Qu

Quality Pasture

How to create it, manage it, and profit from it

by

Allan Nation

A division of Mississippi Valley Publishing, Corp.
Jackson, Mississippi

First reprint July 1996

Library of Congress Catalog Card Number: 95-094359

ISBN: 0-9632460-3-8

Photographs by Allan Nation

Cover Design by Heritage Graphics, Jackson, MS

Manufactured in the United States of America

This book is printed on recycled paper.

Table of Contents

In 1975, the University of Nebraska estimated a farmer could make a middle class living with 97 acres of corn or 461 acres of wheat.

In 1991, the University of Nebraska estimated that same standard of living would require 1327 acres of corn or 3317 acres of wheat.

Today, a middle class living is still possible from only 100 acres of quality pasture.

Preface

The widely held belief in North America that "grain is cheap" has had a devastating impact upon our ruminant agriculture. Our dairy production costs are double those of Ireland and triple those of New Zealand. Grain-finishing pushes our cost of beef production to three times that of Argentina, Australia and New Zealand. Whether or not such huge production-cost disparities can continue in a world of ever-freer trade will be determined in time.

What is true today is that a pound of dry matter from grazed quality pasture can substitute for a pound of concentrate (grain/meal mix) on a virtually one-for-one basis. With grazed pasture costing from one-seventh to one-fifth that of concentrate, the immediate profit implications to North American farmers for every pound of grain replaced by pasture is clear. What has not been so clear is how one creates high TDN, concentrate-replacing pasture. It is to this end that this book is directed.

I have not tried to detail the thousands of grasses and legumes that are available, their climate peculiarities and seeding rates. There are other excellent books that do that well. Rather what I hope to accomplish with this book is to give you a sense of the "whole" that pasture-based agriculture requires. The timing of breeding and lactation, the type of genetics used, the necessity for control over grazing time and area, and the thoughtful development of an annual forage "flow" are more essential than the seeding rate of a particular grass or choice of species.

Much of the information in this book has been borrowed from practical graziers in New Zealand, Ireland and Argentina as the North American prototype is a work in progress and unfinished. Because of the lack of practical information at home, we are forced to travel the world to sift out ideas we can use here. Needless to say, the current practitioners of quality-pasture agriculture in North America must be of a pioneer spirit and be willing to withstand the "negative reinforcement" of their peers and most of agricultural officialdom. The idea of substituting pasture for grain and direct-grazing for machine harvest threatens much of the current structure of North American agribusiness. Despite the opportunities it offers for tremendously increased farmer income and environmental quality, this is an industry that has had to grow in an extremely hostile and derogatory climate. That it has been able to grow, and grow rapidly, indicates the underlying strength of its premise.

I have tried to include enough stories about real people doing real things to show that this is not just a pipe dream. Grassland agriculture **is** the most profitable form of agriculture when it is structured and managed correctly. It can be done. It is being done. You can do it!

Allan Nation
January 1995

Chapter 1: We Are All In The Energy Business

Everyone who attempts to run an enterprise at a profit is really, at the heart of the matter, in the energy business. Profits and losses are just a scorecard of how efficiently we use the energy resources available to us.

There are four major sources of energy: solar, fossil (oil and coal), animal and human.

The most expensive energy source is human energy. It is so expensive that the whole history of human productivity has involved its replacement with lower-cost animal and fossil fuel. The least expensive is solar energy. Ironically, because this energy source is free, very little human energy has been directed toward its maximization. Between the two extremes, fossil fuel and animal power are intermediate in cost. Fossil fuel, unlike animals, does not have an on-going maintenance cost when it is not being utilized. Animals, however, can replace themselves by breeding.

Since only solar energy is free, the most profitable business in the world would be one that uses the least amount of human and intermediate energy and the maximum amount of solar energy. There is such a business.

It is called agriculture.

The real job of farmers is to capture free solar energy in a plant through the magic of photosynthesis. This solar energy stored in plants is the basis of all animal life on earth. As the Bible points out, all flesh is grass. Because it is the only production industry that runs on a free energy source, agriculture is the largest source of new wealth created each year.

Pasture, due to its total ground covering and long growing season, can capture more total solar energy falling on an acre of ground than any other crop. This solar collection advantage makes perennial pasture the most profitable crop that can be grown. Unfortunately, pasture is not directly convertible into human energy and we must use a ruminant animal to convert the solar energy stored in the plants into a form we can utilize.

Luckily, this solar energy converter is also self-mobile and can cover large areas to collect the solar energy stored in plants and bring it back to us to use in a very dense, human-energy-convertible form. This is a real win-win situation. The animal converts solar energy to a human energy form at the same time it harvests the solar energy stored in the crop. In all other forms of agriculture, higher-cost fossil fuel and human energy must be used to gather the stored solar energy in the plants.

Farming For Thinking People

This freedom from the onerous chore of having to gather stored plant energy allows us to use our human energy in thinking. There is a reason graziering is correctly called "The thinking person's form of farming." We do the thinking. The animals do the work.

Thinking is the one human-energy activity that cannot be replaced with other lower-cost energy forms. The lowest value use of human energy is doing what is correctly labeled "mindless work." The more time we can spend thinking about what we are doing and the less time we spend actually doing it, the more productive we are. Sometimes this thoughtful planning requires some upside-down thinking, with the kind of results that make our neighbors look as us as if we're nuts. We are nuts--grass farming nuts! (Entrepreneurs take note. We've marked some of these upside-down opportunities in this text with an upside-down cow.)

The extra value created solely by thinking is the second largest source of new wealth in the economy. If we combine human thought and creativity with a solar powered agriculture, we have a one-two knockout punch for creating maximum wealth.

Note the energy conversion sequence. Solar energy to plant energy to animal energy to human energy. This is also the sequence your management efforts should follow for the greatest financial impact with the possible exception of the last one, the animal to human conversion, which I will discuss shortly.

You Must Be A Grass Farmer First

You are a grass farmer before you are a beef, sheep or dairy farmer. The pasture is where the energy conversion chain starts. As a result, there is far more financial leverage in spending your time feeding and caring for your pasture than in feeding and caring for your animals.

Following the energy conversion sequence, your efforts should be prioritized:

1. Use your management skills to time your animals' genetic maturity, breeding, birth and lactation period to the green growth cycle of natural pasture in your region. (Natural pasture is not native pasture, but the predominant species most widely used in your area.)

2. Use grazing management and periodic overseeding to develop a dense pasture capable of maximum sunlight interception and conversion.

3. Use your management skills to keep the pasture in a green, vegetative state. Mature pasture is not converting sunlight to plant material at its maximum efficiency. Immature pasture keeps the plant-to-animal conversion rate at its maximum.

4. Use your management skills to extend the grazing season through the use of stockpiled pasture during both the winter and summer slumps. The **growing** season and the **grazing** season are too entirely different things. One is dictated by your climate, the other by your management. Every day your animals can gather their own feed is a day you won't have to spend utilizing far more expensive fossil and human energy to bring it to them.

5. Extend the growing season by using more cold (or heat) tolerant plants to keep a green photosynthesis going for as many days of the year as possible. Sunlight wasted is profit lost forever.

6. Maximize the conversion of quality pasture to animal product with growing or high-value-product-producing animals.

It is not cost effective to improve the quality of the pasture beyond the needs of the class of animal grazing it.

7. Match stocking rate as closely as possible with the pasture growth rate. Nitrogen fertilization is most cost effective when it is used to smooth the seasonal forage growth curve rather than to maximize production.

Non-Seasonal Breeding Causes Grazier Depression

Some people may quibble over this exact sequencing and I am not willing to fight over any of them but the first one. Matching the animal's breeding-and-lactation curve to the pasture growth cycle is the single most important management input in grassland farming and usually the one most resisted by new graziers and quite often the last implemented.

It is true one can make improvements by applying pasture and grazing management to a non-seasonal situation, but it allows one to only "pick the low hanging fruit," if you will pardon the horticultural analogy. While picking this "easy" fruit can be quite exhilarating as green-season feed costs initially drop, the profit improvement curve quickly flattens out and becomes stagnant. This "hitting the wall" is the root cause of the "grazier depression" seen in almost all non-seasonal dairy-graziers in about their third year of converting from confinement to pasture. Sadly, many continue to beat their heads against this wall for years.

As Confucius advised a thousand years ago, "The way out is through the door."

The wall will never give.

High Returns From Consumer Marketing

If we were consuming all of our own production, the transfer of stored solar-energy from animal to human would be as easy and seamless as producing it. However, because we must sell our produce to other humans and because selling has nothing to do with nature and everything to do with human nature, the return-to-human-energy-expended is extremely high. It is so high, in fact, that many marketers soon seek to shift the lower return-to-human-energy production phase to others. Quite often a very little effort in direct-consumer-marketing can offset rather severe climatic production disadvantages in net profit return.

In conclusion, the most profitable agricultural model is one that maximizes free solar energy, replaces higher-cost fossil-fuel energy with lower-cost animal energy and allows humans to spend the majority of their time thinking. If your operation is not making the profits you think it should, run it through this model and see if you can't readily find your profit leaks.

Remember, agriculture structured correctly will be almost effortless and **the** most profitable field of endeavor in the economy. Go for it!

Chapter 2: Creating Quality Pasture--Bottoms Up

Most North Americans have never seen what a high-energy, quality pasture looks like. It is dense, diverse, young in age, leguminous and relatively weed free. It is well-drained and can breathe with a crumbly, porous soil. Due to copious amounts of organic matter, it can absorb rain by the tankcar-load and is alive with earthworms. Such high-energy pastures do not just happen. They are created by the grazier's management. Creating and keeping a quality pasture is not an easy task. It requires thoughtful grazing management and frequent inputs of lime, phosphate, legume and grass seed.

It never ceases to amaze me that dairymen who think nothing of spending $180 to grow an acre of corn will not spend $10 to $15 a year to grow an acre of quality, perennial pasture, which can return them many times the profit of corn. I fear only the tiniest handful of us have grasped what being a "grass farmer" truly means.

In our search for lower-purchased-inputs, we have shot ourselves in the foot by ignoring agronomic inputs that can raise the energy level of the pasture. The reason we have to purchase so much outside feed is because our pastures are not producing enough energy (TDN). Why? Usually because they are not leguminous enough, have too few young grass leaves, and are frequently near-monocultures of naturally low-energy grass species such as orchardgrass rather than high-energy grasses like ryegrass. High energy grasses require soils that are high in organic matter, calcium and phosphate. To obtain the latter requires creating the former.

I hear the comment all the time that the reason we grain feed dairy cows and finish beef steers with grain is that "corn is cheap." No, it's not! A pound of TDN from corn costs five to seven times that of grazed pasture. It is this huge cost differential that makes pasture inputs like annually adding small amounts of legume seed and high energy perennial and annual ryegrass so cost effective with dairy graziers and beef finishers. The big money in grass farming is in replacing TDN from grain with TDN from grazed pasture.

% Of Total Diet

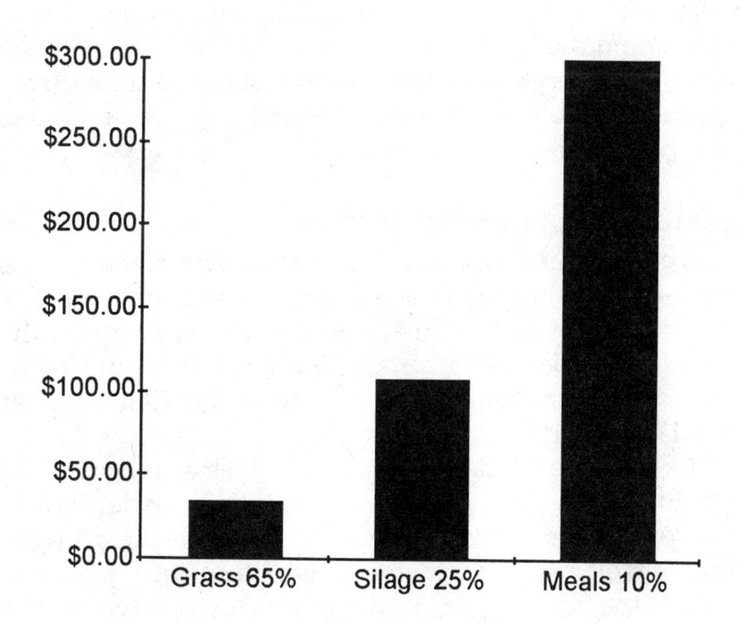

Source: ACOT Council for Development in Agriculture

Organic Matter Is Nature's Fuel

A major problem in creating quality pastures in North America is that most of our non-prairie soils are naturally low in organic matter. Organic matter is the fuel for the bacterial fires in the soil, which operates as a factory producing plant nutrients. The organic matter is burned to create carbon dioxide, ash and other residues. This provides carbonic acid in the soil-water, and the solvent effect of this acidified water on calcium, potassium, magnesium, phosphates, and other minerals is many hundreds of times greater than that of rain water.

Decomposition by micro-organisms within the soil is the reverse of the process represented by plant growth above the soil. Growing plants, using the energy of the sun, synthesize carbon, nitrogen and all other elements into complex compounds. The energy stored up in these compounds is then used more or less completely by the micro-organisms whose activity in the soil makes nutrients available for a new generation of plants.

Soil-organic-matter is the source of all soil nitrogen. In the later stages of decay of most kinds of organic matter, nitrogen is liberated as ammonia and subsequently converted into the soluble or nitrate form usable by the plants. Low-organic matter, low-nitrogen soils result in the extreme clumpy growth seen around manure pats in many of our pastures.

Soil Must Be Able To Breathe

Your pasture's soil is a living, breathing creature. It must have passageways through the soil to exhale its carbon dioxide just as you do. An acre of corn in Northern Iowa on a warm July day will exhale 25 times more carbon dioxide than a human being. Without organic matter the soil becomes compacted and cannot cycle carbon dioxide out and water in.

Organic matter decline under clean tillage is dramatic. That same field of Iowa corn burns enough organic matter in a warm day to equal 1.6 pounds of coal, and a 40-acre field of corn is burning organic matter with an energy output equal to a large 40-HP steam, traction engine. Without a ready reserve of organic matter to supply the energy, the soil cannot change plant-food elements to a usable form and plants cannot grow.

Soil-organic-matter is primarily the dead roots of grass and other plants. These particles provide water-holding capacity in the soil, help keep the soil open for air penetration, buffer herbicides and salt-based fertilizers, and tie up poisonous heavy metals like aluminum. Without pre-existing soil-organic-matter, ammoniacal nitrogen will not work. (Nitrate of soda is water-soluble and thus can be directly picked up by the plant roots.)

When ammoniacal nitrogen is applied to a crop, this does not go directly to the crop but causes the microbial breakdown of existing soil-organic-matter into plant-usable nitrogen. Without soil-organic-matter to capture it, anhydrous ammonia quickly escapes to the air.

The amount of soil-organic-matter is the number one variable in crop yield if all other factors are constant. Organic matter is the soil's sponge. It can absorb copious amounts of rain and slowly release it to the plant during periodic dry periods. High-organic-matter soils can absorb as much as four or five inches of rain without producing runoff. This can greatly increase usable natural precipitation. Conversely, the lack of soil-organic-matter can exacerbate the lack of soil moisture.

In the Mississippi Delta where continuous cropping has almost completely exhausted the soil's organic matter, irrigation is now needed by many farmers to grow naturally drought-resistant cotton in a 55-inch rainfall climate. It is not that the droughts are getting worse, as farmers often claim, but that their soil organic matter is getting worse. USDA research in the 1930s showed that rotating cropland through sod-forming pastures for three to five years increased usable rainfall in Iowa by 6.4 inches a year over continuous corn. Grass crops absorb 87.4 percent of the rainfall compared to only 69.6 percent for a field of corn. In Iowa, this is the same as increasing rainfall by 7.2 inches per year.

Warm Winters Can Cause Organic Matter Decline

Southern farmers face a very difficult task of maintaining soil-organic-matter as the soil temperature stays high enough in the winter to allow soil-organic-matter to be converted to ammonia and carbon dioxide and escape with no benefit. For each fall of 10° Celsius or 18° Fahrenheit in annual temperature, the average organic matter content of the soil increases two to three times, provided the precipitation-evaporation ratio is kept constant.

For example, virgin soils in Northern Missouri will have an organic-matter content of 3.54 percent versus 2.20 in Southern Missouri versus 1.94 in Southern Arkansas. The tremendous drop off in soil-organic-matter as one moves southward is the primary reason for the rural poverty in the South.

A four percent organic-matter soil will produce twice the amount of corn-yield per acre of a two-percent if all other inputs are held constant. Conversely, if we add organic matter to the South's high-rainfall and long-growing-season, the results can be quite dramatic. First-year corn yields in Mississippi following the plowdown of five years of fescue and legumes have been as high as 300 bushels per acre with supplemental nitrogen! In University of Georgia tests, 100 bushels of corn were grown with no nitrogen at all following the plowdown of a five-year-old fescue pasture.

Research at the University of Maryland's Coastal Plains station found that corn yields following several years of bluegrass sod were two to three times that of continuous corn or continuous soybeans, regardless of the amount of nitrogen fertilizer used!

However, such high yields only occur for the first two years following plowdown as the soils's organic matter is quickly depleted in the South's warm climate. Restoration of soil-organic-matter by the plowdown of leguminous cover-crops such as is commonly done in the upper Midwest will have no positive lasting effect in the South due to the warm soils' fast nitrogen cycling. Only the periodic rotation of the land through pasture combined with the use of winter-active legumes as a cover crop can rebuild soil-organic-matter levels in warm winter areas.

Short-season, winter-dormant grass-crops such as bermuda do not build organic matter as quickly as long-season, cool-season crops like fescue. Where short-season, sub-tropical grasses are used, these pastures should be overseeded with winter-active annual grasses and legumes to build soil-organic-matter.

In the North, allowing the surface of the land to go through the summer bare will result in the same quick burnout of organic matter as occurs in the South in the summer. Vegetation is the skin of the earth. Plow it away and things start going downhill very rapidly.

The spreading of non-composted manure on the land and the plow-down of highly carbonaceous crop residues also will cause a depression in available soil nitrogen as soil bacteria increase to decompose it. This can greatly lower subsequent plant growth unless supplemental ammoniacal nitrogen is used to make up for this phenomenon. Soil-organic-matter can only be "made" by the increase in soil nitrogen held in a narrow nitrogen/carbon ratio. Compost is better than raw manure, but green grasses and legumes are superior to compost.

It is virtually impossible to be an organic farmer without being a grass farmer first. Perhaps the reason organic matter is so seldom seriously discussed is the only way to build significant amounts, particularly in warm, winter climates is through the practice of thoughtful grazing management over time. There are no instant fixes to low soil-organic-matter levels.

High-TDN Grasses Require High Organic-Matter

In the context of high-TDN pasture, organic matter is particularly important because high-energy grasses like ryegrass and perennial clover require a relatively high organic matter of four to five percent to survive the summer dry period. It is not heat that kills cool-season perennial grasses, but the lack of soil moisture. Irrigated perennial ryegrass is used in the Central Valley of California where summer daytime temperatures commonly exceed 100 F (35 C) and endophyte fescue will grow as far south as Orlando, Florida, in soils kept constantly damp.

Damp soils are also usually higher in organic matter. In cool and almost-constantly wet Ireland, many upland pasture soils are 10 to 12 percent organic matter and lowland soils are almost peat.

However, there is a big difference between damp soils and wet soils. We do not want wet soils as they are cold and starved for nitrogen and air. Good surface and internal drainage are very necessary to produce quality pasture.

Grass Is A Mirror Image

A grass or legume plant below ground is a mirror image of its above-ground self. If the grass is continually kept grazed short, its root system doesn't grow any deeper than 2 to 4 inches. This keeps the moisture-retaining, drought-buffering sponge-zone very shallow, making the plants susceptible to droughts.

Under a pulsed-grazing system, like rotational grazing, the

grass grows tall (and the roots grow deep) and then is grazed off. This shocks the system so that the root system dies back to match its above-ground self. These dead roots then become new organic matter.

Rotationally grazing legumes, such as alfalfa, builds organic matter the fastest because they are living off of nitrogen in the air rather than breaking down pre-existing soil-organic-matter for their nitrogen needs.

Nothing builds soil-organic-matter as fast as pulsed grazing, but we are still talking three to five years to get low-organic-matter soils to the point they can support a quality pasture. This is a source of great frustration to new graziers who need their pastures to do it all and do it all immediately!

Frequent pasture-liming is also an important part in building soil-organic-matter. Liberal organic matter is tied to liberal amounts of soil calcium. Just as it "ain 't the heat, but the humidity" that hurts, it is the lack of soil calcium rather than the soil pH that hurts. It is possible to have a high pH and low soil-calcium content.

Lime Is A Pasture's Premier Fertilizer

It is unfortunate, that lime is seen primarily as a means of altering soil pH rather than the pasture's most important fertilizer. 200 to 500 lbs. of agricultural lime should be applied each year, regardless of soil pH, to create a high-energy pasture. This annual application is necessary because the surface decay of the grass residual creates a very acid zone at the soil surface that can prevent the germination of clover seeds. Most clover seeds will not grow if planted deeper than the clover seed is tall, so this top eighth of an inch is the most important soil strata in keeping clover (and TDN) in your pastures. This highly acid, topmost layer of soil is hidden in most soil tests by the less acid subsurface layers.

This acid surface also keeps earthworms from feeding and allows the buildup of a dead grass thatch and a sod-bound root zone. Earthworms are a major way of providing carbon dioxide release upward through the soil and water movement downward. Earthworms help to quickly recycle surface manure into the soil and prevent pasture refusal. Their casts (manure) are extremely rich in plant nutrients and have extremely stable soil-conditioning properties.

Benefits Of Lime

However, to thrive, earthworms require a greater amount of soil-calcium than is normally available. If for no other reason than keeping your pasture earthworm friendly, annual liming would pay for itself, but New Zealand grazing consultant, Roger Martyn, lists additional attributes from small annual applications of finely ground, face-powder-consistency, agricultural lime.

- Helps prevent weeds such as dandelion, plantain, chickweed and buttercup.
- Helps with the movement and absorption of phosphorous, nitrogen and magnesium.
- Bacteria, fungi, protozoa and other soil life so important for nutrient cycling are more abundant in calcium rich soils.
- Releases important trace and growth nutrients by its pH altering effect.
- Clover requires twice the calcium of grass. Abundant calcium is necessary for clover nodulation. No lime, little clover.
- Creates soil tilth and structure so that air and water can move more freely through it by causing clay particles to stick together. Soil must be able to breathe to grow great grass.
- Allows pastures to hang on longer in a drought.
- Improves the palatability of grass and clover, makes the pasture softer for animals to graze, and lessens grass-pulling in new stands.
- Reportedly makes animals more docile and content.

Applying lime "a little and often" is far better than large amounts every few years due to the problem of constant surface-acidity buildup and the use of supplemental N. Putting more lime out at a time does not speed soil-pH modification, as this is a very slow process, but it can cause a temporary soil-phosphorous deficiency.

Research at Louisiana State University's Hill Farm Research Station found annual ryegrass responded as well to the application of a small amount of lime as it did to several tons of lime. In sandy Coastal Plains soils the primary benefit of liming is the prevention of aluminum toxicity by slowing the breakdown of soil-organic-matter. It is very difficult to maintain, much less build, soil-organic-matter in hot, wet climates without frequent small amounts of lime.

Lime should only be applied in the rainy season to insure

that it is washed off the grass before the animals return to the paddock. It usually requires two inches of rain to wash the lime from grass leaves. New Zealand grazing consultant, Vaughan Jones, said many of the North American forages he has tested are very low in both calcium and magnesium. Both of these problems can be rectified by using dolomitic lime.

Gypsum Allows Clay Soils To Breathe

Another calcium soil-amendment is gypsum or calcium sulphate. This is primarily a byproduct of the process of producing water-soluble phosphate fertilizer. Gypsum is pH neutral and does not raise nor lower soil pH. This makes it useful as a source for both calcium and sulphur in high pH soils. Most gypsum is 18 percent sulphur.

Gypsum moves through the soil profile much faster than lime and is recommended if deep-rooted legumes such as alfalfa are to be grown in areas that have a highly acid subsoil and where aluminum toxicity is a major problem. University of Georgia research has shown an excellent alfalfa-yield response to gypsum fertilization. Gypsum should be applied at the same 500 lb. annual rate as lime.

Gypsum is also useful for creating better soil structure and porosity in tight clay, crusting, low-organic-matter soils. As previously discussed, soils must be able to breathe to live. Gypsum reduces the amount of swelling in wet clay soils and helps create and preserve both large and small pores in the soil structure. This allows soils to drain excess water better and thereby stay warmer. Wet soils are cold soils and warm up much slower in the spring than well-drained soils.

It is also useful for lowering the sodium content of soils as calcium will replace sodium in the soil's exchange sites. In Australia, small amounts of gypsum are applied through irrigation water to help prevent sodium buildup in the soil on irrigated pastures.

It is ironic that the disposal of phosphate-fertilizer-gypsum is currently viewed as a major environmental problem, but this "problem" product could help a lot of pastures if it were spread like lime, a little, often. Environmental entrepreneurs take notice!

Importance Of Phosphorous

Phosphorous is found in every living cell and is essential in both plant and animal nutrition. In animals it is, following lime, the second largest mineral component of bones and skeletons. Race horse owners have long noted the superior bone strength of horses raised in the phosphate-rich, central plateau of Kentucky.

Approximate nutrient content of various common phosphate and potash fertilizers.

Material	% Phosphorus (P_2O_5)
Normal superphosphate*	20
Triple superphosphate	45
Monoammonium phosphate	48
Diammonium phosphate	53
Ammoniated superphosphate	16
Basic slag*	10
Bone meal*	24

* May not be readily available commercially

Material	% Potassium (K_2O)
Muriate of potash	60
Sulphate of potash	50
Sulphate of potash magnesia	22
Potassium nitrate	44
Potassium carbonate	65
Sodium potassium nitrate	15
Monopotassium phosphate	35

Source: **Southern Forages** by D.M. Ball, C.S. Hoveland, and G.D. Lacefield

Animals forced to graze phosphate-poor soils grow very slowly and develop phosphate-deficient-related diseases. The results of phosphate deficiency are readily seen in the unthrifty, disease-susceptible calves from the phosphate-poor, sandy soils of the Atlantic and Gulf Coastal Plains. Many of these soils contain less than 500 pounds of phosphorous per acre in their top six inches compared to five times that amount in much of Indiana and Ohio. The lowest soil phosphate percentages in the nation are found in the Norfolk and Tifton soils of the Carolinas, Georgia, Florida and Alabama. If Southern graziers would start to religiously lime and phosphate their pastures, no doubt the reputation for "poor-doing" Southern stocker cattle would largely disappear.

In the context of creating quality pasture, phosphate is particularly important in that copious amounts of available phosphate appear to be a key in successfully growing perennial ryegrass. Graziers in Argentina told me they thought perennial ryegrass wouldn't survive in their hot climate until they started applying phosphate every year. Now, they report great success with it in a climate very similar to southern Missouri, Kentucky, Tennessee and northern Mississippi and Alabama. Vaughan Jones told me that in New Zealand perennial ryegrass will only last a couple of years if annual phosphate fertilization is discontinued.

Research at Ohio State in the 1930s found that the milk from 130 cows or the bones in 240 grass-fattened steers completely drained all the available phosphorous from the top six inches of one acre of pasture. Like lime, a program of annually applying 200 to 500 lbs. of phosphate per acre is necessary for a high-energy-producing pasture. However, lime and phosphate should not be spread together. Lime is best spread in the winter rainy-season to insure it is washed off the grass blades before grazing. Phosphate is normally spread in the early spring at or near greenup and is the best carrier for trace element fertilization.

Broomsedge As Warning Sign

The primary indicator plant of a pasture deficient in lime and phosphorous in the Eastern half of the United States is broomsedge. In the northeastern United States, poverty grass or moonshine grass serves as the same warning flag. Low-phosphorous-requiring plants will form a dense sod and crowd out the higher-TDN legumes and grasses. Only phosphorous fertilization will make the preferred high-energy grasses and legumes aggressive enough to redominate the pasture.

Brassicas, a major low-cost source of supplemental TDN, are particularly susceptible to low-soil-phosphorous. Conversely, plants with large root systems such as cereal rye and oats are much less responsive to phosphorous fertilization.

Lime, organic matter and available phosphorous are all parts of the same whole. Liming soils can help make soil phosphorous available to plants.

Phosphorous does not exist in a free form in the soil but is held as a compound with another element. Phosphorous is held in the soil in four ways:

- Compounds of calcium and phosphorous or magnesium and phosphorous.
- Combinations of phosphorous with organic matter.
- Compounds of iron and aluminum and phosphorous.
- Compounds of phosphorous in rock from which soils are formed.

Of these four, compounds of calcium and magnesium are the most available to the plant. These compounds are found in acidulated, commercial-superphosphate fertilizer.

As organic-matter-percentage increases, the response from phosphorus fertilization decreases. This is backward from what one would suppose for organic phosphorous, which is only marginally available to the plant. It is supposed that soil-organic-matter delays the absorption of the phosphorous by soil iron and aluminum, which is much less available to the plant than organic phosphorous.

Many researchers in the 1930s noted that frequent, small limings appeared to make soil phosphorous more available. In fact, where lime was applied as annual fertilizer, rather than as a pH modifier, crop yields in moderate-to-acid soils were just as high as where superphosphate had been applied. It appears that lime increases the availability of pre-existing soil phosphate by allowing the existing soil phosphate to shift from being tightly held by iron and aluminum to the much more plant-available compound of calcium phosphate. Conversely, applying large amounts of lime at one time, as is so often recommended for pH modification, will result in symptoms of phosphorous starvation and poor plant growth. Remember, a little, often, is nature's way of fertilization.

Care should be taken in applying large amounts of acidulated phosphate to a pasture, particularly in sandy, low-organic-matter soils. The quick uptake of these highly available phosphates can make animals grazing these plants lethargic and sickly for a time. For this reason, there has been a shift away from superphosphate to natural reactive phosphate rock (RPR) in New Zealand. Lime and RPR should not be spread together as it is the organic acids of plant decay that make RPR available to the plant.

It is commonly thought that RPR can't be used in high-pH soils, but this has been found to be untrue in pasture situations since the soil surface is always acid due to continuous surface-plant decay.

Although much of the RPR fertilizer used in New Zealand comes from the United States, it currently is not widely advertised nor readily available here as the phosphate rock industry is afraid to antagonize their primary customers in the commercial fertilizer industry by promoting its benefits. This reticence is a major opportunity for someone willing to specialize in pasture-friendly fertilizers.

Lime Takes Precedence Over Phosphate

Because lime and organic-matter percentage will greatly affect the subsequent availability from the application of commercial phosphate fertilizers, it is recommended that if budgets are limited, lime should take precedence over phosphate fertilization.

For graziers in clay or loam soils, phosphate fertilization is often an act of faith because the phosphate is quickly tied up in slowly available forms. A soil low in phosphate is like a dry sponge. Until enough phosphate has been applied for the sponge to become saturated, little will be available for the plants. Also, in permanent pasture situations it usually takes a minimum of two years before you will see a visual response in your plants from phosphate fertilization. Conversely, phosphate drawdown is so slow that the yield declines early on are almost imperceptible. New Zealand graziers shelter their profits from the tax man in good years by increasing their phosphate fertilization and then draw on this account in poor years by skipping the annual application.

Animal manures are very low in phosphate value. A ton of cow manure is approximately the equivalent of 100 lbs. of a 3-5-10 mixed fertilizer. This is a gross imbalance in the ratio of nitrogen and phosphate to potassium, and gross imbalances can be bad for our animals' health. High soil-potassium levels are a major cause of milk fever.

Phosphate can be used in confinement situations to help prevent both bad smells and disease. Phosphate is an ammoniacal fixer and can prevent the loss of free ammonia from manure and urine when added to the cow's bedding. This also prevents objectionable smells. One ton of superphosphate will fix 140 lbs. of actual N. Research at Ohio State concluded the annual financial return on the cost of adding 45 lbs. of 16 percent superphosphate to a ton of fresh cow manure prior to spreading was 412 percent!

An additional side benefit of this practice is that the superphosphate is refixed into an insoluble form, slowing its release, and thereby helping to prevent animal health problems from a too-rapid uptake. For this reason, this is an ideal practice for pasture, but a very poor one for annual crops where fast response is desired. Phosphate is also an antiseptic and inhibits bacterial activity. Many graziers use phosphate as part of the bedding in lambing sheds and where baby dairy calves are being raised.

Potassium Overload

In nature, too much of a good thing can produce severe health problems in your animals. Keeping soil phosphate and potassium levels balanced is a very important factor in good animal health. This is particularly difficult if your animals are being fed supplemental grain, or you are spreading poultry or hog manure on your pastures. With the exception of sandy, pervious soils, mucks and peats, most soils in the United States have sufficient potassium. A growing problem in dairy pastures is excess potassium due to the supplemental grain feeding of the cows. Keep in mind a ton of corn contains almost ten pounds of potassium. Unlike calcium and phosphorous, which is constantly exported off the pasture in the bones and milk of the animals, the potassium eaten in the forage and grain is almost completely recycled in the urine. The amount of potassium in the soil continues to build and can increase to unhealthy high levels.

Grass Tetany

Grass tetany results from animals grazing low magnesium forages and can sometimes occur on water-logged soils even if properly fertilized with magnesium. However, grass tetany can also occur from an imbalance of low phosphorous and high potassium and nitrogen--a combination that restricts magnesium uptake in the plants. This form of grass tetany is primarily a problem on soils fertilized frequently with raw broiler litter or dairy manure. Keeping legumes in your pasture mix will usually prevent grass tetany, however, grass tetany is not the only problem caused by too high a level of soil potassium.

Milk Fever

Soil potassium buildup appears to be a major, growing health problem for grain-supplemented dairies. There appears to be no problem with high levels of soil potassium in lactating cows. In fact, high soil-potassium levels appear to make cows more heat-tolerant and grasses more cold-tolerant, but dairy scientists now say there is a definite link between milk fever and high potassium levels in dry and close-up cow forages. Many also believe high soil-potassium levels contribute to a wide array of calving problems and metabolic disorders such as displaced absomaseums. Alfalfa hay and small-grain silage are very high in potassium and are not recommended for dry cows. Dry and springing cow-forages should not be over 1 to 1.5 percent potassium. Hog and chicken manures are much higher in potassium than ruminant manures. Hay purchased from confinement hog spray-fields and poultry producers should always be tested for potassium content before feeding it to dry and near-term cows.

Benefits Of Composting Manures

An excellent management practice is composting. Composting is a speeded-up version of a natural decomposition process. Microorganisms feed on manure, newspapers, wood chips, meat scraps, or any other wastes from the plant or animal kingdoms. In the presence of air, the organisms reduce these complex compounds into a stabilized organic material similar to humus, the organic fraction of the soil. Being mostly organic matter, compost improves soil structure, adds to its ability to hold water in dry years and enhances soil biological activity, including earthworms.

Composting takes all the major and minor trace elements needed for plant growth and turns them into a slowly-available-to-plant form that is highly resistant to leaching. Studies have shown that a single application of compost can benefit crops for at least eight years. However, compost is not a major source of soil nitrogen as it runs only about two percent N, and this, like the other fertilizer elements, is only slowly available over time.

A major benefit of composting to graziers is that it prevents the pasture refusal that occurs when fresh cow manure is spread. The slow release of plant nutrients is also ideal for a pasture situation and is something that commercially available pasture fertilizers should be designed to mimic. However, commercial fertilizers are designed for fast release, which is good in a rowcrop situation, but can be very bad in a pasture. As with superphosphate, muriate of potash should be applied in multiple small amounts rather than in one big load as the fast uptake in the forage can make cattle sick, particularly on low-organic-matter, sandy and sandy loam soils.

Many graziers prefer potassium sulfate to muriate of potash as it leaves sulfur as a byproduct in the soil and many soils are sulfur deficient. A product known as Sul-Po-Mag has long been a favorite for graziers seeking legume-rich pastures in sandy soil regions in that it provides both sulfur and magnesium with the potassium. Potassium fertilizers are best spread in the fall.

Another fertilizer element necessary in much of the South for good legume reseeding is Boron. This should be applied annually at the rate of 1.5 lbs. per acre for clover and double that for alfalfa. This can be spread with your phosphate.

New Zealand graziers have gotten excellent animal and clover responses to very small amounts of sodium, selenium, cobalt and copper. Unfortunately, the United States lags far behind New Zealand in the whens, hows, and whys of trace-element fertilization. Currently it is somewhat expensive to have trace elements custom-blended with your phosphate. Vaughan Jones assures me that as soon as U.S. co-ops see the competitive advantage custom blending pasture mixes creates they will start to do it and the price will become much more competitive. Currently in New Zealand custom blending is done with push-button equipment for five to ten New Zealand dollars per ton (US$3-$6).

Supplemental Nitrogen

Nitrogen is most farmers' favorite fertilizer because the plant's response to it is almost instantaneous, while lime, phosphate and potassium take at least two years to create a measurable response. Legumes, because of their high TDN, would be included in a quality pasture mixture even if they didn't fix nitrogen in the soil. That they do is truly serendipitous; however, the amount of nitrogen legumes produce is almost always below the maximum the pasture's grasses could utilize. This nitrogen shortfall is reflected in a lower-than-possible stocking rate. Since the animal-to-overhead ratio is the second-most important indicator of dairy profits after feed costs, skimping on nitrogen fertilization can be penny wise and pound foolish.

In the northern Dairy Belt, land taxes often run $30 to $50 an acre and yet many dairymen use up to four acres to produce the yearly feedstuffs for a dairy cow due primarily to their lack of pasture fertilization. Research in Northern Ireland has shown that to maintain a dairy cow for the entire year from the offtake (pasture and pasture silage) of one acre of perennial ryegrass will require around 250 lbs. of actual N. The newest, high-nitrogen-producing white clovers available today will produce around 250 lbs. of N if fertilized annually with lime and phosphate. However, a legume-based system will still have seasonal shortfalls of N production. This nitrogen shortfall worsens as the overall climate becomes warmer as we will shortly discuss.

Nitrogen Is Cheaper Than Grain

In the ultimate irony, many American dairymen prefer to make up a grass shortfall with increased grain feeding, which costs many times more than what supplemental nitrogen fertilizer would have cost to grow more grass. Of all the possible purchased-solutions there are to a seasonal shortfall in grass production, nitrogen fertilizer is the cheapest.

Response, in yield of grass to extra nitrogen is very good with cool-season grasses up to 320 actual units of nitrogen per acre. Up to this level of nitrogen, each extra pound of nitrogen should produce 15 to 20 pounds of grass dry-matter. This has a feeding value approaching the equivalent weight of concentrates!

The real trick in keeping nitrogen costs low is to make sure the extra dry matter the purchased nitrogen grows can be directly grazed by the animal. Increasing nitrogen application rates from 120 units per acre to 360 units per acre will require an increase in overall stocking rate of 40 percent to be economically viable. Because most stocking rates are relatively fixed for the entire grazing season, while pasture growth rates are highly variable, nitrogen fertilizer is most economical when used as a pasture-growth-curve leveler. Like all other fertilizer elements, nitrogen is best applied in multiple, small applications rather than all at once.

In his seminal book, **Grass Productivity**, Andre Voisin recommended that a grazier's yearly nitrogen application on cool-season grasses be split into multiple small portions with one-sixth of the total just before spring growth begins, one-third at the end of the spring-grass-lush, and one-half in the autumn to build a stockpile of grass for subsequent wintergrazing. Voisin found that with timely nitrogen applications he could increase the grass growth-season by nearly one month a year, diminish the effect of the summer grass growth slump, and even out the roller-coaster-growth-curve of cool-season pastures.

Cool-season grasses can grow at temperatures lower than clover rhizobia, and soil bacteria can start nitrogen production. By applying nitrogen in the late winter, he enabled the grass to begin its growing season before that of the natural soil-nitrogen-production cycle.

These late-winter applications are particularly important if the fall was droughty and the grass was carried into the winter very short. These short-grazed autumn pastures will be very slow waking up in the spring due to low root reserves for growth.

Voisin noted that with a late-winter nitrogen application he could begin grazing when the cherry trees were just beginning to bud, but if he didn't apply nitrogen, the grazing season began when the cherry trees were blossoming. He found a cool-season grass's slowing growth due to the onset of summer heat could be reinvigorated with an application of nitrogen as well. This late spring application greatly diminished the effect summer has on grass growth.

Care must be taken with spring nitrogen applications so that they are not made so late that they actually worsen the spring-growth surplus. Voisin found that one unit of nitrogen would grow 5.30 units of grass in the spring, but only two units in the fall. He recommended that in a ten-paddock dairy-cell only the first six should receive a late-winter application of nitrogen. He also recommended that the first three paddocks should receive 134 lbs. of calcium nitrate (20 lbs. of actual N) and the next three should receive 89 lbs. (13 lbs. of actual N). Two of the four paddocks would receive no nitrogen and would be set aside for haying or silaging. Two would receive no nitrogen but would be grazed in the spring rotation. This staggered rate of application helps give a "cut" to the spring rotation and helps prevent clover bloat by increasing the grass percentage. Each year the rotation should start with a different paddock to prevent favoring certain forage species over others.

Cattle that have been wintered on hay and feed should not be allowed to graze but two hours on the first day. Their grazing period can be gradually increased each day. If the cattle are not gradually allowed to build their rumen microbia for spring pasture and legumes, severe bloat and other problems can occur.

New Zealand grazing consultant, Vaughan Jones, recommends that paddocks that are to be dropped for silaging not receive supplemental N as this will lower their carbohydrate content and make them harder to ensile.

Urea is the cheapest form of nitrogen and just as effective as ammonium nitrate as long as the weather is cool and damp. Urea cannot be used in hot, dry conditions.

Southern Pastures Need Nitrogen

Subtropical grasses such as bermuda and bahia are much more efficient converters of nitrogen to dry matter than cool-season grasses and the uppermost limit of N-to-dry-matter conversion rate has not been determined. Some believe it may be as high as 1000 units of N per acre if applied in multiple applications.

By applying 30 to 40 lbs. of actual N every 28 days, dairymen in East Texas and Florida are able to maintain stocking rates as high as 2 to 3 Holsteins per acre. Balancing such extremely high summer production per acre with the much lower production (one cow per acre) of the cool-season annuals used for wintergrazing keeps Southern graziers at their computers. Most do it by dropping as much as half their land out of grazing for hay during the mid-summer peak of growth. Much of this hay is then fed back in the autumn awaiting the growth of the cool-season annuals.

Southern graziers face a very difficult problem in trying to rely strictly on legumes for their nitrogen needs because Southern soils do not have much of a nitrogen reserve to draw on. This is due to the constant high-biological activity the hot summers and warm winters produce. The USDA Yearbook of Agriculture on **Soils and Men** estimated that for every fall of 10° C or 18° F in annual temperature, soil nitrogen reserves (organic matter) increased by two to three times.

It is particularly critical that Southern graziers keep a green and growing crop on their land year-round to capture and utilize the ammoniacal nitrogen that is being produced and that will be lost forever without a green cover on the land. A beneficial effect of this low-soil-nitrogen for Southern graziers is that they do not face the explosive spring growth that Northern graziers have such difficulty utilizing. This slower growth makes spring pastures much easier to manage in the South.

Percent N in various fertilizers and amounts of these materials required to supply various levels of N per acre.

Fertilizer Material	% N in fertilizer	Pounds of N desired per acre					
		30	60	90	120	150	180
Anhydrous ammonia	82	40	75	110	150	180	220
Urea	46	60	130	200	260	320	390
Ammonium nitrate	33.5	90	180	270	360	450	540
Ammonium sulphate	21	140	280	430	570	710	860
Nitrate of soda *	16	190	380	560	750	940	1120
Calcium nitrate *	15	200	400	600	800	1000	1200
		Gallons of liquid per acre					
Anhydrous ammonia	82	7	14	21	28	35	42
Solutions	32	9	17	26	34	43	52
	21	13	27	40	53	66	79

* May not be readily available commercially.

Source: **Southern Forages** by D.M. Ball, C.S. Hoveland, and G.D. Lacefield.

Earthworms And Nitrogen

Many graziers are concerned about the detrimental effect nitrogen will have on their pasture earthworms. The secret here is to follow nature's guide and use multiple, smaller applications rather than one big application. Little detrimental effect is seen as long as a surface-applied N source is used and the application rate is kept at 40 lbs. of actual N or less per application. This would be around 90 lbs. of urea or 100 lbs. of ammonium nitrate. See chart for conversion of actual N to pounds of fertilizer per acre.

Earthworms--Your Underground Pasture Helpers

New Zealand research indicates a good crop of earthworms can increase your pasture growth rates by at least 25 percent. Research in Illinois indicates they can cut fertilizer bills by as much as $20,000 to $30,000 a year. Pastures with healthy earthworm counts require less fertilizer, less subsoiling and less pasture maintenance. Earthworm-rich pastures hang on longer in droughts and drain faster during wet periods.

Here are a few of the other benefits of a healthy crop of earthworms in your pasture:

- Earthworms can generate the equivalent of 200 lbs. of potassic phosphate per acre per annum. They also make calcium, magnesium, zinc and boron more available to the plant.
- Earthworms break down dung more quickly, turning it into plant food, reducing fly breeding ground and internal parasite larvae.
- Earthworms greatly help soil drainage. The pencil-thin burrows that earthworms drill allow rainwater to penetrate deep in the subsoil and prevent standing surface water that can kill grasses and legumes.
- These same burrows allow the soil to breathe. They transport oxygen downward to aerobic bacteria and allow carbon dioxide to get out and benefit the carbon dioxide breathing plants at the surface.
- These burrows remain in place for several years because the worms coat them with a sticky, nutrient-rich mucus. These allow plant roots to penetrate subsoil hardpans and create subsoil moisture wicks.
- Horizontal burrows allow plant roots to quickly grow laterally in compacted soils, and thereby reduce the effect of soil compaction.
- Earthworms recycle surface mulch and manure into nutrient-rich humus. In as little as 10 years, earthworms can completely renew the top two inches of topsoil.
- Earthworm deposits contain 5 to 10 times the amount of soluble plant nutrients as the original soil.
- Soil processed by earthworms is always closer to neutral pH than the original, whether acid or alkaline.
- Earthworms spread beneficial microbes through the soil.

• South Dakota State University research indicates fields with high earthworm populations had water infiltration rates four times as high as those with no earthworms.

• Earthworms eat harmful soil nematodes that feed on clover roots.

Earthworms love:
♥ legume-rich pastures
♥ damp, cool conditions
♥ dense pasture kept at a high residual
♥ small, frequent doses of fertilizer
♥ crumbly, porous soils
♥ darkness

Earthworms hate:
☹ tillage
☹ pasture pugging
☹ bare ground
☹ sunlight
☹ coarse soils
☹ large applications of nitrogen or potash at one time
☹ lack of organic matter
☹ hot, dry weather
☹ soil acidity

The conditions that create a healthy habitat for earthworms are precisely those that are created by a healthy, legume-rich pasture. Earthworms hate tillage, pasture pugging, bare ground, sunlight, coarse soils, large applications of nitrogen or potash at one time, lack of organic matter and soil acidity. They love the damp, cool conditions created by maintaining a dense pasture at a high residual. They are particularly sensitive to the lack of soil calcium. New Zealand grazing consultant Vaughan Jones says the primary benefit of pasture liming should be thought of as "feeding the earthworms." Because earthworms create plant-available phosphate and potassium, liming should take precedence over phosphate and potassium fertilization.

Soil pH must be at least 5.6, and an annual topdressing with a small amount of lime (200 to 500 lbs. per acre) is necessary to keep the top fraction of an inch of the soil surface from becoming acid due to plant decay. The lime used for surface application should be of a face-powder consistency and soft to the touch. Some species of earthworms will multiply rapidly following an application of lime.

Research in Egypt, England and Germany suggests that earthworms are more affected by the changes in surface soil pH created by nitrogen fertilizer than by the fertilizer itself. Smaller, more frequent applications of N, rather than one large one, and annual liming appear to be the solution to the observations of high earthworm deaths from heavy N fertilization.

In coarse, tight, heavy clay soils, regular small applications of gypsum will help create the softer more granular and open soil that earthworms like while providing the necessary soil calcium.

Dung worms require regular amounts of dung and will quickly disappear in a non-grazed field. Dung worms die during dry weather or during freezing conditions but leave behind eggs that will continue the species when better conditions return. All species of earthworms go dormant during hot, dry weather.

Large applications of liquid manure will kill earthworms by sealing the soil surface and suffocating them to death. All applications of manure, both liquid and dry, and all fertilizer elements are better when spread in smaller, more frequent amounts rather than all at once.

Tillage operations should never be done in the early morning or after dark when earthworms are at or near the surface. It appears that the earthworms can sense the onset of tillage and will dive deep and avoid death if given the chance.

In New Zealand, earthworms are often sown onto pastures but this should only be done after several years of liming and trace mineral fertilization have created a hospitable home for them. An earthworm farmer who specializes in a "pasture blend" of worms is Rangimarie Worm Farm, RD 3, Motueka, New Zealand. Growing and selling "pasture worms" could be a profitable sideline for you as well.

In conclusion, the management that creates healthy, leguminous pasture and high animal performance are exactly those that will benefit your pasture's earthworms.

Hidden Herd Aids Plant Growth

There's another herd out there in your pasture and fields that you need to be aware of. It's the huge herd of millions of bacteria in your soil. Thanks to these little critters, the manure, urine and dead plant material in your pasture can be recycled to grow new plants. Too often, because these little critters are out of sight, we unintentionally abuse them and hurt our crop and pasture production.

The USDA estimates that a double handful of unabused soil contains more life forms than there are people on earth. A double handful! In addition to microbes, you'll find protozoa, nature's smallest animal; nematodes, which are tiny eel-like animals; yeasts, fungi, actinomycetes and algae. These creatures are divided into two basic groups--aerobic (air breathing) and anaerobic life (non air breathing). The aerobic critters live in the top 5 inches of the soil and the anaerobics in the lower soil surface. Denying oxygen to the aerobic group kills them, and exposing the lower group to air kills them. This is why many farmers are turning to no-till and minimum-till farming. A deep turning plow puts aerobic life at the bottom where it dies and anaerobic at the top where it dies. To keep these little critters happy, we must be careful to never turn our soil deeper than 5 inches.

Too often microbes are thought of as something only clover-based grass farmers need to be concerned about. This is because of the nitrogen-fixing properties of the microbe *Rhizobium* along with legumes. But microbes also are necessary to convert phosphorus, sulfur, chlorine, boron, and molybdenum into a form for plants to use. While plants derive most of their energy directly from the sun, microbes must obtain their energy either directly or indirectly from plant material in the soil. This is why God gave ruminants their sharp cloven hooves--to push dead-grass material into the soil and thereby feed the little critters beneath the soil, which feeds the big critter above it. The more organic matter there is in the soil, the more microbes there can be and the faster the nutrient cycle can move to grow more plants.

An article in the **American Journal of Botany** estimated that the total length of the root system of a single winter rye plant was 377 miles and that when the root hairs were totaled in, the length was estimated at 6,214 miles! In a single acre of winter rye, it is estimated that the area of root and root hairs would cover 30,000 acres! Needless to say, winter rye is considered a leading builder of organic matter.

Also, high-organic-matter soils are high in fungi like *Fusarium, Gliocladium,* and *Basidiomycetes.* As the organic matter of the soil declines, these fungi die off one by one until only an occasional *Fusarium* is left. Yields and protein content also decline as these fungi die. Under poor soil conditions the *Fusarium* has been found to attack poorly nourished roots or a plant with low resistance and become an active parasite.

Pasture Analysis Better Than Soil Test

A pasture forage analysis is much better for picking up possible soil mineral deficiencies and in planning a fertilization program for grazing animals than a soil test. Afterall, the animals are eating the pasture not the soil. A pasture analysis shows what the pasture is actually getting from the soil and thereby bypasses much of the human interprolation used with soil tests. Recent tests of various soil testing labs found a huge range of recommendations from exactly the same soil samples. Soil tests are good for soil pH measurement and one should be taken about every five years.

Pasture forage tests measure some of the elements in parts per million so cleanliness and accuracy are of the essence. Samples must be gathered only from green growing plants. Soil, weeds, dead leaves and perspiration can distort results.

You should always first wash the hand you will be using for pasture sample gathering. Collect and throw away the first few handfuls you gather to neutralize your hand with the pasture.

Don't sample paddocks that have been fertilized or limed within two months or grazed within two weeks.

Avoid sampling near dusty roads, gateways or water troughs. Samples should not be taken from frost damaged plants or from grass growing in urine and dung patches.

Use a strong brown paper bag (not plastic or ink-coated paper) and hold it with your non-picking hand or under one arm.

With the non-picking hand remove all old dead pasture, foreign matter and soiled leaves before putting it in the bag.

If possible aim for 80 % grass and 20 % clover, or all clover, or all grass. Discard the clover stems as they will usually be contaminated with soil.

Collect two loosely heaped handfuls of pasture for each bag. These should come from as many as 15 different individual pulls across a reprentative paddock. Leave the bag open until you are ready to dry the sample. Tightly packed pasture will heat and deteriorate. Dry the samples at 180 F (80 C) for 12 hours or air dry them in a clean, warm dry environment for a few days.

Never mix samples from around the farm. Initially get a sample from each of your major soil types and in subsequent years test different paddocks, in case there are highly localized deficiencies.

A New Zealand pasture analysis currently costs approximately US$100 for a lab analysis, interpretation and recommendation. Details can be found in the resource section.

Think About It...

♣ Quality pasture has copious amounts of organic matter, is alive with earthworms, is dense, diverse, young-in-age, leguminous, and relatively weed-free. Are you growing quality pasture?

♣ Soil-organic-matter, made up of the dead roots of grass and other plants, helps soil breathe with porousness for air penetration, acts as a buffer for herbicides and salt-based fertilizers, and ties up poisonous heavy metals like aluminum. Such high-organic-matter soils can absorb as much as four or five inches of rain without producing runoff. Think of it as a sponge. What would a doubling of your effective rainfall do for your farm?

♣ Following pasture plow-down, soils produce high corn yields for only two years before being depleted in a warm climate. Only the periodic rotation of the land through pasture, combined with the use of winter-active legumes as a covercrop can rebuild soil-organic-matter in warm winter areas. What's your plan for keeping yields high?

♣ Allowing the surface of the land to go through the summer bare in the North results in the same quick burn-out of organic matter as occurs during the winter in the South. What are you going to use as a cover crop?

♣ Soil-organic-matter can only be "made" by the increase in soil nitrogen held in a narrow nitrogen/carbon ratio. Compost is better than raw manure, but green grasses and legumes are superior to compost. Which will you use on your pasture?

♣ Heat doesn't kill cool-season perennial grasses, lack of soil moisture does. While damp soils are usually higher in organic matter, damp soils are not the same as wet soils, which are cold and starved for nitrogen and air. Is your soil damp or wet?

♣ Nothing builds soil-organic-matter as fast as pulsed grazing. Are you committed to the three-to-five-year period it will take to improve low-organic-matter soils?

♣ Frequent pasture-liming builds soil-organic-matter, but lack of soil calcium, rather than soil pH hurts. What's your pasture's calcium level?

♣ The top eighth-of-an-inch is the most important soil strata in keeping clover (and TDN) in your pastures. Is surface acid interfering with your earthworm numbers and activity?

♣ Lime should only be applied in the rainy season to insure that it is washed off the grass before the animals return to the paddock. Phosphate is normally spread in the early spring at or near greenup and is the best carrier for trace element fertilization. Lime and phosphate should not be spread together. Are you applying these fertilizer elements nature's way, a little, often, and in the correct seasons?

♣ Is your budget limited? Lime should take precedence over phosphate fertilization.

♣ Gypsum creates better soil structure and porosity in tight clay, crusting, low-organic-matter soils. Wet soils are cold soils that in the spring warm up slower than well-drained soils. Do your soils need a feeding of gypsum?

♣ Phosphate is an antiseptic and inhibits bacterial activity. Have you used it as part of the bedding in your lambing shed or where baby dairy calves are being raised?

♣ Ruminant manures and hay purchased from confinement hog spray-fields and poultry producers should always be tested for potassium content before feeding it to dry and near-term cows.

♣ Paddocks that are to be dropped for silaging shouldn't receive supplemental nitrogen since this will lower their carbohydrate content and make them harder to ensile. Nitrogen is best applied in multiple, small applications rather than all at once.

♣ Cattle that have been wintered on hay and feed should not be allowed to graze but two hours on the first day. Are you gradually increasing their grazing time at turn-out?

♣ A deep-turning plow puts aerobic life at the bottom of the soil where it dies and anaerobic at the top where it dies. To overcome this, turn your soil no deeper than five inches.

♣ When was the last time you took a pasture walk?

Chapter 3:
Starting A Quality Pasture Program

The more diverse the varieties of plants and legumes in a pasture, the more stable the annual forage production curve becomes. Nature creates optimum, sustainable output through species complexity. For example, diverse plant communities are very resistant to disease and the more mature a diverse plant community becomes, the more resistant it is to outside invasion and climatic disruption by drought, flood and freeze. Plant communities create their own micro-climate that furthers their own best interests. Without rain there is no rain-forest, and without the rain-forest there is no rain.

Predators and their prey are also in symbiotic harmony in that prey species compete with each other for resources. These populations are kept in check by the predator, which attacks the sick and the weak. If the prey population grows beyond the range's carrying capacity, more become sick and weak and susceptible to the predator. However, the predator is an important part of the survival of the whole. If we remove the coyote to save the sheep, the rabbit population explodes, eats the grass and starves the sheep to death. In other words, the presence of the coyote allows more sheep to exist rather than fewer.

Complexity, Life at the edge of Chaos by Roger Lewin notes that scientists hate the word "holism" because it sounds mystical and religious, but a study of nature will almost always bring you to the view that everything in nature is hooked to everything else. You cannot, as the scientist is wont to do, change just one little thing in isolation of everything else.

New diverse plant communities will end up in radically different ways depending upon the specific conditions under which they were started. In other words, my pasture will always be different from your pasture due to the initial differences in climate and rainfall in the establishment year. Small initial changes can become quite huge in nature over time. This is called "The Butterfly Effect," in that in nature a hurricane in Jamaica may have been started by the tiny wind of a butterfly's wings in Africa many weeks before. The book said that most species in a diverse environment won't make it. If you started out with 125 different species of plants and animals in an environment, they will soon winnow themselves down to 15 or so. And my 15 will be different from your 15 for the above mentioned reasons. The conclusion of this book is that order and stability in nature comes from complexity. Get your pasture salads tossed as soon as possible.

Diversity Stabilizes Forage Curve

"Wow!" was the word that jumped out of my mouth when I first saw Forrest Stricker's pastures near Robesonia, Pennsylvania. He had taken the advice of making your pastures a salad to the point where they actually looked good enough for me to eat. They were a riot of diversity. Puna chicory, orchardgrass, alfalfa, brome, perennial ryegrass, timothy and white clover all grew in a jumbled, intermingled mass. The only description for it was literally a "pasture salad."

Forrest's dairy cows thought it was pretty good stuff too. They were making milk on it as low as $1.79 cwt. in the spring, to a mid-summer high of a very respectable $2.40 cwt.

"By adding deep-rooted plants like puna chicory and alfalfa, we get much better season long production. Clover and ryegrass can fade quickly on you in a mid-summer drought," he said.

Pennsylvania went through two severe droughts and four mini-droughts during a six year period in the late 1980s and early 1990s. That long, almost continuous, "dry spell" taught Pennsylvania graziers the greater stability mixing pasture species can bring. This is particularly true when deep-rooted species like alfalfa, Puna chicory and Matua prairie grass are used.

Forrest establishes his pasture mix by planting cereal rye behind silage corn. Then he just spins the seed mixture into the rye in late winter with a cyclone seeder and then grazes the rye with a fast rotation in the spring. His cows go through the rye at least four or five times at a high stock density and this hoof action helps plant the seeds.

Larry Lohr of Somerset, Pennsylvania, is nearing the end of a long transition from a corn-silage-based confinement system to an all-grass system. "Every year we would take seven acres out of corn and put it to grass as the herd grew," he said. "The extra margin in grass dairying has allowed us to grow our cow numbers at 15 percent every year." Larry is a believer in the new low-tannin reed canarygrass mixed with alfalfa, Puna chicory, red clover and ladino clover. "I've found the canarygrass won't let you down in a wet year or a dry year," he said.

Penny Wise Dollar Foolish

"I can't understand some people's mindset. Here we are growing a crop capable of making at least a thousand dollars an acre with dairy cattle and we're not going to spend five to ten dollars an acre for extra seed? It's just ridiculous," said Dr. Gerry Jung, retired Northeastern ARS pasture specialist.

Farmers need to look at where their costs are coming from. "The biggest cost is for feed," said Jung. "Spending a little money on lime, P and K, can allow you to grow legumes, which can cut both your feed, because of their high TDN, and your nitrogen bill. Ryegrass can cut your grain bill because it is high in energy, as can brassicas for the same reason. Stockpiled fungus-free fescue can cut your winter hay expenses. Spending a little money on your pasture every year saves a lot of money in other places of your operation."

A program of plowing down and planting three to five acres in brassicas each year as the New Zealanders do, can help smooth out the mid-summer slump in forage production, extend the grazing season later into the winter and, due to its very high TDN, allow a cut back on grain feeding. (Brassicas are turnips, rape, swedes, kale etc.) These brassica acres can then be seeded to birdsfoot trefoil in late winter after they are grazed off. The lack of grass will allow a good stand of the poorly competitive birdsfoot to get established and then these acres can be overseeded with grasses and legumes the same year in the fall or the next spring.

Small scale, on-going pasture renovation is common in both Ireland and New Zealand and needs to become common in the USA in order to have high performance quality pastures.

Grazing Management Controls Your Pasture Mix

Graziers can control the species mixture in a pasture to a large extent with their grazing management. A pasture's composition can change in just two or three years.

• If you graze the pasture short in the spring, you are going to favor perennial ryegrass and thin orchardgrass.

• If you shorten the rest period of an alfalfa/ryegrass pasture, you will shift it toward grass dominance. If you lengthen the rest period, you will shift it toward alfalfa dominance.

• Dairymen interested in cutting feed costs need to first incorporate legumes in their pastures and, second, consider adding a high energy grass like perennial ryegrass.

• Nitrated orchardgrass just doesn't have enough energy in it to make much milk, ryegrass does. If you're going to cut the grain feeding down you have to use high energy forages to do it.

• Most of the problems with keeping perennial ryegrass have to do with grazing management more than cold winter weather. Perennial ryegrass needs to be grazed short in the spring in order to tiller and thicken the stand. Most graziers let their pastures blow up on them in the spring and the ryegrass self-smothers and doesn't tiller. Lax spring grazing results in a predominantly orchardgrass pasture.

• Drought will thin a stand of perennial ryegrass, particularly in low-organic-matter soils recently converted from long-term cropping. An on-going program of overseeding both ryegrass and legumes should be viewed as the cost of doing business.

Answers To Commonly Asked Questions

Should I plow up all of my existing pastures?

Definitely not. Apparently many farmers find something therapeutic in the "starting over" sense clean tillage gives them, but it will set you back many years. Pasture subdivision and, in most cases, a program of annual liming should be your starting point.

There is a saying, "Plant nothing but fence posts for your first three years." I recommend you heed it. Most areas of the country will require a small acreage in brassicas or annuals to balance the forage flow. By moving these areas around your farm you can gradually shift your pasture to newer more improved species.

What if my pastures are sod bound? Do I plow them then?

Pastures become sod bound due to close continuous grazing and the lack of earthworms and soil life. Pasture subdivision and lime (or gypsum) will get you a lot farther and faster than plowing.

Why is initial pasture subdivision so important?

A grass plant's roots grow as deep as the grass grows high. If a grass plant is constantly subjected to close, continuous grazing it cannot develop the root mass needed to become a healthy, drought resistant grass plant. In high rainfall climates the amount of subdivision needed to accomplish this is relatively small, say eight to ten paddocks.

What grasses should I plant?

If you are starting out with clean tilled land, your local extension service will be able to provide you with a list of the most reliable grass species for your area. Do not plant a large acreage in the latest "Wonder Grass" you see advertised. These grasses all need superior grazing management and soil fertility to perform as promised. Save them for later when both your skills and soils have improved. However, try to plant the most improved species of the grasses and legumes common to your area when you plant.

What are the key things that create quality pasture?

Legumes and grass young in age so that it is primarily leaf. Clovers are the main indicator plant of good soil health. Don't give up on them when they are hard to grow initially. They are just telling you your soil health isn't right yet. Good soil health produces healthy, high-production animals. We are what we eat! Increased pasture subdivision beyond the initial 8 to 10 paddock stage will allow us to control the animal's grazing so that we can match the degree of leaf removal to the performance we want from the animal. Removing only leaf produces very high animal performance. The ability to manipulate animal performance through grazing management is a skill that can be developed over time.

Is there anything I can do to instantly create quality pasture?

No. In high rainfall areas it will take the soil a minimum of three to four years to regenerate itself. In lower rainfall areas this will stretch to seven to ten years. You must have patience. There is no other way.

Do I need to drag (harrow) my pastures after each rotation to speed the manure breakdown?

No. Slow manure breakdown is caused by poor soil life which is usually caused by inadequate liming (or gypsum in high pH areas). The dragging spreads the maure smell over the whole pasture and makes selective grazing impossible. The ability to selectively graze is necessary to maximize dry matter intake. Pasture dragging can also increase internal parasitism if done during cool, wet weather. Research at the University of Vermont found no increase in dry matter production from routinely dragging pastures.

Do I need to mow after each rotation to even up the pastures?

No. Under heavily stocked fast pasture rotations on lush green pastures, mature clumps of grass can provide needed dry matter supplementation and can help increase animal performance. If your pastures are extremely clumpy, it indicates your stocking rate is too low or your rotation is too long. Maintaining a fast, 10 to 14 day rotation until mid-summer will help keep pastures from clumping excessively.

Excess production should be removed from the pasture as hay or silage. Mowing and leaving it on the surface of the pasture can smother grasses and legumes and promotes the build up of a highly acid, soil-surface thatch. This surface thatch will prevent successful pasture overseeding and legume reseeding.

Do I need to mechanically aerate my pastures?

No. Tight sods are caused by keeping pastures short with continuous grazing and poor soil life which is usually the result of the lack of annual liming (or gypsum). I have not been able to find any independent research that shows any measurable increase in grass growth from mechanical aeration. Research at the University of Vermont found no increase in dry matter production from any kind of mechanical pasture manipulation.

Pasture Management New Zealand-Style

New Zealand pasture management is definitely not low input. At $3000 an acre, land must produce at its maximum and the average dairyman spends some $45,000 a year on fertilizer--primarily for lime and phosphate to grow clovers. Nitrogen is used sparingly to boost ryegrass growth in the autumn and to grow annual summer grazing crops such as corn (maize), millet and brassicas. Perennial ryegrass needs a high organic matter (5 percent), high-phosphate soil to survive and is not a crop you plant once in your life and forget about.

Small annual lime applications prevent rotting vegetation from acidifying the surface of the soil, keep plant calcium levels high, stop weeds and thistles, help prevent bloat, improve dry weather pasture resilience and greatly improve earthworn numbers. Heavier lime applications are used during periodic paddock renovations. Plantain and dock are prime indicator plants of the need for liming.

Care is taken not to force the grass to grow too fast as this can make the animals sick due to low magnesium. "Cows like a thick soup, not a thin watery one," Vaughan Jones said. This is why he likes the slow release of clover N and of reactive rock phosphate over water-soluble Superphosphate.

Heavy use is made of tree windbreaks to lower the summer winds that produce drying and to make the animals more comfortable in the winter. All stock are wintered outdoors.

New Zealand grass farms are in a constant state of renovation with 10 percent of the land area plowed down for summer annual crops and replanted in the fall with improved grass and legumes each year. In the hot Northland, as much as half of the farm is plowed each year and replanted due to the short life of perennial ryegrass at high temperatures. (Three years.)

Standard practice in renovating pastures is to rotary plow to kill the sod, then chisel plow in lime and plant to corn. After grazing off the corn, the corn land is chisel-plowed twice in the same direction the rows are running and drilled with grass and legumes. Many New Zealand graziers prefer turnips, kale or rape to corn. As soon as the new grass has matured to the point where it resists being pulled out of the ground, the new stands are lightly grazed. Only very young, light stock are used in the first winter and spring as care must be taken to avoid pugging on these sodless soils. This constant renovation allows New Zealand grass farmers to be adding the very latest in grass seeds and legumes and keep pasture productivity at its maximum.

Landscape And Its Effect

I grew up in the almost table-top flat landscape of the Mississippi Delta. A major attraction of one of the parks in a nearby city was a man-made "hill" about 15 feet high. Children came from miles around to roll down this hill and play "king of the mountain." However, as similar as this flat landscape appeared from a car window at 60 miles an hour, farmers soon learned an alluvial plain was actually highly variable due to the natural forces of hydrology and siltation.

A river delta is formed by the main river spilling its water and silt load through a sieve of small very slow moving streams. If you look down on a plowed delta from an airplane, you will see that it looks like a marble cake. The soil colors range from white to grey to black in coils and semi-circles delineating the old stream beds. Each of these soil colors had different properties and would grow different crops. For example, the land along the banks of the bayous and rivers was always higher than the land farther from the stream. It was sandier because the heavy sand dropped out of suspension before the clay. The land sloped slightly downward as it stretched away from the stream bank becoming gradually more dark and clayey until it formed the gummy sticky soil known as "buckshot." As grass farmers we knew the sandy, droughty soil near the stream bank would grow excellent Coastal bermuda while the gummy, black clay of the backlands would grow excellent fescue. The intermediate zone between these two extremes would grow excellent dallisgrass interspersed with fescue. If you put the coastal on the heavy, wet soils it died. If you put the fescue on the upland, dry soils it died. Our success in grass farming was totally dependent upon understanding the subtleties of a seemingly changeless landscape. And so it will be where you live.

The beauty of pasture subdivision is that it allows you to break your farm up into smaller management zones. It is much easier to "see" what is going on in a five acre paddock than a 500 acre pasture. Your initial pasture subdivision program should be to delineate these landscape and soil changes. This will allow you to graze similar soils and grasses the same way. Your landscape will also help decide what species of animal will be your centerpiece operation. Here are some ideas on landscape subdivision:

• Only the top of the hill receives the quoted rainfall for your area. The side of the hill receives much less due to fast run off and the bottom of the hill receives much more due to the run-off from the hillside. This makes the side of a hill droughty and the bottom of a hill wet.

• In areas with fractured subsurface rock or limestone, rain falling on top of the hill will percolate down through the hill and reappear slightly above the bottom of the hill as a band of springs, seeps and sub-irrigated pasture. Avoid putting roads or walk-back lanes in this area as it is wet almost year-round. Roads and lanes should always be built on the side of the hill above the seep zone, never at the bottom of a hill.

• South facing slopes are much more productive than north facing slopes. They green up faster in the spring, grow longer into the fall and are ideal livestock wintering areas. Keep in mind the side of the hill is much warmer than either the top or the bottom as the cold air being heavier flows down hill. However, south facing slopes are also naturally droughty and very prone to complete summer dormancy of cool-season grasses. In the Deep South, south facing slopes are ideal for deep-rooted subtropical grasses such as Coastal bermuda. Keep in mind south facing slopes will be much hotter than the hilltop in summer. Where are your Holsteins grazing on summer afternoons?

• North facing slopes are less productive than south facing slopes. Green-up is slower, and their deep soils are prone to pugging for much of the year. In the far north, north facing slopes trend toward bush. Because they are only actively growing during the high sun months, deciduous hardwoods are often better enterprise choices for very steep north-facing slopes than pasture.

North facing slopes are much less susceptible to drought than south facing slopes. In the South, north facing slopes will frequently grow cool-season perennial grasses. Watch the roadside where you live. Note the tremendous difference in grass species on the south facing slope of the highway berm and the shadier north side of the road. Plan on grazing the north facing slopes during the hottest part of the day.

• East facing slopes have a less harsh, hot sun than west facing slopes. Cool-season grasses are more sustainable in hot, dry climates on east slopes than on the much hotter west slope. Again drive an east-west road near where you live and look at the differences between the plants on the two sides of the road. Note how cool-season grasses tend to concentrate around natural water courses and drainages but virtually disappear on well-drained west facing slopes. Remember it is the lack of moisture, not the heat, that kills cool-season grasses.

• Valleys are very productive during the drier summer months but are absolutely the worst place to have livestock during the winter and spring mud season. They are both wetter and much colder than the side of the hill above them. Where are your animals in the winter?

• Cows do not like grazing on steep slopes. In order to graze a steeply sloping hillside with cattle, both the top and the bottom of the hill must be fenced off and the animals forced to graze there. This is stressful for the cattle and productivity will suffer. If your farm is steeply sloped, consider making sheep your primary enterprise rather than cattle.

• Both sheep and cattle prefer to graze on the contour of the land rather than up and down a hillside. Do not subdivide a hillside in long paddocks in an up and down fashion. Run the fences horizontally with the contour of the land.

Enterprise Selection By Climate

If you study world livestock production patterns, you will find certain enterprises tend to concentrate in certain climatic zones. These are:

Hot and wet: Beef cow-calf
Hot and dry: Meat goats & fine-wool wethers
Cool and wet: Dairy cattle
Cool and dry: Ewe-lamb

Establishing Perennial Pasture In Cropland

Most land that has been in cropping for several years is likely to be low in organic matter, have residual herbicides tied up in the soil and be saturated with annual weed seeds. As a result, when we are trying to start a quality pasture in a crop field we are usually starting below zero and we cannot expect this land to perform or respond to management similar to land that has been in pasture for many years.

• If the choice is between buying cropland or pasture, always buy the pasture. This will put you years ahead in reaching optimum profitable production. This is particularly crucial if you plan to use organic farming methods. However, in many areas depleted cropland is the biggest, and possibly only, resource available. Just keep in mind that it will take many years to get the soil life and organic matter up to the point you would have started from with an older established pasture.

• It is better to gradually convert a farm from cropping to pasture than to manage a whole farm of newly established pasture. This is particularly true if heavy dairy cows are to be used as the pasture harvester.

• A new pasture in low-organic-matter soils should always be established as a grass-only sward with supplemental commercial nitrogen as the N source. Ideally, we would like a pasture that is 70 percent grass and 30 percent legumes. However, because of the low-soil-organic-matter in cropland there is little available organic nitrogen in the soil and if legumes are included with the initial planting they will totally dominate the pasture and shade the grasses out.

• Because of the heavy weed seedbank in the soil and the poor soil coverage of the grass in its establishment year, some type of weed control will have to be employed. The absence of legumes will expand your herbicide options.

• Adding annual ryegrass in your initial planting will give you a thick first-year pasture and help with your weed problems.

• You can start to add the legume component in the second year in the South and the third year in the North if the soil has enough available calcium and phosphate to support legume growth. In many instances it will take three years or more of annual lime and phosphate applications to get these very necessary elements high enough for legumes to survive.

• Perennial ryegrass, the preferred grass species for high TDN pasture, will not survive in low organic matter, low phosphate soils and should be avoided in initial cropland conversions. Endophyte-free fescue and Matua prairie grass are good alternatives to perennial ryegrass for initial plantings. However, most graziers now plant a "salad" of several species. These "salad" mixes are now commercially available and are premixed for your area of the country.

• New grass swards are highly susceptible to drought and insect attack and may frequently have to be replanted or thickened with subsequent overseeding.

• New grass swards are easily damaged in wet weather. Provision must be made for a place to put the animals when it rains.

• No hay or silage should be fed on new grass stands.

• No grazing should be initiated until the grass can be torn off with your fingers without the roots pulling loose from the soil. Ideally, new stands should intially be grazed with sheep as they are both light in weight and offer good natural weed control. If cattle are used, they should be very light calves weighing less than 400 lbs.

• Many graziers like to let the grasses go to seed in their establishment year to build roots and start a soil/grass seedbank. They then take the mature grass off as dry cow hay and/or bedding.

• Pastures capable of holding up heavy Holstein cows in wet weather will take a minimum of three years and in most cases five years to develop. Sheep, stocker cattle and lighter cows, like Jerseys, are much more user-friendly with newly extablished grass farms.

The Healing Power Of Pasture

Research by University of Georgia agronomist, Joel Giddens, builds a powerful case for a perennial grass-crop rotation system similar to that used in Argentina, particularly in areas with warm winters. One somewhat surprising finding of Giddens' research was the ability of sod-forming grasses to build nitrogen in the soil **without** associated legumes. His research found that fescue builds organic nitrogen at the rate of approximately 66 pounds per acre per year. After 6 years of continuous fescue, the soil in the study showed an accumulation of 394 pounds of organic nitrogen with no clover.

Cropland in fescue for 5 years produced a subsequent corn crop of 95 bushels per acre with no additional nitrogen source. Cropland fallowed for 5 years without sod-forming fescue produced only 40 bushels of corn.

How sod grasses build nitrogen in the soil is not exactly known, but Giddens suspects that it is from non-symbiotic N_2-fixing bacteria that use organic matter from grasses. Some 19 pounds of yearly increase can possibly be traced to organic nitrogen in rainfall, but the remainder came from another source in the soil. To rule out the possibility of blue-green algae producing the nitrogen, grasses were grown in greenhouses to eliminate this as a source. The grasses still built nitrogen. Where blue-green algae was introduced, the algae under the grasses produced higher N levels due to the soil-shading effect that produced a higher-moisture surface condition.

There was little difference in nitrogen building by soil pH. More neutral soils built nitrogen slightly faster than acidic soils.

Giddens' research also showed that Southern soils deteriorated rapidly under tillage losing approximately 10% of their organic nitrogen content per year. Tilled soils, which were continuously moist, lost organic matter and nitrogen at a rate 200% higher than forested soils.

His research also found little benefit in the South from many widely recommended organic-matter-building cover-crops and rotations. There was no subsequent yield benefit to the following corn crop by using nitrated rye as a cover crop. There was no yield benefit to the corn crop from using a soybean rotation. There was no organic nitrogen buildup in the soil from summer-annual grasses. It appears that only perennial, sod-forming, cool-season grasses have the ability to build soil-organic nitrogen.

The use of clover and succulent winter annuals such as oats showed very little long-term benefit to building the soils' organic matter because of rapid decomposition in the South's warm winters and hot, wet summers.

For example, turned-under crimson clover showed only a third of the organic carbon remaining after 6 months, only 20% after 12 months and only 13% after two years. Turned-under oats showed only 29% organic carbon remaining after 6 months, 21% after 1 year and only 8% after 2 years.

The Southeast's high rainfall causes extremely rapid volatization of applied-nitrogen sources. For example, 10 milligrams of nitrogen applied as NO_3 to 20 milligrams of moist, fescue roots completely disappeared in 48 hours whether kept aerobic or anaerobic. On sandy loam soil, nitrogen losses due to volatization and leaching can exceed 50% at low rates of application.

Rye grown as a green manure crop to corn showed no benefits to the corn crop. Turned-down crimson clover showed a major yield increase for the subsequent corn crop. For example, turned-down crimson clover plus 160 pounds of nitrogen produced a corn crop of 183 bushels per acre, but the 160 pound rate grew no more corn than an 80 pound rate in fields fallowed without legumes. The legumes contributed organic nitrogen, but also provided additional benefits in improved soil structure, according to Giddens.

Soybeans contributed no nitrogen to the corn because of volatization during the subsequent winter fallow period. However, they did contribute nitrogen to a subsequent rye crop. Removing soybean pods takes away the majority of the nitrogen from the plant. In fact, corn yields from fallowed ground were higher than corn yields following soybeans. Yields of corn following cowpeas were significantly higher than from fallowed ground when either the pods or the whole plant was removed proving its superior nitrogen fixing ability. (For more on cowpeas see Chapter 5.)

Giddens' research shows the extreme difficulties faced by Southern row crop farmers trying to maintain yields without a long, multiple-year, sod-grass rotation.

Can Grass Save The World?

Australian grazier Alan J. Yeomans believes it can. Yeomans is the son of P.A. Yeomans, who invented the Yeomans Plow and developed a low-input system of irrigation known as the Keyline Method that has been widely studied around the world.

Addressing an ecology conference in Australia, Yeomans

said cattle are getting a bum rap on increasing global warming with their rumen-produced methane. The major cause of global warming, Yeomans believes, is the tremendous increase in atmospheric carbon dioxide caused by the burning of fossil fuels and the heavy use of "inversion" soil tillage, which has destroyed the soil's organic matter.

Yeoman's said the increase in world atmospheric carbon, if precipitated out of the air, would form a layer of carbon the thickness of a cigarette paper. Good fertile soil with an organic content of 10% contains a carbon content equal to a layer of carbon 3/8 inch thick, or 100 times the amount of atmospheric carbon released by all of man's industrial activities from the beginning of time.

If we could increase the organic matter content of the world's soils by just one percent, we would take the world's atmospheric carbon dioxide content of the air back to what it was in pre-industrial days. The best way to do this is to institute a program of "pulsed" grazing.

When a grass grows tall, its roots grow long. When it is subsequently grazed off, the roots die back due to what he calls "grass shock," leaving carbon in the soil in the residue of the dead grass roots. This is the fastest way known to build soil organic matter.

By rotating the world's arable land periodically through a grazed perennial grass crop, always using cover crops, and minimizing tillage and nitrogen fertilization, farmers could dramatically decrease the world's carbon dioxide level in just a few years while just as dramatically increasing their profits.

Pasture And Pollution

Until recently the focus of clean water enforcers has been almost entirely upon nitrate-leaching into streams and groundwater and its effect upon human health. High nitrates in drinking water can cause spontaneous abortion and the "Blue Baby" syndrome where newborns cannot get enough oxygen. Controlling nitrates to the point whereby they no longer threaten human health is relatively easy for grass farmers. However, surface-water nitrate-leaching also causes algal bloom in salt water and is having a major impact upon our major fisheries such as the Chesapeake

Bay and the Gulf of Mexico. Free leachable soil nitrates can come from commercial fertilizer, animal manure or rotting legumes.

Nitrate levels high enough to cause human health problems have been relatively rare. However, concentrations of inorganic N in runoff as low as 5.3 parts per million can support growth and reproduction of algae. Tests in Alabama found field runoff losses of free N as high as 68 parts per million from a single application of eight tons of broiler litter per acre. Broiler litter, because of its high free nitrogen content, is a particularly bad nitrate polluter.

Management practices to reduce nitrate leaching include the following:

- Limit manure spreading to the pasture growing season.
- Use nitrogen-feeding winter cover crops (usually rye) behind nitrated rowcrops.
- Use deep-rooted, nitrogen-feeding pasture plants like Matua and Coastal bermuda for maximum soil-nitrogen-capture.
- Spread no more than four tons of raw manure per acre, per year, no closer than 100-feet from a stream and/or composting prior to spreading. Composting greatly lowers the leachable free nitrogen in manure and makes all the nutrients more stable and slower in release.

Phosphorous Cleanup More Difficult

Solving the problems caused by nitrate leaching will be a cake walk compared to those caused by phosphorous. Phosphorous can cause algal bloom capable of killing fish in fresh water at parts per million as minute as those between 0.002 and 0.09. Tests by the ARS have been unable to locate a single stream in Pennsylvania that meets the Clean Water Act standards for phosphorous.

Organic phosphorous, unlike nitrate, is stable in the soil and will not leach. Phosphorous problems occur with surface manure spreading and subsequent runoff and the use of acidulated phosphorous fertilizers such as superphosphate and triple superphosphate, which are water-soluble. Reactive rock phosphate does not cause pollution because it is not water-soluble.

Owen Carton, manure specialist for the Irish Extension Service, told me the solution is for farmers to have a nutrient budget just like a financial budget. The nitrogen and phosphorous in the manure must balance the uptake and use by the plants in order for there to be no pollution. Confinement production systems, which concentrate the nutrients from many hundreds of acres of corn and soybeans, face the biggest problems in balancing their accounts. Of course, graziers are not entirely without sin.

While there are a lot of people fighting the idea of fencing their livestock out of the streams, cattle really appreciate clean stock water. Wisconsin dairyman, Dan Patenaude, got a good increase in milk production when he went to piped water and stopped using the creek that runs through his place for stock water. Research shows that green permanent pasture is as good a nutrient sponge as forest, but we need to be aware of the potential for problems.

What Can You Do To Keep Your Act Clean?

- Plan a nutrient budget.
- Cut down on grain feeding. Use more pasture.
- Take extreme care with silage effluent.
- Grow grass in with alfalfa and other legumes.
- Only spread manure during the green growing season and never closer than 100 feet from a stream bank.
- Increase the composting of winter-produced manure.
- Use more outdoor extensive (non-barn) wintering. (See the section on Shelterbelts for details.)
- If you are using a creek or stream for stock watering start planning for a piped-water system now! In Ireland, one drop of manure in a stream is a $1000 fine. It could (probably will) happen here too.

The Importance Of Pasture Walking

As a grass farmer, your most profitable activity will be walking and observing your pastures. Not riding over them on a horse, an ATV or a pickup, but slowly walking, taking your time and really looking down into them. Every pasture should be walked over at least once a week. It is probably better to do this a few paddocks each day, rather than trying to cover all in one day.

Wisconsin dairy grazier, Alan Henning, said he makes a

game of his pasture walks by hitting a golf ball into the next paddock and then going and looking for it. The key point here is to always be looking down into the pasture rather than across it. A major part of being a master grazier is to learn to observe what is going on in your pasture with both your plants and animals.

Here are some tips on successful pasture walking from New Zealand grazing consultant Vaughan Jones:

• Are your pastures dense or is there bare ground visible? Bare ground can collect no sunlight and therefore will never make you a dime. A handful of grass and legume seed tossed on that patch of bare ground can add it to the profit column. Therefore, always take a small sack of seed with you on your walks. Also, carry a corn knife or grubber for any pasture thistle you may discover.

• Notice how your land breaks and drains. A patch of standing water several days after a rain is bad news. This may indicate the soil is too tight and needs an application of gypsum to add porosity or you may need to cut a drain there.

• Cows that are low in selenium scour as they walk and leave strung out manure pats. Cows that are scouring due to lack of selenium hold their tails high when they dung and keep their tails and behinds clean. Other indicators of low selenium are mastitis, retained afterbirth, abortions, foot and leg problems.

• A cow with a dirty tail usually indicates worms, not selenium deficiency.

• A cow with manure spread from side to side on the rump, indicating the cow's anus is itching is a good sign of coccidiosis.

• Your grazing animals should be docile, hold their head up when they walk, have bright open eyes and a sheen to their hair coat, even in winter. Wild, crazy cattle and a brownish tinged, rough-hair coat is a good indicator of mineral deficiency.

• If cattle enter a paddock and almost immediately bawl to get out, something is wrong. A grazier should never ignore a bawling animal as it is a sign of distress. If an electric wire has not fallen into the water tank and there is plenty of water available, it could be a mineral imbalance that is making the grass taste bad. A lack of sodium will make grass unpalatable. Many New Zealand graziers will fertilize with salt to make their pastures taste better.

A good sign of the lack of sodium is animals licking each other.

• Healthy luxurious stands of clover are a sign of good soil health and as a result are a prime indicator plant. Poor growing clover usually means poor-doing animals.

• If you see clover growing better in your dung pats than in open pasture it is a good indication of low soil phosphorous. If the grass grows better in a urine patch it is an indication of low nitrogen or sulfur. If the clover grows better in a urine patch it is an indicator of the need for potassium.

• A poorly fertilized soil tends to quickly get a clumpy appearance due to uneven growth rates. In well fertilized soils, unpalatable clumps are much less a problem.

• Animals with dry brown hair, especially around the ears is an indication of copper deficiency. Slow clover regrowth following grazing and less than expected average daily gains also indicate copper deficiency.

• Animals with hunchbacks and poor growth is a sign of boron deficiency. There will be little clover and very little soil life.

• Ill health, anemia, pot bellies, swollen heads, pale runny eyes and loss of appetite indicate a shortage of soil cobalt. Also your clovers will refuse to nodulate.

• Cows like short grass. Never let your pasture get over six to seven inches tall. If it gets over a foot tall, drop some paddocks for hay or silage.

• Thin and watery manure indicates too low a dry matter in the pasture. Mow up to one third of the paddock the afternoon **before** the cows enter it to increase dry matter. This practice will also help keep fast growing pastures under control.

• The critical factor in keeping a healthy pasture is not to overgraze to the point where you bare the soil during hot dry weather. If the soil is bared to the sunlight, the wet soil-microbes that are essential for healthy pasture can be killed and replaced with dry soil microbes. These dry soil-microbes exude a waxy substance that prevents water from entering the soil and can keep your soils droughty long after the drought has ended.

Supplemental grain feeding can take the pressure off a stressed pasture. During droughts or winter, grain can be an excellent pasture stretcher. The grain should be fed on the ground underneath the electric fence. There is only three to four percent wastage using this method, not enough to pay for feed troughs.

• A thatch on your soil prevents successful oversowing and indicates poor earthworm numbers. A well balanced, high fertility soil should have 40 earthworms per spade of soil. Your earthworms should be slimy and clean. If soil sticks to them, it is a good indication of the need for calcium. If your earthworms are sick, your cattle are going to be sick as well.

• Cows should never be allowed to get dirty from lying in manure. Their skin has to breathe and they lick each other and can get terribly parasitized. Dirty cows indicate too little shade. Either provide plentiful shade or none at all. Don't have your cows shading up in too small, manure-covered areas.

• Walk back over your rotation for several days. How fast is the manure breaking down. Is the soil surface covered with a thatch of dead material? Is there evidence of earthworms and soil life? If not, why? Do you need to lime? Nature is always trying to tell you what she needs, but you must be out there and observant.

Walking with some sort of grass measuring tool whether it is an electronic or a mechanical meter will teach you what 5000 lbs. of dry matter looks like compared to 2000 lbs. compared to 1000 lbs. This knowledge will be rather quickly internalized and you will be able to quickly figure how much feed your cattle have available, whether you need to speed up or slow down your rotation, add nitrogen or stock numbers, cut for silage or begin to feed.

This ability to "read" your pasture is where you stop being a rancher or dairyman and start being a grass farmer. You can't do it from the truck or from an office 200 miles away. It can only be done by being out there in the pasture, observing and thoughtful.

Tip: Ask your extension service to purchase an electronic pasture dry matter meter and lend it to new graziers trying to teach their "grass eye." Many states and counties now have these available. Does yours?

Think about it...

♣ The more diverse the varieties of plants and legumes in a pasture, the more stable the annual forage production curve becomes.

♣ Spending a little money on your pasture annually saves

you a lot of money in feed costs.

♣ Your initial pasture subdivision program should be to delineate landscape and soil changes. This will allow you to graze similar soils and grasses the same way as well as help you determine which species of animal should be used for your centerpiece operation. Which enterprise and grasses does your landscape indicate will be to your best advantage?

♣ What changes can you make in your grazing management to control the species mixture of your pasture?

♣ Small scale, on-going pasture renovation produces high performance quality pastures. Do you have a renovation program for your farm?

♣ By rotating the world's arable land periodically through a grazed perennial grass crop, always using cover crops, and minimizing tillage and nitrogen fertilization, farmers could dramatically decrease the world's carbon dioxide level in just a few years while just as dramatically increasing their profits.

♣ What subdivisions can you make using your farm's landscape to its best advantage?

♣ Certain enterprises tend to concentrate in certain climatic zones. What criteria did you use to choose your primary enterprise?

♣ Does your climate and rainfall give you a natural competitive edge?

♣ Remember, feed the pasture before the animals, let the animals do the work, use your energy thinking.

♣ When was the last time you took a pasture walk?

Chapter 4: Quality Pasture In Temperate Climates

Year-round grazing in the temperate areas of the US requires the use of permanent pasture (fescue, ryegrass, or bluegrass), Korean lespedeza or summer annuals, and cereal rye.

Here is a brief outline of the year's grazing program:

April to early July--permanent cool season pasture. (Fescue, bluegrass, perennial ryegrass mixed with white clover)

Early July to the end of August--supplement permanent pasture with two hours of daily supplemental grazing on brassicas, sudan grass or corn. Apply 40 lbs. of N in August on permanent pastures and begin to stockpile for winter use.

In early September--plant land from summer annuals to oats and cereal rye. Graze oats and cereal rye from **late October until December**. Oats will provide good fall grazing but will freeze out in mid-winter leaving only cereal rye.

Graze stockpiled permanent pasture from **December to March**. Graze cereal rye from **March to permanent pasture in April**. Rye ground is then planted to a supplemental crop for summer grazing.

The above is a proven system but it is land-extensive and makes no provision for seasonal imbalances such as during the spring lush. The two major weak spots are the September to mid-October period and the month of March. Pasture can be stretched at these times with supplemental grain-on-grass feeding or with stored forages. A problem with an all-grazing approach is if enough land is provided to get through the season's "flat spots" the pasture will be grossly under-harvested at other times of the year such as the spring. The "put and take" system used by university researchers is seldom feasible in commercial situations as most purchased animals require a long graze and a lot of weight gain to avoid negative marketing margins. So, if you want to be a purist, year-round grazing is possible. However, most graziers feel a system whereby at 45- to 60-day stored feeding period is planned-for can actually be more profitable because it allows a higher over-all stocking rate.

A system whereby the spring lush is mechanically harvested, stored and fed back during the September-October and March flat spots is a more land-intensive system but requires more machinery input. Many graziers find total pasture removal in the September-October period (to allow maximum stockpiling for winter) and again in March (to prevent pasture pugging damage) actually cuts total stored feeding time. Self-feeding systems such as direct-grazed silage stacks work particularly well in the September-October period due to the normal seasonal dryness of the weather. However, mud-free feeding structures are best for March use.

A good grass farmer always tries to have his animals directly harvest as much of his annual feed budget as possible but will also always have a stored feed back-up system for insurance. A good grass farmer doesn't hesitate to use stored forages to prevent long-term pasture damage regardless of the time of year.

Compromise With Grass And Clover Swards

The most common perennial clover used for grazing is white clover. It can be grown in every state in the US and every province of Canada (with irrigation where necessary). Keeping a high percentage of your pasture sward in white clover can accomplish two things. It can decrease or eliminate your need for supplemental nitrogen and it can increase animal performance over what a grass-alone sward would produce.

Nitrogen. Research in Northern Ireland shows a ryegrass/ white clover sward containing 30-40% clover dry matter, during the growing season, will carry 80% of the stocking rate of a ryegrass sward receiving 300-350 kg fertilizer nitrogen per hectare (240-280 units of N per acre). Please note the percentage of clover required is expressed in dry matter terms.

Animal Performance. However, the proportion of clover required in a sward to improve individual animal performance depends on the type of stock and the grazing system adopted. For example, sheep in rotationally grazed swards can show enhanced performance, with an average clover level of 5-10% over the season, due to their ability to selectively graze clover. In cattle systems, swards need to contain a minimum of 25-30% clover in order to enhance individual animal performance.

Grass/white clover systems require a compromise between the lower percentage of clover required for animal performance and the higher percentage needed for nitrogen fixing. A clover content of about 30% dry matter has been determined to be the best compromise between the quantity of herbage produced per hectare and the nutritional value of the herbage. If the clover content is very high overall yield decreases, since there is not enough grass to utilize the nitrogen fixed by clover, and while the nutritional value of the available herbage rises, the risk of bloat in cattle is also increased. However, too little clover will eventually result in poor production. Compromise. Compromise.

The most accurate method of assessing clover content is to measure the proportion of clover dry matter in the sward. This is unlikely to be practical at the farm level. A more practical method of estimating clover content in a sward involves visual assessment of ground cover, that is, the proportion of the ground which is covered with clover leaves. However, there almost always appear to be more clover present than there is on a dry matter basis because:

- Clover leaves are more conspicuous due to their horizontal position compared to the more upright position of grass leaves.
- The dry matter content of clover is generally lower than that of grass.
- Clover leaves often appear above grass leaves because of their growth habit.

For these reasons the clover content of grass/clover swards often appears to be much higher than the actual clover content as assessed on a dry matter basis. There is a broad relationship between clover ground cover and the proportion of clover dry matter in a sward as shown in the table below developed by the Hillsborough Research Station in Northern Ireland.

Relationship between clover ground cover and clover content (% in dry matter) within a grass/clover sward:

% clover ground cover	% clover in dry matter
20	5
40	20
60	35

Fluctuations occur in clover content throughout the growing season.

Keep in mind, that our target of 30 to 40 percent clover dry matter is an average of the whole growing season. In most situations, the clover content of swards is at its peak in mid-summer. The spring target should be 30% **ground cover,** indicating that adequate clover has survived the winter and will be able to compete with grasses that grow more quickly than clover in spring. By mid-June, clover ground cover should be increasing to around 40%. In order to achieve the target of 25-30% average clover dry matter in a sward over the entire season, a peak of 50-60% clover ground cover is required by early August.

Clover must compete with grass for its survival and the grass has all of the advantages. The grass is usually taller than the clover which allows it to shade it out if grazing management gets lax and it has a more extensive root system. This allows the grass to "take a licking and keep on ticking" while the clover plant is much more susceptible to drought, pests, diseases and severe winter conditions. As a result, maintaining a high percentage of white clover usually requires an annual program of overseeding.

How To Promote Clover Growth

Care must be taken in the establishment year to not overgraze a newly planted grass/white clover sward.

- Do not apply nitrogen fertilizer.
- Do not apply liquid manure.
- Do not cut for hay or silage.
- Even when using a clover-safe herbicide do not spray until the clover has reached the first true leaf or trifoliate stage.

White clover stands can often be increased through the use

of grazing management. Here are some tips:

- Graze grass swards to the one inch level after winter dormancy.
- Do not let pastures get away from you in the spring and become tall and rank.
- Rotationally graze during the summer so as to provide a minimum of three to four weeks rest.
- Avoid severe pasture pugging.
- Overseed annually to give clover an edge.

Survival Of The Fittest
Clover Must Compete With Grass To Grow

Clover
☹ Can get shaded out by grass with lax management
☹ Susceptible to drought, pests, winter conditions because of shallow root system

Grass
☺ Taller
☺ Hardy because of its more extensive root system

A Year Of Grazing Cool-Season Pastures

Each season offers different challenges for the grazier. By understanding Nature's grass cycle, graziers can maximize their animals' performance. Here's a quick study of what's happening, when, and what to do about it:

Spring. Now is the time to calve, lamb and maximize compensatory gain on over-wintered stocker cattle. The combination of low light intensity and rising temperatures results in fast-growing grasses. But the bad news is that while these grasses may be high in protein, they are low in soluble, non-fiber carbohydrates and dry matter. Consequently, animals must consume a huge amount of fresh spring grasses in order to fill the rumen with enough nutrients and dry matter to effectively grow and produce. The low carbohydrate (sugar) level in these grasses puts a drain on the protein content since there may not be enough energy (or sugar) in these grasses to process all the protein for the animal's use. If energy is too low, animals will use their body fat to help digest nitrates.

To aid rumen digestion of protein and minimize proteins lost as urea, feed supplements of soluble carbohydrates, such as molasses, meal, or grain. Chicory, clovers, or other such pasture species add diversity and increased nutrients to the pasture salad. Free choice hay or straw adds fiber and aids digestion.

Make very fast rounds of 5 to 14 days with dairy cattle. Set stock beef cattle and sheep. Allow dairy cattle to just top the grass and move them to the next paddock. In the Northern one-third of the country, 50 to 60 percent of the land area will probably have to be shut up and routed to silage harvest to keep pasture growth from getting out of control.

Early Summer. Still on a fast rotation. Stems and seedheads are beginning to emerge now, adding fiber to the grass. The fast grass growth during this period no longer limits animal performance. The only limiting factor now is how much grass an animal can physically consume. Now is the time to ratchet back grain feeding and make really cheap milk from pasture.

To maximize gain, mow one fourth to one third of each paddock in front of the animals. This will both keep dry matter intake high and prevent pasture growth from getting away from you. This is a good time to use small, strategic applications of nitrogen fertilizers to reincorporate silaged areas, maintain digestibility and protein for high intakes, and to start to build a forward stockpile of grass for the coming summer grass growth slump.

A good tactic useful in all seasons is to separate animals by grazing habits, bunching the competitive, voracious grazers together and keeping the smaller, more timid grazers in other groups. Eliminating stress from this competitive environment can actually help slower animals graze more effectively.

As grass growth slows, slow your rotation with dairy cows and start it with beef and sheep.

Mid Summer. Heat and prolonged day length causes grasses to decrease in quantity and quality. The amount of moisture a pasture receives now affects the quantity and quality of grasses. The hotter and dryer the conditions the lower the protein content, energy value and digestibility of the grasses. Slow rotation and start to ration the stockpile of grass you grew in late June. Increase grain feeding to dairy cows to stretch available pasture.

Wean beef calves and lambs and drop brood stock to maintenance to save grass. Set stock the weaned calves and lambs and keep pastures under control by rotating yearling cattle, sheep or cows through them periodically. Protect soil moisture by leaving enough residual to keep soil surface completely covered.

Supplemental corn and brassica crops can be useful here in providing extra, highly digestible dry matter and carbohydrates. Limit grazing of brassicas to two to three hours per day. Chicory, red or white clovers can also provide quantity and quality summer feed. Ample drinking water, particularly for lactating animals and those grazing brassicas, is of prime importance.

Autumn. Under irrigation, or in high rainfall areas, the moisture content of fall-grown grasses maximizes digestibility, but fiber content may again be low. Small, strategic applications of nitrogen fertilizers can boost grass quantity, digestibility and protein content and help build a forward stockpile of grass for winter use. However, nitrogen can worsen the difference between rumen-fermentable proteins and carbohydrates contained in the grass. Supplementing with additional carbohydrates such as molasses or grain can aid digestion and minimize protein and energy waste. Chicory and clover are ideal additions to the fall pasture salad. Balance fiber needs with hay or straw.

Leave a higher grass residual on each rotation to build a feed reserve for winter use or shut up one third of the paddocks for stockpiling for winter use. Seed summer-grazed corn areas to oats and cereal.

Sell heavy yearling beef cattle and lambs. Move new crop dairy replacements to a specialist grower. Dry off low milk producing dairy cows and prepare to dry off whole herd by Christmas.

Winter. All brood stock should now be dry. If you are new to MIG, now is the season to start learning your trade. Grass growth, if any, is minimal during this period and stockpiled pastures should be tightly rationed out to prevent the dry stock from top grazing the best of the pasture early in the winter. The rule should be to give the dry cow a little ice cream every day and then make her eat the box it came in as well.

Taking each paddock to a very low residual is a good idea in winter. This will promote tillering and clover growth and allow the soil to warm early the following spring. Apply 200 to 500 lbs. of lime (gypsum in high pH soils) on closely grazed soils after grazing.

Hold stocker cattle to one pound of gain per day through pasture rationing in the early winter and supplemental feeding in the late winter. Do not feed to gain in excess of one pound as this will hinder spring compensatory growth.

Tightly ration out brassica crops such as kale and swedes with time limited, on-off grazing in conjunction with stockpiled pasture and/or supplement these low dry matter crops with hay.

In late winter, frost seed all grass paddocks with 2 to 3 pounds of red and white clover. In areas with well-drained, high pH soils add one pound of alfalfa as well. Frost seed last year's grazed brassica paddocks with 5 to 10 lbs. per acre of birdsfoot trefoil. Do not add grasses to these paddocks until the following spring.

Apply phosphate to grazing paddocks and manure slurry to silage paddocks just prior to spring green-up for best utilization for the following season. Do not put manure slurry on paddocks that are to be grazed within 30 days. Compost can be applied to either grazing or silage paddocks with good results at any time from late February to August.

Overlooked Forage Plants

Here are some forage plants that are commonly overlooked. For details on planting, seeding dates and recommended forages for your area, contact your state forage extension specialist.

Quackgrass. Research at the University of Minnesota indicates that quackgrass, considered a noxious weed in much of the upper Midwest, is equal in quality and mineral content to timothy and smooth bromegrass for forage when harvested at an immature stage.

When harvested at similar maturities, quackgrass had a higher crude protein content and a lower neutral detergent fiber (NDF) than smooth bromegrass. It was also more palatable to sheep than smooth bromegrass. With no nitrogen fertilizer, Quackgrass yields exceeded those of planted orchardgrass and reed canarygrass. With nitrogen fertilization, yields were nearly identical.

The University of Minnesota study concluded that quackgrass appears to be a viable alternative to reed canarygrass and smooth bromegrass in the upper Midwest. Eradication of natural quackgrass stands to permit establishment of reed canarygrass or smooth bromegrass for forage production is not a viable economic option.

Eastern Gamagrass. Eastern gamagrass, an extremely high-quality native warm-season grass, appears to be poised for a major comeback as both a forage and perhaps as the long-sought-after perennial grain crop.

Gamagrass is a wild relative of corn that flourishes in the southeastern states and Mexico and produces a seed that is higher in protein than corn. The plant grows to a height of six to eight feet and has produced as much as seven tons of dry matter to the acre with supplemental nitrogen, and two to five tons with no supplemental nitrogen.

Gamagrass has leaves that closely resemble those of a corn plant and are much wider than most grasses. This high leaf content has made gamagrass a decreased plant under continuous grazing as cattle select it above other species.

Under management-intensive grazing, the plant can provide high quality grazing during the months cool-season plants (such as fescue) are in decline. Gamagrass is considered a good low-cost perennial replacement for such annuals as sudans, sorghums and millets that have traditionally been planted for quality summer grazing.

The range of gamagrass extends from Nebraska to Massachusetts, southward to upper South America. The natural habitat for gamagrass in the tall grass prairie was in wet bottomlands. It is the only grass known capable of making a cross with corn and produces viable hybrids.

The native gamagrass reproduces primarily through underground rhizomes and is a very poor producer of seed.

Matua. Matua has the longest growing season of any cool-season, perennial grass. It is deep-rooted, drought-tolerant and loves nitrogen.

This very high quality "specialist" grass is best used as a complimentary grass to cool-season natural pasture, but its grazing management is so strict it should not form the basis of your whole pasture system.

Matua is best used with high-value animals like dairy, for the finishing period of grassfed animals, or for "popping out" stocker steers prior to being sold.

Because of its deep and extensive root system, matua is much more drought tolerant than most cool-season grasses and prefer drier soils than perennial ryegrass and fescue.

Matua is a non-winter-dormant grass. It will grow all winter if temperatures allow it. Matua grows at a much lower temperature than perennial ryegrass or fescue and will grow later and green up sooner than these two grasses.

Matua must be rotationally grazed on a 25- to 30-day rotation. Grazing should be initiated at the 10- to 11-inch level and cattle rotated off at the 3- to 5-inch level.

Matua will self-smother if allowed to lodge. It must be taken into the winter no higher than the three-inch level. It cannot be taken into the winter in a tall, rank stage and stockpiled like fescue for mid-winter use. Winter-kill is more the result of self-smothering than cold. Matua in Pennsylvania taken into the winter in a tall, rank stage suffered a 98 percent stand loss.

Matua will not tiller under grazing. To thicken the stand, you must allow for annual natural reseeding. Allow the stand to make a seedhead each August, shred (mow) the stand after seed has been produced, and then apply 40 to 50 lbs. of actual N at that time for fall grazing.

Graze the Matua in the fall and allow your fescue and other

cool-season grasses to stockpile for wintergrazing. Matua must be grazed at least twice in the fall to avoid winter kill.

Matua is not susceptible to the U.S. strain of Hessian fly.

Brassicas. Forage brassicas may offer North American grass farmers a way to balance their yearly pasture production, provide a high-quality late-summer and fall graze, and extend the grazing season far into the winter in the colder parts of the continent.

Wisely used in Northern Europe and New Zealand, brassicas have been overlooked by most North American grass farmers and researchers. Few crops offer as much potential as do the brassica forage crops in their ability to improve livestock carrying capacity from August to January at northern latitudes.

Brassicas include rape, kale, turnips, swedes and cabbages. Dry matter yields for no-till brassicas have exceeded 5,350 lbs. per acre after 90 days and have sometimes exceeded 7,135 lbs.

Brassicas can be used in short-growing-season climates to stockpile a feed wedge of highly digestible forage then can be grazed off as needed. Brassicas grow well in cool weather and can withstand cold temperatures with little damage to the plant.

Brassica forage is available when forage yield of cool-season grasses is relatively low and warm-season grasses are declining in quality. For instance, in a trial in southwestern Pennsylvania, dry matter yields of rape in November ranged from 4,370 to 5,530 lbs. per acre, while orchardgrass yielded 1,160 lbs. per acre. In addition, dry matter digestibility, as measured by in vitro dry matter disappearance, averaged 90 percent with rape and 60 percent with orchardgrass.

Summer-planted turnips accumulate dry matter yield in October just as corn does in August. Turnips in Pennsylvania accumulated the energy equivalent of 115 bushels per acre of corn between early August and early November in one trial.

The regrowth from a heavily grazed (July) stand of rape in northeastern Pennsylvania exceeded 4,190 lbs. per acre by early October.

Mature forage rape is one of the best crops for fattening lambs, flushing ewes, grazing stocker cattle, dairy cattle and hogs. Crop maturation has little effect on digestibility of brassicas and makes them ideal for stockpiling.

Turnips. An acre of winter-grazed turnips will support

twice as many sheep as an acre of wheat, according to Steven P. Hart of the El Reno Forage and Research Lab. The cost of planting turnips as a forage crop are about the same as wheat.

Turnips planted in late September and early October are ready to graze in late October. Crude protein levels of 16 to 20 percent and total digestible nutrients of 80 percent make turnips on a par with grain. Turnips are also very winter-hardy and can take the cold better than wheat.

Turnips provide summer energy for dairy cows. Australian dairymen are using grazed turnips to replace grain as an energy supplement for dairy cows on late summer pastures. Turnips are highly digestible but low in protein and must be used in conjunction with pasture grazing.

In Victoria, Australia, turnips are used in a pasture renewal program with the turnip area being used as a sacrifice paddock or feeding area after grazing to build fertility before being planted to improved-grass-varieties the following spring.

Most Victorian farmers feed the turnips with a movable, temporary electric fence two to three hours after milking. This provides about a third of the cows' daily feed requirement. With this strip-grazing technique there is almost 100 percent utilization.

Turnips allow better summer management of cool-season pastures as over-grazing can be avoided. Also, turnips can create an instant long rotation with a low grazing pressure to protect and enhance clover growth and survival.

The secret to turnip success is an early planting that produces a canopy before moisture becomes growth limiting. Late maturing turnips can be grazed more than once if first just lightly grazed.

Grazing Corn. The direct grazing of standing corn (green-feeding) is an accepted dairy practice in the summer dry areas of New Zealand. In parts of Canterbury, the crop has proven to be a reliable alternative to parched and unpalatable cool-season grasses and helps relieve heat-related grass endophyte problems. In Argentina, grazing corn is the standard way of finishing steers for slaughter in the difficult late summer/early fall period. In recent years, the grazing of standing green corn has spread to North America and there are now high protein varieties bred with grazing in mind.

Summer milk production often increases when grazing standing corn as long as the feeding is combined with the grazing of protein rich grass and clover mixtures. Corn does not have enough protein to act as the sole grazing crop for lactating dairy cows. The corn should only be grazed for three to four hours following the morning milking and the cows moved to grass/legume pastures for the remainder of the day.

Using electric fence to break the corn field into paddocks will prevent undue trampling of the crop. Strip grazing, whereby one wire crosses the whole field and is gradually moved forward, is the most common method used to graze corn. Often the corn is knocked down with a tractor prior to grazing so the cows can see where the electric fence is.

Corn can be used as the sole grazing crop for fully grown beef steers that are being fattened for slaughter. Growing cattle (less than 850 lbs.) will need alternate pastures of grass/legume mixtures for sufficient protein.

For a greenfeed crop, seed is best drilled in seven inch rows on a firm seedbed at 65 to 75 lbs. per acre. This high seeding rate will give maximum bulk of leaf with fewer thick stalks.

Sowing on at least two dates four to six weeks apart should provide a succession of green, leafy corn between the feeding off of one block and starting on another. Too many farmers delay grazing until the crop has reached full flower or tasseling when the sugar level is low and the corn is consequently least palatable to stock. Aim to always have grazing finished before the crop develops full flower. Careful timing of sowing and starting grazing earlier can assure a plentiful, nutritious greenfeed for what is normally a difficult feeding period.

Wayne Willkomm of Glen Haven, Wisconsin, reported he grazed steers on Baldridge 500A grazing corn with no apparent problems.

"It's just like a milking parlor," he said. "When I opened the first paddock they ate a little grass between the rows first. Then they started on the leaves, cleaned them up and bit the stalk off to 18 inches. Now, when I open a paddock, they march right in, line up like at a feed bunk and start stripping leaves."

Wayne planted four times in a time-staggered pattern to try to spread the optimum grazing as long as possible. He is experimenting with producing corn-grazed Argentine style finished slaughter steers. For additional information on Argentine grazing methods see the chapter on beef production.

There has been some experimentation using corn as a wintergrazing crop in heavy snowfall regions in Canada. A major problem has been low yield due to the lack of summer heat units needed. In areas with enough summer heat units to grow a high tonnage crop, wintergrazing corn has proven to be very cost-effective.

Corn is not a low-input crop. It requires nitrogen, early weed control and a high tonnage yield to be cost-effective. Direct agronomic costs (not including harvest costs) for no-till corn have ranged from $120 to $200 per acre. If mechanical harvest is used rather than direct grazing, direct costs increase $80 an acre.

Common Weed Helps Prevents Bloat. Research at Massey University in New Zealand has confirmed many graziers' observations that the common cool-season pasture weed, dock, does help prevent bloat in cattle grazing alfalfa, red and white clover and, in fact, when consumed in small amounts actually enhances the nutritive value of these forages.

Dock and non-bloating legumes such as lotus, sainfoin, birdsfoot trefoil and crown vetch have been found to contain a substance known as condensed tannins (CT). CT not only prevents bloat when consumed in small quantities but helps to precipitate protein from consumed forages. Gains in productivity of 10 to 15 percent are thought to be possible by including CT-carrying forages in a pasture mix.

The Massey researchers hope to eventually be able to genetically engineer forage legumes to include CT, which will not only render them non-bloating but allow increased animal gains and milk production.

Think About It...

♣ White clover can decrease or eliminate your need for supplemental nitrogen and it can increase your animal performance over what a grass-alone sward would produce.

♣ A good tactic to use in all seasons is to separate animals by grazing habits, bunching the competitive, voracious grazers together and keeping the smaller, more timid grazers in other groups. Eliminating stress from this competitive environment can actually help slower animals graze more effectively.

♣ What tactics will you use to make sure your animals eat some "ice cream" and "part of the box" every day?

♣ Which forage species have you overlooked?

Chapter 5: Quality Pasture For Warm-Temperate And Subtropical Climates

The southern temperate to subtropical zone of the United States offers tremendous potential for quality pasture enterprises. However in no other region is the term "grass farmer" as appropriate. Quality pasture in this region is not a "natural." It is entirely man-made and requires relatively high and continuous agronomic and management inputs. While costly on a per acre basis, thanks to high stocking rates these inputs translate into some of the cheapest beef and milk in the United States. When the Deep South finally wakes up to the potential offered by quality pasture, the results will be truly awesome.

Bahia, a South American subtropical grass, and Osceola white clover, a Florida developed subtropical white clover, provide the base forage for Harlan and Dorotheanne Rogers Bar HR Ranch in Southeast Mississippi. By overseeding the bahia and white clover with annual ryegrass and annual clovers, the Rogers have worked out a virtually year-round pasture program for the several hundred registered Charolais cows and the 2500 stocker cattle they and their son, Bernie, graze each year.

In the Deep South, the five-month-long, always hot, and frequently dry, summer prevents the use of perennial cool-season plants. Heat-loving, water-and-nitrogen-efficient, subtropical

African and South American perennial grasses such as bahia, dallis and bermuda are used as the base forage.

A major management problem with these grasses is that they grow and mature very quickly, necessitating high stocking rates and very fast rotations (10 to 15 days) to keep the grasses young and vegetative in order to produce adequate animal performance. This necessity for constant grass management has resulted in most Deep South graziers staying with beef cows and calves rather than the forage-quality sensitive stocker and dairy cattle.

Once the weather turns cool in the fall, these subtropical grasses quickly slow in growth and go dormant. This leaves a five- to six-month gap in the annual forage production. These grasses quickly lose their quality in the heavy winter rains and require protein supplementation if used as standing hay. As a consequence, many Southern cattlemen will feed as much or more hay as graziers far to the North despite the warm winter. However, as the Rogers have proven, this extended hay feeding is entirely unnecessary.

To overcome this winter gap in forage production, cool-season annuals such as annual ryegrass, oats, wheat, rye and mixtures of the above are used. To provide early fall growth has traditionally required disking the land to remove warm-season grass competition and provide a water-holding environment for the sparse and infrequent early fall rains. This required the use of expensive "heavy metal" tractors and disks that are otherwise unneeded in a Deep South grazing program.

Cutting Back On Heavy Metal. A major proponent of the "less than heavy metal" approach to grass farming, Harlan Rogers has been trying to find ways to cut back the disking expense traditionally used in an annual ryegrass program. "Last fall as an experiment we took 500, three-hundred-pound stocker cattle, and grazed 50 acres to a one-inch residual, and then overseeded with 25 acres of Marshall ryegrass and one pound of Osceola clover. Those 50 acres had just as good a stand of ryegrass as the land we broke ground with tractors," he said.

"We've spent way more money disking ground than we've had to grow ryegrass. We've cut back on the use of prepared seedbeds as much as possible. All a ryegrass seed has to do is be able to touch the soil to grow. We now just scratch the soil surface with the disk rather than trying to totally destroy the (warm-season) grass."

The Fall Flatspot. Fall is traditionally the most difficult period for graziers in the Deep South. Autumn rainfall is almost completely dependent upon tropical storms and hurricanes, and this is usually a feast or famine situation. Cattle should be held off winter annuals to allow a forward stockpile of growth that can be used during the slow-growing mid-winter period. Graziers have found grazing these winter annuals too early produces a much longer hay-feeding period than restricting the intake of the animals in the autumn (very slow rotation) and, if necessary, feeding supplemental hay or silage at that time.

The ryegrass is allowed to grow to six to eight inches in height before grazing is initiated and then the grass is taken down only a few inches at a time per rotation. Leaving of a lot of leaf surface allows the grass to capture as much of the minimal winter sunlight for regrowth as possible. In the relatively warm winter temperatures of the Deep South, it is often the lack of sunlight that is the most limiting factor in grass regrowth. Fortunately, bahia-grass quality rises as its growth rate slows in the fall and is capable of producing good average daily gains (1.5 lbs. per day) in late September and October.

To provide an earlier and more reliable fall pasture than annual ryegrass, Rogers seeds three bushels of oats per acre on August 30 on part of his land. Oats need very little moisture to germinate and grow, and won't come up and die in a fall drought like annual ryegrass can do. Oats allow his stocker cattle to start grazing in early October, whereas, ryegrass is frequently not ready to graze until mid-November. Oats, however, can freeze out in mid-winter and so are always backed up with 20 lbs. of annual ryegrass per acre overseeded in November.

To avoid the ryegrass-killing fall droughts, annual ryegrass is not seeded until late September. The annual ryegrass and two annual clovers--Crimson and Arrowleaf--are spun on the pastures by the local co-op along with 150 lbs. of ammonium nitrate. "I know you aren't supposed to put clovers in with fertilizers, but this way I get my ryegrass and clover spread for free. We've been doing it for years with no bad results," he said.

Broiler Litter Fertilization. Broiler litter provides most of the ranch's P and K needs, and hen litter provides soil calcium and keeps the soil pH high. Care is taken to not spread too much broiler litter at a time as excessive amounts can set grass growth back. A ton of broiler litter contains approximately $40 worth of N, P and K at current fertilizer prices. If it can be purchased for $8 to $10 a ton, it is a good fertilizer buy.

Mississippi State now recommends spreading no more than four tons of broiler litter per acre per year. Due to the very slow release of nutrients, it is recommended that one application be made per year. This should only be done during the growing season to prevent nutrient leaching. Broiler litter is very high in potassium. This can result in animal health problems. Also, all efforts should be made to keep clover in pastures where broiler litter is being used as a fertilizer. This will help prevent grass tetany, which can be a major problem in broiler litter fertilized pure grass stands.

Clovers Very Cost Effective. Crimson is a very early maturing cool-season clover and starts to grow rapidly in mid-February and signals the end of the winter crunch period. Arrowleaf is a late maturing cool-season annual clover and keeps pasture quality high as the ryegrass starts to mature in late May. "Two more weeks' gain at two pounds a day on 1000 steers is 30,000 lbs. of beef. That will buy a lot of clover seed," Rogers said.

He also puts in one pound of Osceola white clover in his winter pasture mix for subsequent summer grazing quality. Osceola is a ladino-type white clover that has been bred to survive the hot, droughty summer conditions of the sandy lower Coastal plain. "I've never had a case of bloat with Osceola clover," Rogers said.

Osceola appears to produce an excellent stand for about four years before starting to thin. He overseeds every acre annually with one pound as a "just in case" measure. Volunteer crabgrass also helps keep summer pasture quality high.

Summer pasture quality is important because Rogers practices sell-buy accounting whereby he tries to sell his heavy feeders and then buy in his light replacements (250 to 300 lbs.) on the same market. This results in his grazing an animal for a year in most cases during which his pastures will produce 575 to 600 lbs. of gain per head. This produces a gross margin before overheads of around $300 per animal. (For a more detailed look at sell-buy accounting read **Pa$ture Profit$ With Stocker Cattle**.)

Rogers said his year-long stocking rate was equal to one mature beef cow per acre. This stocking rate includes all land needed to produce supplemental hay. Stocker cattle have free choice access to low-quality baled "pasture clippings" at all times to keep dry matter intake balanced on the washy annual pastures. Cows are allowed free choice, low-quality hay when being fed broiler litter to prevent possible digestive upsets.

Use What You've Got To Gain An Edge. Rogers has virtually eliminated his equipment costs by farming out his machinery work to others. He said if you don't have the investment in machinery you aren't tempted to use it and will try to find a way to let your animals do the work for you.

A long-term cross fencing program has reduced the farm to mostly 18-acre paddocks. "Every year we go in and cut our paddocks in half again," he said. Unusual in South Mississippi is the Rogers' widespread use of privet hedge for perimeter fences. These tall hedgerows provide windbreaks and shade for the cattle and privacy for the ranch.

The Rogers have continued to expand their operation by buying nearby cheap cut-over timberland and fertilizing it with broiler litter to get it up to speed as a high-producing pasture. Harlan Rogers is careful to always stay slightly overstocked and make sure animal investment always takes precedence over land acquisition.

Seasonal Dairying In Texas

Bermudagrass has never been thought of as a good grass for dairy cows but a group of East Texas dairymen are finding out it can make lots of milk and money if managed correctly. The secret is to "use the bermudagrass as fast as it grows and then manage to grow some more."

This was Dr. Bill Oliver's advice on how to manage Coastal bermudagrass for stocker cattle 10 years ago. Oliver worked at the Northwest Louisiana Hill Farm Station in Homer, Louisiana, and is now retired. In the late 1970s, Oliver found that Coastal bermudagrass could produce over a 1000 pounds of gain per acre in a 5 month grazing season if it was kept young and growing rapidly.

This research was picked up on by Clifford Davis, an East Texas dairyman, who found the same management techniques Oliver advised for stocker cattle could be applied equally well to dairy cattle.

Davis' success was in turn picked up on by Steve Roth, an Iowa dairyman looking for an escape from snow and machinery costs. Roth, with the help of Davis' county agent, Johnny Cates, added management-intensive grazing to Oliver's and Davis' findings on creating quality bermudagrass and built a prototype 200 acre, 500 cow, management-intensive grazing, Coastal bermudagrass dairy in Grand Saline, Texas, 60 miles east of Dallas.

The financial success of Roth's prototype in the last three years has already spawned two dozen imitators in Roth's home county and has attracted a steady stream of dairymen from all across the South, Southwest and Mexico to "kick the tires."

To his extreme credit, Roth has been free with the financial results of his dairy. Roth's figures show that a management-intensive grazing, Coastal bermuda-based dairy could pay itself out completely in less than five years! Cows, milking parlor, land, house, Cadillac, everything! Returns per cow were in the thousand-dollar range and on a per acre basis were over two-thousand-dollars per acre, per year!

In just three years from start-up Roth has built another 320 acre dairy, turned over the operation of both dairies to his sons, and "retired" to the stocker business on a third new 150 acre farm. "It has never been my intention to become fully employed," he said with a smile. Steve's wife, Pam, is into competition horseback riding and they now travel extensively pursuing her hobby.

The Roth dairies all have deep sandy soils with a base of Coastal bermuda. This is undersown (drilled by a contractor) into cereal rye and annual ryegrass each fall. Crimson and Arrowleaf clover are oversown during the winter. This grass combination provides virtually year-round pasture with the exception of supplemental hay feeding in the fall "flat spot" and again in January and February. All hay is made from surplus pasture. There are no barns, only a high throughput, milking parlor. All haying and machinery work is done by contractors. Each dairy has only one used tractor.

Steve originally started out with a stocking rate of three

Holsteins per acre, but has found two per acre work much better with less need for supplemental hay. The original farm is divided into 40 permanent paddocks of approximately five acres in size. Each paddock has its own concrete stock tank. These permanent paddocks are subdivided with a portable electric fence when necessary to increase stock density or lengthen the rotation.

If he had it to do all over again, Steve would build larger permanent paddocks and would use more temporary fence to make variable-sized paddocks. "How big should a paddock be? The correct answer to that changes every day. You need a system that allows you to be as flexible as possible," he said. Steve's secret to making milk with Coastal bermuda is to keep it young and growing fast. This requires two things--lots of nitrogen fertilizer and lots of cows to eat the grass as fast as it grows.

Steve fertilizes every 24 to 26 days with 40 to 60 lbs. of actual N per acre. In late June, when the grass is growing at its fastest rate, a stocking rate of four Holstein cows or more is required per acre! 40 percent of the farm is dropped from the rotation and hayed to increase the stocking rate.

Potassium and Sulfur fertilization have also been found to be critical on Coastal bermuda. Steve believes he will eventually go to a New Zealand-style micro-nutrient fertilization program as well.

The cows are managed on a fast ten-day rotation in the summer to keep the Coastal bermudagrass young and vegetative. Steve said his Coastal pastures will average 18 to 20 percent protein and 70 percent TDN. This compares to 20 to 25 percent protein and 80 percent TDN for ryegrass.

Steve said the grass becomes more lignified and less digestible as the heat peaks in late July and August. This needs to be taken into account in your breeding season decisions. "The secret to success in southern dairying is to have your cows near the end of their lactation or dry in late July and August." As the days cool in the late summer and fall, the Coastal becomes highly digestible again and almost as good as spring pasture.

From an all Holstein herd, Steve is now leaning toward Jerseys and crossbreds. "We found out that the Jerseys make just as much milk per day in the summer as the Holsteins and half the year is summer here in Texas." All breeding is done natural-service by Limousin bulls and all replacements are purchased.

Steve no longer uses any drugs in the treatment of mastitis for fear of traces getting in the milk tank. He now grafts calves onto the mastitis cows for 30 days and their suckling takes care of it. Total bills for both vet and vaccines average $8 a cow per year and the cow cull rate is down to 15 percent per year.

All calves are raised on whole milk, meal and pasture using McCarville-style feeders for 30 days and then sold to local graziers as stocker calves. "When beef prices were high we averaged $350 for our 30-day-old calves versus $60 for day old Holsteins. That's a big payoff for 30 extra days."

Steve and Pam recently built a large new home on their newest farm. The 150-acre farm is used solely as a "run-off" for dry cows and to grow out the nearly 1000 baby calves the two dairies produce a year. "People ask me how I can afford to buy a farm just to graze dry cows? I bought this whole farm for what I spent on dry-cow hay last year. People just don't put a pencil to things."

The dry cows receive only pasture and no feed.

Why Nitrogen Is Necessary

At SGF's Texas Grazing Conference we talked a lot about the intricacies of how to use bermudagrass with high performance dairy cattle. Several attendees were concerned about the speakers' continued references to frequent heavy applications of nitrogen as being inconsistent with a "sustainable" system. They wanted to know if the same animal performance could be achieved by not applying the nitrogen and just using more land.

I put this question to Dr. Burt Smith of the University of Hawaii. He said, unfortunately, the answer is no. If bermudagrass got better with extensive management and lower inputs, the South would long ago have been the dairy center of the country.

Animal performance on bermudagrass tends to be high in both the spring and fall when the temperatures are cool and fiber percentage is low, but dismal in summer. This is because tropical grasses such as bermuda, increase in fiber content as the heat rises. It is this increase in fiber (silica) in the grass, more than the animal's physiological reaction to the heat, that is the primary cause of low animal performance on tropical grass. The animal's system plugs up with indigestible cellulose and if it can't get out the back end, the animal can't get more in the front end.

Nitrogen fertilization forces the grass to grow very fast and, thereby, lowers the fiber content of the grass and increases animal performance. The trick is that this grass must then be harvested as fast as it grows to keep it young and vegetative. The grass should not be allowed to get over five inches tall and should not be grazed less than two inches. This necessitates very high stocking rates (two to four cows per acre) and very fast rotations (10 to 17 days) or near set-stocking.

Burt recommends that you not start applying nitrogen to tropical grass until the weather turns really hot (90 F plus, 30 C plus) and the clovers fade. Then crowd your performance animals in to achieve the necessary high stocking rate and route part of your pastures to hay and/or silage making or beef cow grazing. These "flex acres" are necessary due to the high variability of summer rainfall.

If the grass in a paddock gets away from you, do not force lactating dairy cows to graze it off. Allow them to top-graze the top two inches and harvest the rest as hay. Shredding pastures frequently produces a surface mulch that prevents clover and cool-season grass seed from coming in contact with the soil surface.

100 lbs. of ammonium nitrate should be applied every 20-28 days to keep the grass fiber low and animal performance high. Due to the high temperatures, lower cost urea cannot be used in the summer. While this level of fertilization sounds, and is expensive, at the recommended high stocking rates used, the actual cost per pound of milk is far lower than the alternatives.

There's a major point I want to make here:

The exercise of keeping the grass fiber low results in a high milk production per acre. But this is a by-product of our goal of improving individual animal milk production and not an end unto itself.

Tropical grass management with performance animals requires an exceptional level of skill, commitment and forward thinking.

• Start with a few acres, learn and provide for maximum flexibility.

• There are many cultivars of bermuda. Choose one suited for your climate and soils. Ask your forage extension specialist for recommendations.

Observations On Deep South Grass Dairying

Dairy quality pasture in the Deep South does not just happen. It is not a "natural" situation and it is not "low-input." For example, East Texas dairyman, Steve Roth, estimates that it costs him $200 an acre in fertilizer, seed and equipment cost to create a dairy-quality Coastal bermuda/rye/ryegrass pasture. However, that $200 investment grows all of the forage needed to support two Holstein cows for the entire year. While the agronomic input sounds large, on a per pound of dry matter basis it is extremely reasonable. In simple cowboy economics, Steve Roth's annual $200 an acre investment in pasture allows the Roth family to pocket about $2000 an acre in profits each year. There are very few legal crops that will allow you to do that year in and year out, but dairy quality pasture will.

With the exception of purchased grain, virtually all input costs--land, taxes, labor, capital structures--are dramatically lower in the Deep South than in the upper Midwest. Egged on by tough state Clean Water regulations and a rapidly falling milk price, Southern dairy producers are shifting back to grass faster than in most other areas of the country.

Interestingly, it is primarily relocated dairy producers from other regions who are moving the fastest in showing the world what Southern pastures can do with intensive management. If all this sounds good to you, c'mon down! You'll find plenty of company.

The following are some of my observations after touring a dozen or so Southern grass dairies.

Autumn Flat Spot Still Looms Large. The four- to six-week autumn transition from warm-season perennials and annuals to cool-season annuals is the primary forage flat spot in the Deep South. I have yet to see a seamless flow across this flat spot from any combination of grasses, legumes, fertilization or irrigation. It appears that some form of stored forage will always be necessary to successfully bridge this gap.

All Annual System Is High Risk. Relying totally on annuals for both winter and summer grazing is both expensive and runs a very high weather and insect attack risk. A sizable percentage of your farm should be in warm-season perennials overseeded with a short-season winter annual. Full-season annual ryegrasses should not be used for overseeding warm-season perennials as they will severely retard the spring and early summer growth of the warm-season perennials. Use full-season winter annuals on prepared seedbeds. Early spring warm-season perennials are more digestible than maturing winter annuals. It is best to route the annuals to hay and silage in the spring and graze the warm-season perennials.

All no-til pasture systems in the Deep South create huge insect problems following the burn down of the crop. Be prepared to spray. Under no-til systems, periodic rotations through dense, shade-producing sorghum-sudan grass will be necessary to keep common bermudagrass under control.

Oats, because of their large size, are very attractive to birds, raccoons and other creatures and must always be drilled rather than overseeded. Also, of the winter annuals, oats will grow the earliest in the fall, but early planted oats are prime army worm attractors. So be vigilant and prepared to spray when you plant early.

Warm-Season Plants. Warm season annuals are more digestible than warm-season perennials. Johnsongrass and dallis grass are the most digestible warm-season perennials but need a high fertility, water-holding (high-organic-matter or clay) soil. Both of these plants are bunchgrasses and are therefore easy to keep legumes in and to overseed with winter annuals. In the middle South on heavy soils, both of these grasses will grow in combination with fescue.

Common bermudagrass is more digestible than many improved bermudas and can be plowed, overseeded and abused in a myriad of ways without fear of stand loss. Just ask any cotton farmer. Common is preferred in summer wet areas, heavy soils, or under irrigation. The improved bermudas should be used on sandy upland soils where droughty conditions are common. All bermudas are sod forming and are therefore difficult to overseed with cool-season annuals and legumes.

Overseeding. It appears the best overseeding method for the planting of cool-season annuals into sod-forming bermudagrasses is the spinning on of the grass seed just prior to the cows being turned into a paddock and then grazing the paddock very short. This method produces a natural "stagger planting" and does not bet the whole crop on one day's climatic conditions. Warm-season grasses that have been overseeded should not be fertilized with N until they have gone winter-dormant.

In a grass dairy, the cheapest input you have is grass and legume seed. Don't skimp on how much you put out there. Remember a pound of cool-season grass and legume can replace a pound of feed on a dry-matter basis. Many dairymen find two overseedings, one at the start of winter and one at the end of winter work best. Seed drills do not form a dense enough pasture to be used exclusively without additional overseeding.

Legumes. Clovers must be overseeded every year in the Deep South. Under Southern climate conditions, legumes should be seen primarily as a high TDN feed replacer rather than as a nitrogen source. Southern grasses without legumes will frequently require grain for energy supplementation.

Irrigation. Irrigation works better on annuals than on perennial subtropical grass. The digestibility of subtropical grasses is higher when grown under slightly droughty conditions. LSU's, Dr. Bill Oliver, said if he had his "druthers" about water and Coastal bermudagrass, he'd much rather have two inches of rain on the first day of the month and not a drop for the rest of the month than rain every day.

Early autumn irrigation to get winter annuals up faster creates problems with warm-season weeds, bermudagrass and insects. Irrigation always creates as many problems as it solves. It is not a panacea.

A combination of irrigated summer and winter annuals and non-irrigated warm-season perennial overseeded with a cool-season annual provides a better and more reliable forage flow than an all annual system.

Breeds And Breeding. Seasonal dairying does not have quite the attraction in the South that it does in the North because climatic conditions are not as extreme and, more importantly, because few Southern dairy producers milk their own cows. However, seasonality in breeding can help make the best use of the grass, and therefore, greatly enhance profitability.

Jerseys make just as much, and frequently more, milk than

Holsteins under Southern summer conditions and will do it for a fraction of the Holstein's feed costs. In fact, Jersey dairy graziers report their cheapest milk is made in the summer, whereas, summer milk costs 25 to 30 percent more than winter milk with Holsteins. Due to their high heat tolerance, Jerseys lend themselves well to a late-winter calving, low-cost seasonal production. The longer your hot season the more the breed decision will shift toward Jerseys and away from Holsteins.

Holsteins work best when bred for a late fall and winter calving season and a once a day (at night) milking during the worst of the hot season. Neither Jersey's nor Holsteins will breed well during the hottest part of the year. A percentage of Northern born and reared Holstein replacement heifers will die from heat stress during their first Southern summer. Northern replacements should always be brought South only in the cooler months of the year.

Limousin bulls are becoming the beef breed of choice for clean up bulls for both Jersey and Holstein graziers. The Limousin produces calves that are either solid red (Jersey) or solid black (Holstein) with little to no dairy look to them. These calves are currently being sold at the top of the beef market in the South.

Fertilization. A regular program of pasture forage testing is crucial due to the South's extremely mineral-deficient soil. Soil tests are of little to no value in a grazing situation. I recommend you start with a New Zealand forage test through Vaughan Jones. (See the resource section.) Jones will tell you the physical manifestations you should be seeing in your cows from what the forage test shows and what will happen when that deficiency is corrected.

Sandy soils retain very little applied nutrients under the Deep South's high rainfall, and fertilization should always be little and often. Applying heavy amounts of superphosphate fertilizer can make cattle sick on sandy, low organic matter soils. Remember, little and often is the key to both productive grass and healthy animals. The routine use of mixed fertilizers rather than separate N, phosphate and potassium is both costly and can produce poor animal health due to excessive potassium buildup. Use what the grass needs, not what the co-op has on hand that day.

Buy a three-point hitch, tractor-mounted fertilizer/lime spreader and spread your N yourself in small amounts following each rotation. You can mount an electric drive cyclone seeder on the front of your tractor and do two operations at once. Keeping one small tractor permanently rigged for overseeding and fertilizing/liming is a real time saver.

Warm-season perennials must be kept very young and fast growing to be of dairy quality. Protein levels of young, two-week-old, highly fertilized bermuda can be as high as 28 percent. Warm season perennials in excess of 20 to 24 days of age are no longer of dairy quality. Rotations must be very fast on warm-season perennials (14 to 15 days) and 30 to 40 lbs. of actual N should be applied after each paddock shift. Keeping subtropical grasses short is not as important as keeping them young in age.

If grass growth exceeds the rate at which the animals can eat it, it should be mechanically removed. Shredding (mowing) pastures should be avoided as much as possible as it produces a highly acid duff on the soil's surface that makes overseeding very difficult. However, shredding is far preferable to forcing the cows to graze old warm-season perennials. The drop in milk production is quick and dramatic.

Subtropical grass hay can be of dairy quality as long as it is cut at less than 25 days of age. After 25 days, subtropical grasses are strictly for dry cows. Subtropical grasses will successfully ensile if cut at 14 to 15 days of age at the same height used for grazing (four to five inches). Older than that they do not have enough carbohydrate to ensile.

Soil temperatures are high enough to grow cool-season annuals for most of the winter in the Deep South and N should continue to be applied following each rotation.

Sandy, acid soils in the South usually have plant-toxic levels of aluminum without liming. The frequent and high levels of N necessary with warm-season grasses require annual small applications of lime to keep the soil surface from becoming extremely acid. This acid layer will greatly hinder subsequent overseeding of cool-season grasses and legumes.

Cows on sandy soils need constant access to minerals. Lack of regular pasture liming and phosphate fertilization can make cattle susceptible to disease and unthrifty on sandy soils. Salt and potassium are particularly important in hot weather to prevent heat stress.

Rotation Length. Rotations should be fast (14 to 15 days) from late February/March to mid-September. After mid-September pasture growth rates will start to slow because of the shortening day-lengths even though air temperatures are still very hot. At this time, the rotation must be lengthened to 30 to 35 days. This is done by cross-fencing the paddocks into smaller paddocks to slow the rotation. A sizable portion of the cows should be dried off at this time, or feed will have to be increased.

Making milk from Labor Day to Thanksgiving in the Deep South is very expensive and should be avoided or at least a minimal part of your operation. Yes, I know many milk co-ops set your milk price based upon your volume of September milk, but put a sharp pencil to it before you try to maximize milk production in the fall in the South.

Leader-Follower Best. Non-seasonal cows should be sorted by stage of lactation and production. High producing cows should be allowed to lead the other cows through the rotation. These cows should only be forced to graze the top inch to inch and a half of the grass sward. High producing cows should be given fresh grass after each milking even if it is only a ten foot strip. The more frequently they are given a fresh break the higher the milk production will be as this stimulates grazing and intake. Multiple small breaks will help prevent cow milling in hot weather.

Dry cows are best kept on a separate farm from the main herd. The grain feeding of cows will eventually raise soil potassium levels to unhealthy levels for dry cows and springers without annual lime and phosphate applications. Dry cows are an excellent way to develop and condition pastures for future dairy expansion.

Supplemental Feeding. Southern dairy cows are grossly overfed. This is because feed recommendations have been for unmanaged, unfertilized low quality, continuously grazed pastures. Why should a cow grazing 20 percent protein pasture be fed supplemental protein? Indeed, why go to all the trouble and expense of creating quality pasture if we are going to feed the cow the same as when we were feeding seven percent protein bermuda hay? Feed is the biggest single variable cost and the one area where profit improvement can come the fastest and be the most dramatic. Overfeeding is particularly costly to Southern dairy producers because feed is much more costly than in other regions.

Profitability and per-cow milk production have little to no relationship in a grass-based dairy. Profits are highest when the cow gets the majority of her feed in the pasture and the smallest part of it from a feed mill. The whole system of feeding cows at the parlor prior to turning them onto fresh pasture is antithetical to maximizing pasture consumption. Feed should be seen primarily as a pasture growth curve smoother. Therefore, supplemental feed should be fed in the pasture (under an electric fence) after the cows have had all the grass they can eat. Not before.

As supplemental feed inputs fall so will the year-long overall stocking rate. Land is cheaper than feed in the Deep South. It is more profitable to have fewer cows, lower purchased feed bills, and less purchased forage than to push for the maximum number of cows per acre. Maximum profitability will be achieved when the cows eat all of the grass you can grow with the least amount of purchased feed.

No doubt as milk prices continue to fall in the South, dairy producers will be forced to re-examine their current costly feeding practices. The Deep South can be the least-cost milk producer in the nation. All it will take is the spread of the know-how of creating and utilizing a dairy quality pasture.

A Review Of Cool-Season Annual Clovers

Cool-season annual clovers are becoming increasingly popular in the South and Pacific West. When seeded in the fall, these clovers can extend the grazing season by providing high quality forage during the period when warm-season grasses are dormant.

One of the keys to good success is selecting the right clover species and variety for your particular location and soil type. Several of the most common annual clovers are described below:

Arrowleaf Clover Arrowleaf starts its growth in the fall but produces most of its harvestable forage from March to late May.

Three cultivars--Amclo (early maturity), Yuchi (intermediate maturity), and Meechi (late maturity) are grown widely in the southern United States on soils ranging from clays to silty loams to sandy soils.

Arrowleaf grows over a wide range of pH, but a pH of 6 or above appears best if other factors are not limiting.

Louisiana recommendations are that eight pounds of Arrowleaf seed be planted between October 1 and November 15 on well-prepared seedbed. For sodseeding, planting should be done between October 15 and November 15. For best result, seed should be scarified as well.

Ball Clover Ball is best adapted to moderately wet loamy clay soils. The prostrate- to slightly-erect stems allow this clover to withstand close grazing. Seedheads produced near ground level under close grazing produce large quantities of small, hard seed, which facilitates natural reseeding.

Peak forage production is in late March to early April. Stands should be seeded during October at four pounds per acre.

Ball clover has bloat potential and care should be taken.

Berseem Clover Berseem is an upright-growing annual clover. Bigbee is a berseem clover Mississippi State University selected for cold-hardiness. Berseem prefers areas with a long, frost-free growing season such as that experienced by the Gulf Coast region.

Although berseem grows well on a variety of soils, it grows best when planted on medium-textured soils. It is also fairly drought and moisture-tolerant.

Louisiana recommendations are to plant between October 1 and November 15 using 20 pounds per acre when seeded alone, and 15 pounds per acre when seeded in a mixture.

Although berseem is considered a non-reseeding clover, Bigbee has successfully reseeded itself in Mississippi.

Crimson Clover Crimson, an upright growing annual clover, has long been recognized as an important legume in wintergrazing programs in the South. It is well-adapted to a wide range of climatic and soil conditions.

When planted early, it produces rapid growth in the fall, but most of its production is in the early spring. It thrives on both light and heavy-textured soils and is tolerant of medium soil acidity.

Under Louisiana conditions, it is recommended that 12 pounds of seed per acre be used when planting in a mixture between October 1 and November 15. All recommended varieties naturally reseed themselves when properly managed.

Pure stands of crimson clover have caused bloat in some

instances.

Persian Clover Persian is an excellent naturally reseeding annual clover. It is well adapted to poorly drained, heavy soils.

It can have both prostrate and erect stems, which develop from low rosettes in the spring. Persian clover grows best on alkaline soils, but will tolerate soils of medium acidity.

Abon, a cultivar developed at Texas A&M University, is the only improved variety of Persian clover. It produces more hard seed and greater forage yields than do common types.

Most of the forage production from this species occurs in April and early May.

When grazing Persian clovers, care must be taken to avoid bloat. Best results are obtained by seeding Persian clover between October 1 and November 15 at a rate of seven pounds per acre.

Subterranean Clover Subterranean is a low-growing annual clover that has prostrate creeping stems with erect leaves. Seeds are produced in a bur, which develops at or below ground level. Thus it has excellent reseeding ability with close defoliations.

Sub cover is tolerant of moderately acid to slightly alkaline soils and there are varieties that will produce well on almost any soil type. All of the recommended bio-types originated in Australia.

It is recommended that 15 pounds of seed per acre be planted between October 1 and November 15.

Overlooked Forage Plants

Here are some forage plants to consider adding to your pasture mix. For details on planting, seeding dates and recommended forages for your area, contact your state forage extension specialist.

Matua. Research at North Carolina State's Vernon James Center near Plymouth, North Carolina, indicates that a one time October overseeding of Matua prairie grass into bermuda may be a viable alternative to the traditional practice of annually overseeding with cereal rye for wintergrazing. A key component of the success of Matua in the South is the complete removal of grazing animals in May to allow the plant to make seed.

In the South, Matua does not function as a long-lived perennial, like fescue, but as a self-reseeding annual. It is necessary to remove the grazing animals for three weeks in May to allow seedset. Once one can walk through and easily knock the seed from the plant with your hand, reintroduce the animals and let them graze off the stems. Unlike most grasses, cattle will readily graze the stems and seeds of Matua.

The bermudagrass pastures should be rotationally grazed with a fast rotation during the summer to keep the bermuda young and vegetative. By mid-summer, it will be difficult to find a single plant of Matua in the sward, but it comes on strongly from seed in October when the temperatures moderate.

Avoiding late summer nitrogen applications helps prevent the bermuda from growing strongly in the early autumn and thereby slowing the regrowth of the Matua.

The above regimen should produce good Matua grazing in November similar to that from cereal rye, but Matua's quality is better than rye and it grows better than rye in cold weather.

Matua stays green all winter and will grow strongly during winter warmups. It also stays in a high quality vegetative state until May, whereas, cereal rye frequently tries to go to seed during warm winters. Average daily gains with lightweight stocker cattle have been in excess of two pounds a day with Matua.

After three winters with Matua/bermuda at Vernon James Center, Matua appeared to offer many advantages to annual overseeding with cereal rye. New volunteer stands of Matua were appearing in other non-overseeded pastures apparently from the manure of animals allowed to graze the seedheads of mature plants.

Johnsongrass. Johnsongrass is native to South Asia and the Mediterranean area of North Africa. It got its name from Colonel William Johnson of Selma, Alabama, whose enthusiasm for the grass and his personal use of it brought the first attention to the grass in the South.

It is best adapted to heavy soils but will make satisfactory growth on any soils that will produce good yields of cotton or corn. Johnsongrass is highly cross-fertile. Under favorable conditions, a plant from one seed may produce a hundred or more stems that will grow from 3 to 6 feet high.

Johnsongrass should be planted at the same time as cotton or whenever the threat of late frost has passed. Use 20 to 30 lbs of seed per acre. Broadcast seed on a prepared seedbed with a cyclone seeder. Disk lightly to cover the seed and firm with a cultipacker.

Allow a seedling stand to reach the bloom stage before grazing or cutting for hay so the plants will develop a good root system. Hay should be cut at the boot or pre-bloom stage.

To maintain a good stand of Johnsongrass hay, do not cut after early September.

The heavy tonnage per cutting makes Johnsongrass hay an extreme soil drainer. Watch your P and K after each cutting.

In tests at Auburn's Black Belt Substation, Johnsongrass was nearly equal to Starr millet and sudangrass as temporary grazing crops for lactating dairy cows. However, Johnsongrass cannot be continuously grazed without reducing the stand. Allow it to grow to maturity once before frost.

Frosted Johnsongrass hay makes good standing hay for fall and wintergrazing with brood cows and heifers.

The University of Arkansas called Johnsongrass superior to sudangrass and millet. Their recommended grazing practices were:

- Start grazing when the plants are in the early boot stage. Apply sufficient grazing pressure to remove the leafy growth in a week to ten days. This will require five or more fenced areas to permit grazing through the summer.
- Topdress with 40 to 50 pounds of actual nitrogen per acre for each four to six week grazing period if moisture is available and additional growth is desired.
- Do not graze from early September until after frost to permit plants to develop good root reserves. After frosted plants are thoroughly dry, they may be grazed off with no damage.

Prussic acid poisoning is likely to occur on plants stunted by drought or frost. Drought-stunted plants should not be grazed until good growth has reached 15 to 18 inches. Frosted plants should not be grazed until thoroughly dry.

Auburn University said that it is a "common practice to thoroughly disk Johnsongrass meadows every third or fourth year to maintain an even vigorous growth." Many producers are able to do this through good grazing management without disking.

Johnsongrass grown as a summer double-crop to winter peas was recommended as a high-quality forage crop in the Black Belt of Alabama and Mississippi, and for use in rotation with small grains to prevent disease buildup.

Auburn's recommended rotation in the 1960s was:

- First year--oats for grazing and grain. Plant Johnsongrass in summer and overseed with Caley peas in fall.
- Second year--volunteering Caley peas and volunteering Johnsongrass.
- Third year--volunteering Caley peas and Johnsongrass. Prepare land or sodseed wheat in October or early November.
- Fourth year--wheat for grazing and grain. Prepare land early; plant wheat in October.
- Fifth year--wheat for grazing and grain. Prepare land early; plant oats in September.
- Sixth year--oats for grazing and grain. Prepare land early; plant oats in September.

Three fields were used in the rotation at Auburn.

Johnsongrass seed is both scarce and expensive. Many of the certified varieties available have been "over-improved" and have too many of the sorghum-sudan characteristics. Agronomists at Mississippi State urge you to look for a nearby seed source you can combine, such as a roadside or an abandoned field.

Seed yields may run as high as 500 lbs per acre. Seeds are dormant when first mature and may remain so for several months.

Dallisgrass. This is the South's longest warm-season grazing crop. Dallisgrass is a warm-season perennial grass, which is well adapted to loam and clay soils with annual rainfalls of 35 inches or more from Texas to southern New Jersey. In drier climates, it does well in moist creek and river bottoms.

Research in Louisiana has shown it to have higher in vitro true digestibility (forage quality) than bahia, common and Coastal bermuda when grown under similar conditions. This is partially due to the higher leaf percentage of dallisgrass than other warm-season perennial grasses. As a result, dallis is one of the two preferred warm-season grass species for dairy and stocker cattle in the South. (Johnsongrass is the other.)

Dallisgrass is a bunch grass that grows in clumps with numerous leaves emerging from a knotted base composed of very short rhizomes. This allows the plant to withstand very close grazing and survive, as its growing points are below the soil's surface. This bunched growing pattern also allows for much easier overseeding of annual ryegrass and legumes than sod-forming grasses like bermuda. Dallis does not respond to nitrogen as well as bermuda, but is an ideal companion grass for white clover.

White clover and dallis are very compatible species since they are adapted to the same soils and climate. Both can tolerate close grazing. White clover and dallis have been shown to provide the most economical production on the black prairie soils of Alabama, Mississippi, Louisiana and southeast Texas. In the more northerly Alabama-Mississippi prairie, fescue, dallis and white clover grown together can provide a year-round, perennial-grass pasture system.

Dallisgrass will frequently volunteer into existing grass stands when phosphate fertilizer is applied. In east Texas, one and a half to two acres of white clover and dallisgrass will support a cow-calf unit from March 1 to late November if fertilized with 60 lbs. of phosphate annually.

Dallisgrass poisoning can occur when cattle are turned into mature stands of grass with seedheads that have become infected with ergot. The cattle quickly become ergot "junkies" and enjoy getting high on the infected seedheads. They eventually get so drunk they become uncoordinated and fall down, but quickly recover when removed from the infected pasture. Mowing infected pastures at a six-inch height removes the problem.

Research at Texas A&M has shown the best new stands of dallisgrass occur when planted at 6 to 8 lbs. per acre in the fall in conjunction with annual ryegrass and clover. The dallisgrass will not emerge until the ryegrass has matured in the following spring. The companion crop prevents erosion, provides wintergrazing and reduces spring weeds.

Kudzu. I am always amused when someone points out that his particular species or breed of animal will "even eat kudzu." Kudzu as a forage is only slightly less nutritious than alfalfa and was originally brought to the South as a legume that could be used during the summer slump when white and red clovers faded in the heat. Its use as an erosion control cover-crop was very secondary to its forage benefits when originally introduced.

In the 1930s and 1940s it was common to plant kudzu with Crimson or southern winter peas to provide both summer and winter grazing.

Kudzu was traditionally deferred until July, August, and September and was time-limited grazed. Like most high-quality forages, kudzu is easily killed with close continuous grazing.

Mississippi State extension in 1949 pointed out that one acre of kudzu could graze three dairy cows per acre if time-limited to no more than two hours a day, but only one per acre if grazed continuously. (Louisiana research found continuous grazing of kudzu tainted the milk flavor. Kudzu is best grazed for two hours following the morning milking.)

Kudzu was also recommended for hogs. An acre of kudzu would support 12 to 15 100-pound pigs or five dry sows with supplemental grain under continuous grazing.

"Kudzu is as good as the best grazing," Mississippi State crowed. In October, following the removal of the cattle or hogs, Mississippi State recommended sowing Crimson and ryegrass or southern winter peas broadcast into the kudzu. These cool-season plants could then be grazed from late fall until April 15 the following year. By allowing the clover, ryegrass, or peas to make seed, the plants would volunteer the following winter. The kudzu was then deferred until July.

Cowpeas. Also known as blackeyed peas, cowpeas were one of America's earliest legume "break" crops. A native of Africa, Colonial settlers saw that corn, cotton and tobacco crops grew better after a year in cowpeas. Both Thomas Jefferson and George Washington were very vocal in the praise of the value of cowpeas as rotation crops.

Cowpeas are higher in nutritive value than most legumes for either forage or human consumption. Eating cowpeas and cornbread on New Year's Day is thought to bring good luck for the entire year in Texas and other parts of the South.

Cowpeas make a good, if hard to cure, hay and a good grazing crop for yearling cattle.

Research in Louisiana has shown that 800 lb. yearlings will gain two pounds a day on cowpeas in the worst of the summer slump. Gains of calves are about half those of yearlings and cannot be considered economical.

Seed costs can be high if bought through a horticultural outlet. They are lower through an established forage seed dealer or direct from the grower.

While traditionally a Southern crop, there are new varieties that can be grown as far north as the Great Lakes states.

Cowpeas do better if grazed down and then allowed to regrow. However, they will withstand continuous grazing. In the Louisiana research, cowpeas supported an average of 1000 lbs. of bodyweight for a July-September graze.

While traditionally grown following small grains or winter annuals, cowpeas can be planted anytime after warm weather is assured and will grow until frost. Cowpeas are traditionally planted by broadcasting at the rate of one and a half bushels per acre for forage. Cowpeas can be grown with corn for a high protein silage or grazing crop.

Annual Lespedeza. Annual lespedeza covered several million acres of the South and lower Corn Belt in the late 1940s providing high-quality summer legume pasture for both dairy and beef cattle. Common or Japanese clover was accidentally introduced in 1846 at Monticello, Georgia. Korean, another major variety of annual lespedeza, was introduced by the USDA at Arlington, Virginia in 1919.

Common dominated the lower South and Korean the upper South and lower Corn Belt states. The legume was primarily used as summer pasturage for stocker cattle and dairy stock following small grain harvest. Unlike alfalfa and white clover, lespedeza could grow on thin, acid soils, with a minimum of phosphate, potash or nitrogen. However, research in Missouri showed that lime on heavily acid soils could frequently triple lespedeza yields.

Lespedeza can be sown in the South anytime from midwinter to early spring. Broadcasting without covering will normally develop satisfactory stands when sown in permanent pastures (non-sod forming), idle land, or on fields planted to fall-sown small grains or annual ryegrass.

The inoculum for lespedeza is the same as for cowpeas.

Lespedeza is highly sensitive to soil temperature and does not start to grow until late spring or early summer. In most of the South, its useful pasture season is only three to four months long.

The most ideal use for lespedeza is for summer pasture following small grains or annual ryegrass. Once established, lespedeza may be managed for successive years through volunteer reseeding.

Lespedeza can withstand close, continuous grazing and can support one mature beef cow per acre using continuous grazing. Average daily gain on stocker cattle for a 100-day graze is around 1.5 lbs.

Lespedeza cannot maintain itself in bermudagrass, carpetgrass, or lightly grazed bluegrass. It will do well in open-sods, such as timothy, orchardgrass, dallisgrass, and tall fescue.

Animal performance from pasture-lespedeza mixes is not as high as pure stands of lespedeza following small grains. Ground lespedeza seed compares favorably with cottonseed and soybean meal as a protein source for dairy cattle.

Lespedeza will reseed itself from the Atlantic Coast states to eastern Texas, Oklahoma, and Kansas. North of the Iowa-Missouri line the value of lespedeza becomes limited. Korean lespedeza is recommended for eastern Oklahoma, northern Arkansas, Missouri, southern Illinois, and across southern Pennsylvania and New Jersey.

Lespedeza can provide a quality legume forage during the seasonal summer slump of perennial pastures and a cheap, high-quality summer pasture for small grain and annual ryegrass graziers.

Tropical Corn. Tropical corn offers Southern graziers a high tonnage, high TDN doublecrop option behind cool-season annual pasture. The extremely drought-resistant Central American corn can be planted in early June and will produce 12 to 18 tons of dry matter per acre by early September. The corn can be used for silage, greenchop or direct grazing. Tropical corn is not recommended for grain production due to low grain yields and very slow plant drydown.

Tropical corn tests high in fiber, but research at Mississippi State's Coastal Plains Experiment Station found the fiber to actually be far more digestible than the lab tests indicated. Both the stalk and leaves have been found to be highly digestible making the plant ideal for whole plant use.

At the dairy-oriented Coastal Plains Experiment Station, the annual ryegrass is cut for hay in May and tropical corn is no-tilled into the stubble in early June, chopped for silage in early September and the pastures immediately no-tilled back to oats and annual ryegrass.

Seven Secrets Of Pasture Success

1. Get animals in sync with pasture.
2. Match stocking rate to pasture growth.
3. Develop a dense pasture.
4. Keep pasture young and vegetative.
5. Extend grazing season.
6. Extend growing season.
7. Match animal enterprise to pasture quality.

Think About It...

♣ Leaving a lot of leaf surface allows the grass to capture as much of the minimal winter sunlight for regrowth as possible. In the relatively warm winter temperatures of the Deep South, it is often the lack of sunlight that is the most limiting factor in grass regrowth.

♣ Is broiler litter an option for N, P, and K in your area?

♣ Are your pastures clover-rich?

♣ What elements on your farm can you use to gain an edge?

♣ How flexible are your paddock subdivisions?

♣ The secret to success in southern dairying is to have your cows near the end of their lactation or dry in late July or August. Have you planned to minimize heat's effect on your dairy cows?

♣ Nitrogen forces the grass to grow very fast. What is your management-intensive grazing plan for managing this fast growth?

♣ What's your backup plan if this fast-growth grass gets away from you?

♣ Some form of stored forage will always be necessary to successfully bridge the autumn flat spot. How have you prepared to get through this grass slump?

♣ Relying totally on annuals for both winter and summer grazing is both expensive and runs a very high weather and insect attack risk. A sizable percentage of your farm should be in warm-season perennials overseeded with a short-season winter annual. What is the pasture mix for your climate?

♣ What climate were your animals bred for?

♣ In a grass dairy, the cheapest input you have is grass and legume seed. How much have you added to your pastures recently?

♣ Cows on sandy soils need constant access to minerals. Lack of regular pasture liming and phosphate fertilization can make cattle susceptible to disease and unthrifty on sandy soils. Salt and potassium are particularly important in hot weather to prevent heat stress. Have you fed your pastures to prevent heat stress in your animals?

♣ Tropical grass management with performance animals requires an exceptional level of skill and forward thinking. Have you been practicing maximum flexibility with a few acres?

♣ Are you ready for the next step?

♣ High producing cows should be allowed to lead the other cows through the rotation. Have you sorted your animals by stage of lactation and production?

♣ Feed should be seen primarily as a pasture growth curve smoother. Therefore, supplemental feed should be fed in the pasture after the cows have had all the grass they can eat. Not before. What's the percentage of feed costs in your operation?

♣ Have you overlooked any forages that grow in your area and climate, which could be added to your pasture mix?

Chapter 6: Pasture Irrigation

Irrigated pasture when used in combination with high-value producing animals can be one of your most profitable irrigated crops. However, grazing and water management must be exceptional for exceptional results. For economical irrigation, irrigated pasture must be dense pasture. It makes no sense to irrigate sub-standard pasture.

• Use annual ryegrass and frequent reseeding of perennials to keep the sward dense. Using dry cows or ewes to graze the paddock to a one inch residual, once a year, will promote plant tillering and dense pasture. Allowing plants to fully mature and go to seed will create open spaces in the pasture sward, which wastes irrigation water.

• Irrigated pasture must be well-fertilized to fully express the growth potential that exists. Fertilizers should be spread out over the growing season to be most effective as irrigation speeds nutrient uptake. In an irrigated pasture, water soluble forms of nitrogen and phosphate are quickly used up or leached out of the root zone.

• Because of the necessity to keep animals off freshly watered areas to prevent pugging and pasture damage, rotational grazing is always used with irrigated pasture. Most irrigated cool-season pastures are maintained on a 14- to 30-day rotation. With stocker cattle and lambs a 10-paddock subdivision is usually adequate. Dairy pastures are usually further subdivided with portable fences so as to give the dairy cattle a fresh break after each milking.

- Irrigation allows cool-season perennials to survive in extremely summer-hot regions such as California, Mexico and southern Africa. Cool-season pastures offer a longer period of quality growth than warm-season pasture-species and should be the basis of irrigated pasture. In the San Joaquin Valley of central California, dallisgrass, a warm-season perennial is added to cool-season pasture mixes (Ladino clover, annual and perennial ryegrass and tall fescue) to keep summer growth rates high. Dallisgrass is a bunch grass and does not crowd out companion cool-season grasses and legumes the way bermudagrass does.
- Maintaining a high summer-residual on cool-season grasses will prevent low-growing bermudagrass from becoming a problem, will slow soil drying and keep plant regrowth and animal production rates high. Periodic paddock rotation through sudan-grass or corn will also shade out bermuda.
- In the Sacramento Valley of Northern California, orchard-grass is used to replace the warm-season dallisgrass. Ladino white clover is California's favorite irrigated legume and was grazed in pure stands in the 1940s and 1950s. It requires frequent waterings to grow in the mid-summer heat and fertilization with phosphorous and sulfur.

Take Care With Hot Weather Irrigations

- Ladino clover and alfalfa are susceptible to "scalding" if irrigated during very hot weather (in excess of 100F/35C). Stands may be completely killed in some cases. Irrigation should only be done at night during very hot weather.
- Birdsfoot trefoil requires less water than Ladino clover, is non-bloating, will grow in alkaline soils and does well on deeper non-hardpan soils. It grows well in the very hot Imperial Valley of California in combination with ryegrass and dallisgrass.
- In winter-cold areas, smooth brome, Kentucky bluegrass, tall oatgrass, orchardgrass, tall fescue, alfalfa and white clover are frequently used in irrigated pastures. Keep in mind the longer the growing season the more cost-effective irrigation is.

• Spot mowing is the best control for minor infestations of buckhorn, dock, thistles and sedges that tend to come into irrigated pastures. Bush-Hog has an excellent ATV pull-behind mower for such spot mowing jobs. Whole-paddock mowing is not recommended unless the pasture is becoming orchard or dallisgrass dominant. Severe weed problems may require a rotation through a tall-growing, shading crop such as sudangrass to regain control.

Bloat Can Be A Midsummer Problem

Irrigated cool-season pastures tend to become legume dominant in mid-summer and particular care must be taken to prevent bloat at that time.

• Feeding hay or straw free choice, fertilizing with nitrogen in early summer just before the slump in grass production, and night pasturing on adjacent sudangrass paddocks are some ways to keep bloat down.

• Ideally, legume content of the pasture should never get over 40 percent of the paddock but this is very difficult to manage for in mid-summer with cool-season grasses. Results from water and free-choice-delivered bloat-preventatives have been variable.

• Stocking rates must be precise to keep costs low. Access to lower cost non-irrigated land during the cold, wet season can help irrigated stocking rates remain high during the warmer dry season. In California, a half acre of irrigated pasture should be able to graze one Jersey cow for 10 months. Dry cows should be contracted out or grazed on non-irrigated pastures as irrigated grass is too valuable to waste on dry cows.

• High-value-producing animals such as dairy, lambs being finished for slaughter, or stocker cattle should be used with high-cost irrigated pasture. Stocker cattle are most cost-effective when grown and framed on non-irrigated range or pasture and then "popped out" during a 50- to 60-day graze on irrigated pasture to release built up compensatory gain. 60 percent of total pasture costs with irrigated pasture are for water and irrigation labor.

Well Drained Soils Best For Irrigation

• Sandy, gravely soils are best for irrigated pasture. Try to avoid heavy clays. Soils that crack in dry weather are poorer candidates for pasture irrigation due to extreme pugging problems during unexpected periods of natural rainfall. Also, coarser soils such as sandy loams make it easy for roots to take up water and nutrients. Clays hold water better but make roots work harder to grow.

• On wet-natured soils, reed canarygrass, alsike clover, strawberry clover and big trefoil can be used to good advantage.

• A stand-off area (deep sawdust, wood bark) is definitely needed with irrigated pastures due to potential pugging during unexpected periods of natural rainfall. I have seen irrigated stands ruined in just a few days of rain. If pugging damage occurs overseed immediately with annual ryegrass to get production quickly back up to speed.

• Irrigation should be little and often so that all water applied is absorbed by plant roots and not lost to ground drainage. The top 10 inches of the soil is most critical for grass growth as that is where the majority of the root mass is. Your aim should be to keep this top 10 inches moist at all times in order to keep cool-season plants in hot weather climates. An irrigation every five to eight days should accomplish this in bright weather. Cloudy weather slows evaporation and transpiration and will allow you to slow the irrigation as well.

• In California, most pastures receive 60 inches of water in 15 irrigations. However, water use can vary from as low as 30 inches to as high as 120 inches depending upon summer temperatures and cloud cover. Monitoring soil moisture levels is important in preventing unnecessary irrigations.

Types Of Irrigation

Borderdyke flood irrigation requires very flat land and a large capital investment in headraces, levees and borders. However, operating costs are low. Flood irrigation is best used in areas where the dry period is definite and long and a governmental water supply infrastructure is in place.

Irrigating from rivers and streams is a very iffy proposition today due to governmental water use regulations. Quite often you will find your irrigation supply cut off when you need it the most.

Centerpivots and linear irrigators have large capital and operating costs but are great labor savers. Care must be taken not to oversubdivide center pivots as the rest period on irrigated pasture is quite short. A major problem with irrigated pasture is letting the out paddocks get too mature. Fast rotations must match the fast growth of irrigated pasture.

When **mined ground water** is used, mineral salt buildup in the soil can be a problem. This can be helped with good drainage, frequent irrigations to leach away the salts, and/or the use of salt-tolerant grass species. Birdsfoot trefoil, bermudagrass, rhodesgrass and Matua prairiegrass are all salt-tolerant species. White Dutch clover, alsike clover, red clover and ladino clover all have a very low tolerance to salt. (See section on gypsum in Chapter 2.)

Portable, high-pressure spray-irrigation has both a high capital cost, a high operating cost and a high labor cost for moving the irrigators around the farm. These are best used in a supplementary manner to keep stocking rates high in normally wet environments, for example, to insure adequate cool-season annual pastures for fall calving dairy cows in the Deep South.

Due to the wonder of compensatory gain, supplementary irrigation is not recommended for stocker cattle in normally reliable, wet climates where drought periods tend to be short.

Low pressure irrigation from dams fed by rainwater, groundwater run-off and even dairyshed wastewater may offer a lower cost yet "environmentally friendly" system. Dairymen who have a large enough reservoir for their dairyshed wastewater can kill two birds with one irrigation--water and nutrient recycling.

Soils where dairy shed wastewater are sprayed must be well-drained in order to prevent the creation of anaerobic septic conditions that can kill the pasture and possibly create a health hazard for the cows.

A **rain-harvesting technique** has been developed by Gerald Van den Bosch in Tasmania and now New Zealand using small-scale dams to hold natural rainfall for use during the dry season. This is creating a lot of interest around the world. Van den Bosch said 5000 to 6000 cubic meters of stored rain water will irrigate an acre of pasture for 120 days. A small dam 700 feet long and 30 feet high can create a reservoir large enough to irrigate 250 acres of pasture for 120 days. Such structures are recommended for areas where rainy season rainfall is reliable (to refill the structures) and the dry season is relatively short (100 to 120 days).

Multitudes of these upland small-scale irrigation reservoirs could greatly alleviate valley flash flooding and downstream rainy season flooding. Unfortunately, strictly interpreted surface water regulations in the West have so far stifled this low-cost irrigation innovation in the United States. However, it may have applications as a supplementary source of irrigation in the Eastern half of the country where surface rainwater regulations do not currently exist or are not being enforced.

Other "downunder" ideas such as **keyline subsoiling**, which slows the rush of water down a hillside and diverts it into the ground, and the use of planned hillside-forests to create **natural sub-irrigation zones** at the bottom of slopes appear to offer ways to maximize the use of naturally occurring rainfall. These "low-tech" ideas need to be investigated more fully in North America where our rainfall tends to be highly variable even in the "wet" areas.

Managing Perennial Ryegrass In Hot Climates

Julia Perreira is an agricultural consultant in Natal, South Africa. She said the primary cause of stand failures with irrigated perennial ryegrass was incorrect grazing management. Perennial ryegrass must be kept shorter than annual ryegrass. Perennial ryegrasses are profuse-tillering plants and tiller throughout the year. If these new tillers are not allowed to receive sunlight they will die out and shorten the life of the pasture.

Spring Management. In the spring of the year, the grass should not be allowed to rest longer than 12 to 15 days between grazings as the new leaves turn over very rapidly. Grazing should be so managed as to take down to three inches periodically but prevent the grass from becoming taller than eight inches between rotations. Continuous grazing with a put-and-take manipulation of stock numbers can also be used to create the rotational effect but is not as easy as rotational grazing.

If perennial ryegrass is allowed to grow taller than eight inches in height during the spring months, autumn production will be severely retarded due to poor new tiller survival.

Summer Management. The rest period should be lengthened as the grass growth slows down in the summer. Never graze perennial ryegrass shorter than three inches and never allow it to get over nine to ten inches in height during the summer. Walk your pasture and make sure new tillers are not being shaded out due to too lax a grazing management.

Autumn Management. Speed up the rotation as the grass begins to grow more rapidly in the autumn. As winter approaches graze the paddocks only slightly to build a forward-feed reserve for winter.

Winter Management. In cold winter areas, increase the rest period between grazing to 35 days or more. In warm winter areas, light grazing provides for a more rapid grass recovery. However, perennial ryegrass can be grazed extremely short in the winter with no subsequent damage to the stand.

Planting Time. Perennial ryegrass can be planted at any time of the year but is best planted in the late autumn, early winter in warm winter areas and in early autumn in cold winter areas.

Seeding Rate. Seed can be drilled at a rate of 20 lbs. per acre or broadcast at a rate of 25 to 30 lbs. per acre. Plant clover with grass. White and Haifa are the best combination clovers in South Africa. If clover seed is broadcast only use lime-pelleted, pre-inoculated seed for ultra-violet sunlight protection

Irrigation Management. Perennial ryegrass is a shallow-rooted crop and requires frequent small amounts of water to be productive in hot, summer-dry areas. One inch of water per week has been the most successful irrigation rate in South Africa. Rainfall should be taken as a 50% effective rate. For example, one inch of rain should be figured as 1/2 inch of water and irrigation should be used to provide the remainder. Take care to not over-irrigate, particularly in winter.

Fertilization Management. Perennial ryegrass requires a higher-than-normal fertility level. P levels should be at least 15% higher than those recommended for annual ryegrass. K levels should be around 150 ppm. Lime to bring soils above 5. Maintenance applications of P should be made in spring and K should be made in the fall. Topdress with 200 lbs. of lime per acre every year if acid fertilizers are used. Supplemental N can be applied in very small rates (25 units of actual N per acre) during periods of the year when rest periods are shorter than 20 days. This may be increased to 35 units of actual N when the grazing cycle is no longer than 20 days.

Care must be taken with supplemental N so as to not promote more growth than can be harvested. Allowing perennial ryegrass to grow taller than eight inches is a major cause of stand decline in perennial ryegrass.

Think About It...

♣ Perennial ryegrass will grow in hot climates with irrigation.

♣ Perennial ryegrass is a high energy grass that can replace grain.

♣ What are you doing to promote plant tillering and dense pasture?

♣ Are your pastures suitable for irrigation?

♣ What is your plan to prevent bloat in mid summer?

♣ Are you irrigating unnecessarily?

Chapter 7: The Competitive Edge--MIG

There are several excellent books available on management-intensive grazing. This is not one of them. However, MIG, as we call it, is a very important part of a quality pasture program. MIG is what puts the steering wheel, clutch and brake on your self-harvesting animal combine.

While per acre increase in stocking rate and gain are usually listed as the primary benefit of management-intensive grazing, Keith Milligan, senior pasture extension officer in New Zealand, gave me a longer list.

1. A **better return on total investment** through a higher stocking rate, increased per head production, and lower death losses from better animal observation due to animal bunching.

2. A **lower labor input** due to more even year-long work load and no high peak periods due to massive haying or feeding.

3. A general **conservation of the environment** due to less over-grazing, better utilization of rainfall and fertilizer due to faster pasture cycling, and the ability to preserve important preferred species of grass.

4. A much **increased sense of peace of mind** on the part of the grazier. You can see your feed bank out ahead of you and by measuring the grass' regrowth can make buying and selling decisions far in advance of the actual "crunch."

Flexible Stocking Rate

Milligan said that while management-intensive grazing could raise per acre production by 20 to 40 percent, MIG in conjunction with a flexible stock policy could increase production **by 60 to 80 percent**! A flexible stock policy changes the stocking rate to match the seasonal variations in grass growth. This flexibility can be accomplished by buying and selling animals but this is extremely risky because the gain per head is likely to be too small to absorb price rollbacks. The alternative to a variable stocking rate is a haying or silage program that takes grass from surplus periods such as the late spring to deficit periods such as the winter. This is the most common program used by dairy and brood stock graziers.

I recommend you plan to take the increase in forage that will result from management-intensive grazing off as hay or silage in your early learning years. Once you've built a comfortable insurance reserve of stored forage, you can start edging up your overall stocking rate. I should warn you that a common mistake novice graziers make is interpolating last year's rainfall and growth rates into the next year. Every year is different. MIG is a real-time system. You must manage for what is happening now and that requires frequent pasture walking.

Keep in mind, 250 paddock subdivisions are not 50 times better than 5 subdivisions in humid environments that produce rapid grass growth and, in fact, could be 50 times worse. In humid environments, including irrigated pastures, a very large number of permanent paddock subdivisions may allow the fast-growing grass to become mature and stemmy before the grazier can get to them. The sole intent of a grass plant is to make a seedhead and the primary task of the grazier is to prevent it from doing so. This difficult task frequently beats the most experienced graziers.

Consequently, I do not recommend that anyone just getting into management-intensive grazing start in the spring season with cool-season grasses or during the mid-summer season with tropical grasses. Concentrate your efforts in the slow growing months, or even better, in winter when the results of your efforts can be dramatic and the chances of your accidentally hurting animal performance are low since your stock will be dry.

Electric Fence Sparks Interest In Grazing

A lot of people ask, "What created the sudden renewed interest in grazing in North America?" I believe the answer can be found in the availability of highly effective, inexpensive "new age" portable electric fence. In the new paradigm of grass as the crop and the animal as merely the harvester, the one element that had always been missing was precision animal control. We had a crop combine with no steering wheel, throttle or brakes. Needless to say the efficiency of the harvest was dismal with only about 30 percent of the grass grown winding up in the cow.

European dairy farmers have long practiced rotational grazing and most dairy farms are subdivided into 20 to 21 permanent paddocks (subdivisions) with the cows shifted on a daily basis. In the humid, temperate climates of Ireland, Britain, Western France and the Netherlands, rigid, permanent subdivisions worked well to match the grasses' rest period to regrowth. However, such rigid subdivisions did not work nearly as well in North America due to our variable rainfall and hot summers. North American graziers needed a much more flexible system, whereby, one could easily speed up or slow down the rate of harvest to match the highly variable growing conditions. Attempts to achieve the level of subdivision needed with permanent fences was both very expensive and greatly hampered the machine harvest of seasonal pasture surpluses.

With portable electric fence, graziers could have an infinite number of paddocks with just three fence reels and some step-in fenceposts. A common comment by graziers has been that they can replace several thousand dollars worth of machinery with a few hundred dollars of portable electric fence.

While it is true most North American graziers do not have the skills yet to fully take advantage of the technology that is available to them, most now know it can be done. For those who really want to soar, the edge of the envelope in maximum productivity is way, way out there.

Keep in mind, there is **no** benefit to rotational grazing if the grass growth is in excess of the animal's ability to eat it. For this reason, beef and sheep are traditionally set-stocked (not rotated) during the spring and early summer on cool-season pastures.

Subdivide By Landscape First

Your first pasture subdivisions should be to group like areas. For example, fence north facing slopes from south facing ones, swampy areas from dry, etc. This initial subdivision will help tremendously in avoiding problem areas and maximizing the off-take of your most productive land. In most cases this will give you the eight to ten paddocks to prevent overgrazing. Try to keep permanently subdivided paddocks large and use temporary fence on a seasonal basis to ration out pasture during times of shortages.

Clean Water Is Critical

How would you like to have an unflushed toilet bowl as your sole supply of drinking water? Such an unsanitary water supply would not only be unappetizing but unhealthy to the point of being life threatening. Unfortunately, many of our livestock are having to get their water from their toilet bowl and are suffering because of it. Dirty stock water is considered the primary transmission point in the spread of animal disease and parasitism.

If you are currently watering your stock out of a pond or dirt tank the cattle can get into, put your money into a fresh water system before tackling management-intensive grazing. MIG will only make this very bad animal health situation worse. If you won't drink it, you shouldn't force your stock to drink it.

Water in every paddock can cut feed consumption. Cows that have to walk to the barn for water seldom walk back to graze in hot weather. Drinking water and urinating is a major way dairy cattle stay cool. (Also, providing water in the milking parlor rather than feed while you milk may even make you more milk. Milking makes a cow very thirsty very quickly.)

Water tanks and troughs should be cleaned frequently as the algae that grows in it is toxic and produces scours in cattle. With today's low-cost plastic-pipe water-systems, there is no reason not to have fresh water available at all times. Many stocker operators have been able to dramatically lower their death loss on newly arrived cattle by simply draining and disinfecting their water troughs daily. Invariably, the stocker operators with the worst health wrecks are those using ponds to water newly arrived cattle.

Water can now be piped for between 16 and 20 cents a foot either in above ground, burst-proof, oil-field hosepipes or below ground in ultra-low-cost flexible PVC pipes. In seasonal grazing areas, low-cost PVC pipe can be laid above ground and drained in the winter to prevent bursting.

In non-rocky soil areas, a below-ground water-reticulation system can be installed for about the same price per acre as a one-wire electric fence system. Several graziers have made waterline layers from subsoiler with a length of chain welded near the bottom of the backside of the subsoiler that can be attached to the end of the hose. These units both trench and pull in the water line in one pass. I know several dairymen in Wisconsin who have plumbed their whole farm with one of these in a few hours.

In several parts of the country, the same people who sell and build electric fence systems also install water reticulation systems. The time is not far off when probably all of these companies will sell hosepipe and connectors as fresh water is critical to the success of management-intensive grazing. The current leading stockwater supply specialist in the United States is Ralph Quillin of Kentucky Grazier Supply in Paris, Kentucky. Many of Ralph's suggestions are incorporated in this section.

Above ground burst-proof hoses are the cheapest solution in rocky areas. These hoses will freeze solid in cold weather but will not burst. A good bit of slack should be kept in above-ground hosepipes as there is a rather amazing amount of contracting and expanding as the weather changes.

Lactating dairy cows require the most water, and sheep and goats the least. There is a direct correlation between dry matter intake and water consumption. As feed intake increases so does water consumption. Therefore, the reverse must also be true, as water consumption goes down so does dry matter intake.

Pipe systems should be designed to deliver a minimum of five gallons a minute at the tank. The following chart is for pipe/size distance for a 5 gallon flow rate:

3/4 inch	1000 feet
1 inch	2000 feet
1 1/4 inch	3000 feet
1 1/2 inch	5000 feet

Large acreages should always use the 1 1/2 inch size pipe.

Water requirements for stock in cold weather are minimal. Research in Canada has shown that snow is an adequate source of stock water for non-lactating beef cattle. Also, little to no stock water is needed by non-lactating beef cattle grazing lush, green pasture such as wheat and ryegrass in cool weather.

Permanently installed stock troughs can be made more effective by providing simple head stanchions that prevent dominant cows from butting subdominants away from the water. This is particularly true with circular water troughs. Quartering a circular trough with two inverted U's made from drill pipe can tremendously increase its utilization.

The higher the stock density per acre, the smaller the water trough that can be used. At high stock densities, the social aspect of watering is disrupted. This allows a relatively small trough to water a large number of cattle as long as the water flow is there. These portable water troughs should always be placed with the valve under an electric fence to prevent the cattle from damaging it. Try to keep water within 500 to 700 feet of the cattle if small portable tanks are used. Close proximity to water allows the animals to graze and drink throughout the day rather than going to water in large groups and less frequently. Snap hosepipe couplings similar to those used on air and hydraulic lines allow one portable tank to be moved along with the cattle from paddock to paddock.

There has been some concern about the water heating to very high temperatures in hoses running on top of the ground. In high rainfall areas, this has not been a problem because the hoses are quickly covered over by grass. In hot arid areas, larger troughs can be used to allow the water to cool, but no ill effects have been noticed from range beef cattle drinking warm water. Research in Pennsylvania has found no increase in stock water use by dairy cattle by lowering its temperature in aboveground hosepipes through the use of white painted pipe rather than black.

Start With Stockpiling

The practice of stockpiling fall grown cool-season grass and then tightly rationing it out over the winter as a replacement for, or a protein supplement to, hay has the highest profit return and should be the starting point for all management-intensive grazing programs. Since wintering stock is 70 percent of the direct cash cost of livestock production, small gains in productivity here can have very dramatic results on your bottom line.

The average growing season for the 50 most frequently used grasses in the United States is 240 days or some three months longer than the average row or vegetable crop. In most of the United States it is possible to extend the green-grass grazing period to 300 days by stockpiling autumn growth.

In the lower half of the United States by using cold-tolerant cereal rye in combination with a perennial long-season grass, a green and **growing** forage crop can be had in excess of 300 days a year. Cereal rye will continue leaf growth at a leaf temperature of 38 degrees F (8 C) and a soil temperature only slightly above freezing.

Winter in the United States averages 160 days in length. However, the actual time of very cold weather, snow and ice is a small fraction of this time. In the northern two-thirds of the United States, the average annual period of snow cover is only 24 days. In the northern one-third, it is only 40 days a winter. Snow is no excuse for not planning to winter graze!

Early spring forage analysis by both graziers and researchers have shown that virtually all of the cool-season grasses can maintain enough quality through the winter-dormant season to provide all the protein needed for a dry cow or ewe or a yearling beef animal. Many of these cool-season grasses will still test out at 12 to 14 percent protein at the end of winter. However, these grasses should be thought of as ice cream in a cardboard box and our animals as children. Like children, our grazing animals if unrestrained will gorge themselves on ice cream in the early winter and by late winter will have nothing left to eat but the empty cardboard boxes. This is precisely the reverse nutrition curve we want for spring calving or lambing.

As a grazier, it is our job to see that the ice cream is carefully rationed out so that it is not a fall feast followed by a late winter famine. What we want to do is to give them a little bit of ice cream **and** then make them eat the box it came in. We accomplish this rationing process best by strip-grazing. By closely rationing out only a small strip of stockpiled grass, we can not only control the nutritional content and quantity but we can force our animals to graze through relatively deep snow.

By planning our stockpiling acres in open areas where the

wind will blow most of the snow away, the necessity of feeding hay can be virtually eliminated with the exception of the worst blizzards. Researchers at Cornell are now wintering dry ewes in upper New York state with absolutely no hay or feed using this stockpile/strip graze method.

Charles Opitz of Mineral Point, Wisconsin is a big believer in extending the grazing season through autumn-saved pasture or stockpiling. He said the trick was to not consume it all in the winter but to save some of your stockpiled paddocks for very early spring grazing. "I like to graze one third of my paddocks in the autumn, one third in the early winter and then save one third for early spring. I like to start grazing this final group of paddocks just before the spring greenup," he said.

"If you don't save some for spring and get started on your pastures early, you'll never get the 'cut' you need in the pasture growth cycle for successful rotational grazing. If you wait until your first paddock is ready to graze with new growth, your last paddock will have blown up and gone to seed before you get to it."

Each year it is important to vary the paddocks grazed in the fall. Autumn-grazing deferment allows the grasses to build healthy root reserves for robust spring growth. The paddocks you graze during the fall will always be your slowest-growing and poorest-doing paddocks next spring.

Unfortunately, warm-season grasses do not maintain quality over the winter the way cool-season grasses do. By spring they are about the same quality as wheat straw. Southern graziers have for many years solved this problem by planting supplemental cool-season annual grasses and/or small grains and have turned their dry cows on them for a couple of hours every other day. It only takes a very small amount of green grass to provide the protein supplement needed for a dry beef cow or ewe with unlimited access to frosted warm-season grass.

Please note, all of the above low-cost wintering methods are designed for use with dry stock. In temperate climates, winter lactation is going to require major intervention on your part, and **major intervention costs**. A recent study in the United Kingdom found that making milk in the winter on stored feed and grain cost 75% more than making milk in the summer from grazed grass.

Spring Pasture Management

When pilots move from propeller to jet planes they must be retaught how to think. The jet is moving so fast that the pilot's mind has to be many miles ahead of his body to avoid a crash.

Spring pasture is the grazier's jet. It requires a lot of forward thinking and very quick action to avoid a wreck. The wreck here is a pasture that has "blown up" and gone to stem and seedhead. Here are some tips for successful spring pasture management:

Start Early. Animals should be turned onto pasture at the first sign of spring greenup. Watch the brush around your farm. When it starts to bud you'd better get your pasture management mind in gear. Don't wait until the first paddock is at the "recommended" height of 6 to 8 inches or the majority of your out paddocks will have made seedheads before you even get to them.

Charles Opitz saves one third of his fall stockpiled pasture for spring. This allows him to start grazing with the precision of a Swiss watch on the 20th day of March each year. These early spring pastures are often quite soft due to freeze-thawing and pug (bog) easily. (See section on wet weather grazing.)

If stockpiled pasture is not available, continue to feed the cows their normal winter feed. Let the cows decide when to quit eating stored feed and hay. This will prevent scouring and rumen upset. Cows nearing calving should be allowed unrestricted access to all the hay or silage they want to prevent milk fever. As most dairymen have noted, most cows will stop eating any supplemental feed once the dry matter of the pasture rises in late spring.

Andre' Voisin recommended a very light early spring nitrogen application as a kickoff for the spring grazing season, but only on one-half of the pasture's paddocks. The remaining paddocks should not be nitrated to avoid overstimulating pasture growth. He wrote that this nitrogen, if applied at the brush-budding stage, would allow two weeks earlier grazing than a clover pasture and put the "cut" in the paddocks that is so useful with rotational grazing.

Voisin warned that spring-pasture nitrogen-applications should be well-timed (early) and sparingly used to avoid an uncontrollable late spring pasture "blow-up."

Move Fast. Spring pasture management is critical. A very fast rotation must be maintained to keep the fast-growing spring grass short, and thereby, young and tender.

Dairymen should set a goal of top grazing every paddock on the farm every ten days. A good grazier can maintain a "topping" 10- to 14-day rotation until mid-summer. This means you may have to shift paddocks several times a day. This fast rotation will pay for itself in very high milk production and pasture that is much easier to control.

Beef cattle and sheep should not be rotated in the spring. Putting small groups of animals in each paddock maximizes average daily gains on yearling cattle.

Do not attempt to break up manure clumps by dragging spring pasture as this will worsen pasture parasitism. Do not worry about uneven pasture clumps of mature grass. They serve a purpose as we shall see.

Keep Dry Matter High. Spring pasture is naturally very low in dry matter and can cause cows to bloat, scour, and lose both milk production and butterfat. Dry matter can be raised by mowing one-third of the paddock the day before the cows are to enter a paddock. The mown grass will dry down and the cows can balance their dry matter needs by alternating back and forth. Dairy cows should be fed grain during the spring lush to maintain body condition.

Andre' Voisin noted that a cow on lush spring pasture craved coarse feeds, and conversely, craved young pasture when on coarse feeds. Managing a pasture to be at its lab-test peak did not maximize animal performance. Maximum performance came from a pasture that was diverse in species and age and high in cow "eating pleasure." (This is why we told you not to worry about the clumps. They serve a purpose in providing dry matter variety.) It was Voisin's observation that the pastured cow by maximizing her inherent genetic "eating pleasure" always balanced her diet perfectly and produced milk at the optimum level. You don't need a nutritionist to balance your diet do you? A cow on a diverse pasture doesn't either.

Walk Your Pastures Daily. Walk all of your paddocks daily in the spring. At some point, you will probably find the pasture growth is in excess of the animal's ability to keep up with it. Later in the spring up to 60 percent of the pasture area will probably have to be deferred for mechanical harvest--preferably for pasture silage--to keep the grazing pressure high enough on the remaining paddocks. Conversely, never restrict your cows' grazing to make hay or silage.

At this point, you should start dropping some paddocks out of the rotation (dairy) and schedule the pastures for silage. Hopefully, by top-grazing and set-stocking you have been able to transfer this surplus out of the wettest part of the spring and into more favorable weather. Soil compaction from machinery on wet soil can hurt subsequent pasture production for many years.

If a paddock(s) unintentionally gets away from you and turns to seedhead and stem, do not force the animal to graze it off. Remove it as dry-cow hay.

Ideally, paddocks scheduled for haying or silaging should be your flatter, more fertile paddocks as haying and silaging is extremely hard on soil fertility. Concentrate your grazing efforts on your thinner, steeper, less fertile soils to prevent needing to machine harvest these areas.

Voisin said paddocks that have been hayed or silaged need to be nitrated immediately after harvest to allow them to quickly build pasture mass for use during the summer dry period. He noted the judicious use of nitrogen in the very late spring and early summer as pasture production starts to droop can help prevent the "summer slump" in pasture production. He said the nitrogen fertilization of cool-season pastures should be concentrated in the second half of the year and only very minimally used in the first half. (See section on nitrogen fertilization.)

Voisin admitted spring pasture management, particularly the dropping and reintegrating of machine cut paddocks, was an annual test of a grazier's skill.

Bentonite Can Help Prevent Spring Pasture Bloat. Pennsylvania nutritionist, Sonny Golden, said that the making available of sodium bentonite free choice has helped stop pasture bloat problems for his grazing dairymen clients. Golden said he found that silica is a very important mineral with ruminants and it should be kept available to the cows free choice at all times but particularly with low dry matter spring pastures and pastures high in legume content.

Golden recommends minerals be provided free choice in

separate compartments. He has found the minerals the cow chooses vary as the pasture changes throughout the season. For example, graziers will note their cows consumption of salt will skyrocket in the spring as they attempt to balance the high levels of potassium in spring pasture. The potassium stimulates the kidneys which increases water and salt intake. This is why high potassium diets tend to help keep cows cool in summer by stimulating water consumption.

Golden recommends that minerals be fed free choice rather than in the feed ration for grazing dairy producers because the grain portion of the ration would fall as their pastures and grazing management got better.

Minerals he recommends keeping available free choice at all times are as follows:

1. A 4 to 1 calcium to phosphorous mineral
2. Potassium Chloride
3. Baking Soda
4. High Calcium Limestone
5. Loose White Salt
6. Magnesium Oxide
7. Sodium Bentonite

Plan For Wet Weather And Mud

Long stretches of wet weather can give graziers fits if they haven't thought through a plan to deal with them. New Zealand's Massey University found a 30 percent decrease in pasture production for the whole season from mud-season pugging. Their research has shown there are but two ways to deal with mud. One is to drain the moisture from the soil and the other is to get the cows off the paddocks before any damage is done. The first option is something we all need to investigate more but for this section we will stick with the second option.

In the early subdivision, provision should be made for an area where the animals can be placed and fed during periods of high rainfall. This is especially critical with annuals and alfalfa to avoid plant damage, but severe, continuous pugging will greatly diminish the productivity of all pastures. A sacrifice paddock can be a pasture with a tight mature sod or a small yard or trap with 3 or 4 feet of sawdust or wood chips laid over it. Here are some ideas on wet weather grazing:

Short Grazing Periods. Three hours of grazing is an adequate amount of time for dry cows to get all the grass they need. Allow cows access to the whole paddock and then get them off! New Zealand research has found little to no milk production fall off if the evening graze is completely eliminated. Even if there is some production fall off, it is better to lose some milk and save the pasture. Do not leave cows on a wet pasture overnight.

Backfence. Cows are not let back on an area previously grazed by using a backfence. Irish research shows stripgrazing without using a backfence can reduce regrowths by about 30 percent.

Have Hungry Cows. By letting the cows get slightly hungry they will graze aggressively with little walking. A hungry cow will eat up to 90% of her feed requirements in two to three hours. Once you see the cows stop grazing and start to lay down to ruminate, bring them in! Always feed grain **after** grazing, not before.

Feed Budgeting. Using a portable electric fence, allocate just enough grass for each grazing period. It is important not to allocate too much. Grass will be wasted and cows will get used to lax grazing. It is better to train your cows to graze down pastures fast and well with as little walking and selectivity as possible.

Slow The Rotation. It is better to severely pug a small part of the pasture than the whole thing.

Multiple Entrances. Provide more than one entrance to each paddock. You want to prevent mud from being dragged onto the grass on the cows feet as they will not eat muddy grass. The wire can be dropped and the cows moved anywhere along the fence to allow the cows to enter and leave over a wider area. This a good reason for using minimalist interior fencing.

Regrass Immediately. Broadcast seed on severely pugged areas immediately. Birdsfoot trefoil takes to such bare ground exceptionally well as does annual ryegrass.

Have A Sacrifice Paddock. Designate a paddock that you are planning to regrass as a "sacrifice area" and put the cattle there. Mounds of sawdust, wood chips or agricultural lime can provide for resting areas to allow the cattle to get out of the mud. Sacrifice areas should not be used for long-term hay or silage feeding but only for standing off the pasture during short, wet spells.

Confine Cattle To Lanes. Your walk-back lanes if kept well drained and in good order can be used as a stand-off area as well. If the lane is used in this way, it is important to split the stock into small groups and confine them to short sections of the lane to prevent them from walking back and forth and destroying the lane. Remember, bored cows like to walk and explore.

Graze Cattle In A Block. Cattle in wet weather should always be confined in a "block" pattern that discourages walking and not a long "strip" pattern. Cattle grazed in a long strip will do excessive walking trying to determine if the grass is better at the opposite end of the strip from where they are.

Build Mud-Free Loafing Areas. Permanent stand-off pads of sawdust or woodchips are another option, however they are best used for providing a place to "put" cattle when off time-limited grazing. They are more properly called "loafing pads" in that they give the animal a dry place to rest. Feeding hay or silage on these pads will soon have them deep in manure and the cattle will be uncomfortable and covered with manure. This prevents the cow's skin from breathing and because cows lick each other can be a source of severe parasitism.

Have Concrete Feeding Areas. The long-term feeding of dairy cows should only be done on concrete. It is better to have several feeding pads with smaller groups of animals than one big pad. Feeding pads should be of a "block" design. Concrete pads should be cleaned every day to prevent bruising and lameness. Cows confined to concrete for a long period will benefit from an occasional walk around the farm's lane system to prevent stiffness.

Breeding Season Must Sync With The Pasture

There is very little management-intensive grazing (or any other pasture management program) can do to dramatically improve your bottom line if you are calving, lambing or kidding out of sync with the growth of the grass in your area. Timing your animals breeding to the grass is the single most important management input in grassland farming, yet most new graziers resist making this change, often making it the last management "tool" implemented, rather than the first. There are many ways of getting your animal's breeding in sync with the pasture. Buying and selling animals is the fastest and the one I recommend.

Give Yourself Time To Learn

A major disappointment of many new intensive graziers is a lowered per head production. Keep in mind that high production per animal and high production per acre are opposite ends of a teeter-totter. If one goes up the other must go down. For example, the potential for a high average daily gain is determined by how tall the grass is when you turn the cattle on a paddock. The actual average daily gain is set by how much grass is left when the cattle leave the paddock. Grazing the grass into the ground so as to leave a sharp graze line between paddocks before shifting produces a low average daily gain. This should only be done with dry stock.

By only allowing the cattle to top-graze the best of the grass sward, average daily gains equal to those of a full feed of grain can be achieved. Young, tender green grass leaves are the ultimate concentrate for ruminant animals.

The only way to break the per head vs. per acre teeter-totter is to use high production animals as first grazers and lower production animals as last grazers. By understanding and knowing how to manipulate grass with the cattle, a grazier can control both his animal's gain performance and the per acre production to a remarkable extent. All of this will come as your "grass eye" develops. Training your "grass eye" takes time and requires practice, observation and contemplation. It will come.

However, I do not recommend you start learning management-intensive grazing with high production animals such as lactating dairy cows, short-season stocker cattle or weaned lambs. Learn with replacement heifers, beef cows and calves, or dry dairy stock that have lower production goals.

Also, it has been my experience perennial grass pastures need about three years of "conditioning" by way of management-intensive grazing before they are ready to really turn a flip for you with the high production animals and classes anyway. So give yourself the time to learn. A early-weaning, beef brood cow herd is an excellent initial rough pasture conditioner or "bush-basher" as they say in New Zealand.

However, a higher value producing enterprise should be your ultimate goal. Take a look at the following chart, which lists average returns per acre for various enterprises. Then explore the options of adding multiple species, as described in Chapter 13.

Management-Responsive Enterprises

In 1992, I followed Jim Gerrish's advice and changed the terminology we were using for managed grazing from intensive grazing management to management-intensive grazing. I did this because I thought it put the emphasis on the correct word--management. However, I now realize when we add the word intensive to management we also need to think in terms of another acronym--MRE for management responsive enterprises. I have seen many graziers who have gotten excited about MIG and increased their management input but didn't change their enterprise. This usually results in the infamous "pushing on a string" syndrome. I.E. we work harder for no great result.

Enterprises & Average Returns Per Acre

Goats $50-200
Beef cow/calf $50-200
Pigs $150
Beef stocker $150+
Beef finishing $200+
Ewe lamb $400+
Dairy sheep $500+
Lamb finishing $1000+
Dairy beef $1000+
Pastured poultry--
eggs $30-50
meat $1000+
Seasonal grass dairy $900-2000

A highly profitable enterprise must be a "whole," wherein, effort and income are closely correlated. Often an increase in management effort requires a new more management-responsive enterprise to be profitable. For example, seasonal grass dairying is the most pasture management responsive enterprise. An increase in pasture quality results in an almost immediate increase in income. Needless to say, this fast reinforcement loop quickly tends to make dairy graziers better green-season grass managers than beef or sheep graziers. The slower the response to increased management input the less interest most of us have in applying more of it. This is particularly a problem in arid environments, which I will discuss later.

Dairy farms traditionally have twenty to forty permanent paddocks because the pasture is being managed for maximum quality and a high number of paddocks helps facilitate this. However, such a high number of paddocks could easily be management overkill (overcapitalization) in beef cow-calf and ewe-lamb where there is a much lower response to pasture quality.

Green-season grazing management with beef cows and ewes is primarily directed toward providing the grass with enough rest from grazing to keep it productive rather than to maintain the highest possible quality. This can usually be accomplished in humid climates with as few as eight pasture subdivisions. There is a very low to negative return to management from increasing pasture quality in excess of the minimal needs of a low-value enterprise. This why the majority of beef cows in the world are still run on range rather than highly improved tame pasture.

Actually the highest return to grazing management with beef cows and ewes comes from using your management skills to facilitate your cows to self-feed themselves through the winter on a very low-cost (no cost is best) feed source. This can be rationed out stockpiled fescue, bermudagrass, corn stalks, wheat chaff or cotton gin waste. Beef cows and ewes are essentially value-adding enterprises. The lower the value of the feedstuff they utilize, the higher the value returned to management.

In other words, **the highest return to grazing management with dairy cows will occur during the growing season and during the non-growing season with beef cows and ewes**.

Growing animals have a much higher return to management than brood animals because a larger percentage of the pasture utilized is used to support growth rather than maintenance. However, growing animals exhibit a phenomenon called "compensatory gain." This allows animals to "catch up" when moved from a lower quality to a higher quality pasture. Research in Northern Ireland whereby steers were kept at high rates of gain year round with supplemental grain were found to reach full grown slaughter weight at almost exactly the same time as steers grazed with no grain and allowed to compensate.

Therefore, the highest return to pasture management with growing animals will come from providing a very high quality pasture for the animal for four to six weeks prior to its sale or slaughter. For example in arid areas, expensive irrigated pastures are most profitable when used as short-term finishing pastures to "pop" (express compensatory gain) animals which have been grown and framed on lower cost (and quality) range. Tests in Oklahoma with steers wintered at low rates of gain have shown average daily gains in excess of four pounds a day when allowed access to adequate high quality spring pasture. Learning how to maximize the use of compensatory gain should be a major management goal for growing animal graziers.

Regardless of the enterprise, your management effort should primarily be directed toward those areas where the return to management effort is the greatest. If your goal is to apply maximum management input for maximum income, make sure the enterprise you choose is highly responsive to management input.

Why ADG Can Suffer With Intensive Grazing

Many researchers have noticed that average daily gains are frequently lower with stocker cattle under management-intensive grazing as compared to continuous grazing. Dr. Burt Smith, Extension Pasture Specialist at the University of Hawaii, said this decrease in performance is largely due to a lack of understanding of cow psychology.

Smith explained that under continuous grazing when forage becomes short or scarce, cattle and sheep will either increase the rate of biting, take larger bites or graze longer. As a result, intake tends to remain constant over a fairly large range of pasture conditions.

However, under management-intensive grazing programs, such as strip grazing, when animals are shifted on daily or twice daily routines, this does not happen. The animal rather than working harder will anticipate the move to the next break.

This is why the concept of pasture residual is so important for high animal performance from intensive grazing. The greater the pasture residual (the ungrazed portion of the sward), the greater the animal performance will be.

Smith said it was important that the right amount of forage be allocated so that high production animals could quickly and easily get their fill and still leave a rather high grass residual.

Also, paddock shifts should always be made on the same

day and at the same time of day for best animal performance.

Management-intensive grazing and continuous grazing are two entirely different grazing environments and the animals know this.

A Day In The Life Of A Cow

The grazing time of cattle almost never lasts longer than eight hours of a 24 hour day. The more grass the cow can take in with each bite she takes the higher her milk production or gain will be. Conversely, if the grass is short or sparse, the cow will not graze longer to make up her deficit. André Voisin, the father of modern grazing, called this irrevocable eight hour day the "cow's union." For this reason, Voisin said cows should be genetically selected for very broad muzzles to maximize intake per bite. He said this one genetic trait was the one most important for increasing a cow's pasture productivity.

Studies at the University of Vermont found that cows do about 60 percent of their grazing during the day and 40 percent at night. To a dairy cow, the morning grazing period was the most important part of the day. 85 percent of the cow's total daytime grazing is done between the crack of dawn and one in the afternoon. Care must be taken not to interrupt this primary grazing period with milking or other activities. In hot weather, more grazing will occur at night.

Dr. Bill Murphy said UV's study showed the cows liked to fill their rumen in the morning and then lay down and ruminate in the early afternoon. In the late afternoon, the cow wants to top off her rumen before night. In their research they noticed the cows would gather at the paddock gate every day at 3 PM and just stand and wait even though there was plenty of grass left in the paddock. "What they were waiting for we couldn't tell, but every day they would be there. Waiting."

Murphy said they now divide the cow's daytime paddock with a temporary electric fence. 85 percent of the paddock is given in the morning and 15 percent is saved for opening at 2 o'clock in the afternoon. This small amount of fresh pasture has broken up the afternoon waiting game by the gate and has increased pasture intake in the cows.

Studies in Ohio also found that pasture intake and milk

production could be stimulated by opening fresh breaks in the late morning and afternoon. Apparently, cows can't resist a fresh, unsoiled break of grass.

Several graziers have noted that if day and night paddocks are of equal size the residual left in the night paddock will be much higher indicating the much lower night grazing. Texas dairy grazier, Steve Roth, now makes his night paddocks smaller than his day paddocks by using temporary electric fence. New Zealand research has found little to no drop off in milk production if the night graze is completely eliminated during wet weather periods.

Night observation of beef cattle with Army starscopes by Dr. Burt Smith at the University of Hawaii found very little grazing occurred on completely dark moonless nights. In hot climates, Smith found the most aggressive grazing occurred in the cool time between the first grey streak of dawn and the onset of the day's heat around 10 AM.

Apparently, for cows at least, breakfast is by far and away the most important meal of the day.

A Review

Management-intensive grazing can increase your per acre production between 20 and 40 percent. This increase will come either as increased animal production and/or increased hay production if the stocking rate is not increased. An increased stocking rate is the most painless way to lower fixed costs. After the initial subdivision expense this increase is almost a pure reward for management and is why management-intensive grazing is becoming the skill that is separating the professional grazier from all the rest.

The following are the real costs of a 200-acre MIG subdivision program as used on the Roth Dairy, Grand Saline, Texas:

Fencing	$41 an acre
Stockwater well	$29 an acre
Water reticulation (troughs and lines)	$32 an acre
Walkback Lanes	$28 an acre
Total	$130 an acre

In summary, if you're just starting management-intensive grazing, I recommend:

1. Get your animals in sync with grass.
2. Availability of fresh water.
3. Group like-management areas.
4. Make provisions for avoiding mud.
5. Concentrate on the slow or no growth months.
6. Do not increase current stocking rates in your learning stage--prepare to make hay or silage instead.
7. Use low production animals.
8. Remember Rome wasn't built in a day.

Think About It...

♣ In humid environments, including irrigated pastures, a very large number of permanent paddock subdivisions may allow the fast-growing grass to become mature and stemmy before the grazier can get to them.

♣ Your first pasture subdivision should group like areas--fence north facing slopes from south facing ones, swamp areas from dry, etc.

♣ If you are currently watering your stock out of a pond or dirt tank the cattle can get into, put your money into a fresh water system before tackling management-intensive grazing.

♣ Stockpiling fall-grown cool-season grass and tightly rationing it out over the winter as a replacement for, or a protein supplement to, hay has the highest profit return and should be the starting point for all management-intensive grazing programs.

♣ Spring pasture is the grazier's jet. Particularly the act of dropping and reintegration of machine-cut paddocks is an annual test of a grazier's skill.

♣ Are you making bentonite available on spring pasture?

♣ Timing your animals' breeding to the grass is the single most important management input in grassland farming. Are you resisting making this change? Why?

♣ By understanding and knowing how to manipulate grass with the cattle, a grazier can control both his animal's gain performance and the per acre production to a remarkable extent. Training your "grass eye" takes time and requires practice, observation and contemplation. Learn with replacement heifers, beef cows and calves, or dry dairy stock, which have lower production goals.

♣ Have you given yourself time to learn?

♣ A early-weaning, beef brood cow herd is an excellent initial rough pasture conditioner or "bush-basher." However, a higher value production enterprise should be your ultimate goal. In your excitement over management-intensive grazing, have you changed your management without changing your enterprise?

♣ Your management effort should primarily be directed toward those areas where the return to management effort is the greatest.

♣ The greater the pasture residual (the ungrazed portion of the sward), the greater the animal performance will be.

♣ It is important that the right amount of forage be allocated so that high production animals can quickly and easily get their fill and still leave a rather high grass residual.

♣ Paddocks shifts should always be made on the same day and at the same time of day for best animal performance. What can you do to get your paddock shifts down to a daily routine?

♣ To the dairy cow, the morning graze is the most important part of the day. Are you leaving your cows undisturbed during this prime grazing time?

♣ Pasture intake and milk production can be stimulated by opening fresh breaks in the late morning and afternoon. Are you taking advantage of this option?

♣ As this book is being written, three universities are offering adult eduction classes in MIG. These are the University of Missouri at Linneus, the University of Southwestern Louisiana in Lafayette, and the University of California at Davis. These very intensive schools are excellent ways for novice graziers to learn the basics of MIG in a "hands-on" atmosphere.

♣ Every year is different. Is your pasture management based on what's happening now, or have you made the mistake of planning this year's management based on what happened last year? A thoughtful pasture walk will give you some answers.

♣ The best time to solve next winter and spring's mud problems is this summer and fall. What's your plan for the next wet weather season?

♣ As Burt Smith said, "The best way to learn to swim is to get in the water and start splashing around. Nobody ever learned to swim by just reading a book about it." Are you ready to make some waves?

Chapter 8: Climate And Its Effect

Man's attempts to alter the climate have not only been costly, but have frequently had negative effects on the health of our animals. This chapter will give you some alternatives that are both easier on the animal and your checkbook.

Shelterbelts

To keep capital costs down, more and more livestock producers are looking at barnless wintering. Just as it is not the heat, but the humidity that makes us feel hot, it is the wind more than the cold that makes us (and our animals) feel cold. Therefore, our first priority should be in providing our animals a shelter from the wind more than any other winter element.

Wind Protection. The greater the height of a shelterbelt the greater the wind protection. Good wind protection is provided for 10 times the height of the shelterbelt on the leeward side and five times the height on the windward side.

Trees provide a much better windbreak than man-made structures because their leaves respond to changing wind velocities and open up to let much of the wind through the shelterbelt rather than forcing it all over the top and creating heavy leeward turbulence. In areas of the country where heavy snow drifts are not a problem, a 50% wind-permeable shelterbelt will give a much more even windflow over a much wider area than a solid or dense shelter. Dense shelters create a very sheltered area close to the shelter but a very turbulent wind area at a distance about five times the height of the windbreak. Dense shelters tend to concentrate the animals (and their manure and pugging) much more than porous shelters.

Gaps in a shelterbelt will funnel the wind at very high velocities through these holes and make it very difficult to fill these holes with new young trees. Care should be taken to make sure the shelterbelt is long and uniform in its density. Cattle and sheep should always be fenced out of a shelterbelt to prevent soil compaction and nutrient overload, which could kill some of the trees and create wind holes in the shelter.

Coniferous shelterbelts are best planted on a North-South axis. This will provide for warming sun on both sides of the shelter-break, will allow the pasture to grow right up to the shelterbelt and will slow the prevailing westerly winds. East-West running shelterbelts should be planted to deciduous trees that will allow maximum winter sun to fall on the paddock but provide summer shade. In non-drifting snow areas, shelterbelts should be kept tall and narrow (one to two rows of trees). On North-South axis a row of fast-growing pine (for height) can be backed by a row of slow-growing conifers to provide a tall but dense shelterbelt.

In the coldest part of New Zealand, graziers plant shelterbelts every 600 feet. These create a much warmer microclimate for both grass growth and animal comfort.

Snow Drifts Can Cause A Problem. In areas where drifting snow is a problem, a narrow one to two row shelterbelt will tend to collect heavy snow drifts in the sheltered leeward area and can create a possible deathtrap for your animals. This can be solved by planting a multiple-row shelterbelt wide enough to catch the drifting snow, or a much better solution is to site the shelterbelt with a deep gully on the windward side. This gully will then catch the drifts and allow a narrower shelterbelt. Both of these solutions will provide a nearly snowless environment on the leeward side for your animals.

Shelterbelts Grow Grass. Wind-slowing shelterbelts keep working in the summer for you as well. Research in Australia has shown that shelterbelts may result in up to 30 percent more grass in dry years by slowing soil moisture loss.

Cold Air Hyrdrology. Cold air is heavier than warm air. It gets as close to the surface of the ground as possible and then rolls down a slope just like rain water runoff. This makes the side of a hill much warmer than the top or the bottom. The warmest and driest place on your farm will be slightly above mid-slope on the South side of a hill in the Northern Hemisphere. Snow will quickly melt here and your pugging problems will be minimized. Spring calving and lambing should be planned to occur on a south facing mid-slope.

Care must be taken to not plant dense shelterbelts across the slope of a hill as this will cause cold air to damn up and remove the warmth advantage of the hillside. Side hill shelterbelts should be planted in a wedge shape to divert downward flowing cold air away from your animals.

Cold air puddles at the bottom of a hill and even more so in a valley. These bottom-of-the-hill sites will be the coldest place and wettest area (due to natural sub-irrigation) on your farm. Where is your barn currently located? Your cattle may welcome getting out of a cold barn and getting uphill where it is warmer.

Action Advice...

♣ First provide a shelter from the wind for your animals.

♣ The greater the height of the shelterbelt, the greater the wind protection.

♣ Trees are better windbreaks than man-made structures.

♣ Dense shelters concentrate animals, manure, and pugging more than porous shelters.

♣ Make shelterbelts long and uniformly dense.

♣ Fence out cattle and sheep to prevent soil compaction and nutrient overload in shelterbelt.

♣ Coniferous shelterbelts are best planted on a North-South axis.

♣ On North-South axis a row of fast-growing pines can be backed by a row of slow-growing conifer to provide a tall, dense shelterbelt.

♣ East-West shelterbelts should be planted to deciduous trees that allow maximum winter sun to fall on paddocks but provide summer shade.

♣ Keep shelterbelts tall and narrow (one to two rows of trees) in non-drifting snow areas.

♣ Avoid a possible deathtrap by planting a multiple-row shelterbelt wide enough to catch the drifting snow, or site the shelterbelt with a deep gully on the windward side.

♣ The side of the hill is warmer than the top or bottom.

♣ The warmest, driest place on your farm will be slightly above mid-slope on the South side of a hill in the Northern Hemisphere.

♣ Don't plant a dense shelterbelt across the slope of a hill.

♣ Plant a hillside shelterbelt in a wedge shape.

Heat And Its Effect

In December of 1965, a climatology symposium was held at the University of California at Berkeley. I found a printed transcript of this symposium in our local university library and thought it answered a lot of questions about why animal performance declines in the heat and what can be done about it.

First, all animals react to heat by decreasing their feed intake. Animals eat less, but more frequently. Apparently this is a way of reducing the body's heat load, which is produced by metabolism.

For most animals, maximum feed intake will be achieved at a temperature of around 75 F/22 C. The performance of growing pigs, laying hens and Holstein cows plummets with the trajectory of a dropped brick as the temperature starts to exceed 80 F/25 C.

For example, a pastured Holstein cow will reduce her feed intake by 50 percent at 90 F/30 C compared to what she will eat at 70 F/20 C. And since milk production is directly related to feed consumption, it will also fall.

On the other hand, the Zebu and Zebu 50 percent crosses will not decrease their feed intake until the temperature exceeds 100 F/35 C. Zebu cattle are able to maintain a constant body temperature until the temperature exceeds 106 F/38 C. Apparently, it is the increase in body temperature that signals the body to decrease feed intake and lower the heat from metabolism.

This ability to maintain a constant body temperature is also thought to be the key to the higher reproductive rate of Zebu and Zebu-cross cows bred in hot climates. Holstein cows and wool-type sheep have shown a tremendous decrease in fertility when the ambient temperature reached 94 F/32 C with a corresponding 65 percent humidity. It is thought this poor fertility is due to the rise in the body temperature in the female that may cause embryonic death. In hot and humid Hong Kong there are 30 percent fewer humans conceived in the summer than in the rest of the year. So apparently this decrease in fertility extends to humans as well.

While Zebu blooded beef cattle have become quite popular in the warm regions of North America, Zebu dairy breeds have not. So far, it has been concluded that the lower milk production of the Zebu dairy breeds in the cooler months economically offset their advantage in the summer.

Since only about 90 to 100 days a year are above 84 F/27 C. even in the Gulf states, it has been generally accepted that even with the lower milk production of the European dairy breeds in the summer, they are the breeds to stay with due to their higher full season milk production compared to tropical dairy breeds.

In the Deep South, this problem can be overcome by not having the cows at peak lactation (or even lactating) during the hot summer months of the year. Research in Georgia and Louisiana showed that August, September, and October were the most difficult months to produce high quality pasture and milk in the Deep South.

The Holstein is the most heat sensitive dairy breed and is most comfortable at a temperature between 30 and 50 degrees F (0 and 10 C). The Holstein wintered outdoors will not show a marked decrease in milk production until the ambient temperature reaches 10 degrees F. Other research has shown that in low humidity climates, the Holstein showed no decrease in production at even much lower temperatures.

The symposium warned that pasture-based dairymen should be careful about choosing this breed in climates where the ambient daytime temperature is above 75 degrees for more than 130 days a year.

Milk production from Holsteins will closely follow the thermometer with decreases on hot days and quick rebounds during cool rainy spells. On hot days, most grazing will occur at early dawn, so dairymen should plan their milking so as to not deny your cows this cheap pasture feed.

One way nature adapts to heat is with a smaller body phenotype. The extremely large framed body of the Holstein presents a large surface area to soak up heat.

The Jersey cow with its small body phenotype is much better adapted to the heat than the Holstein, but less well-adapted to the cold.

Cows will increase their consumption of water by 400 percent during hot weather and tanks and troughs that are adequate during the cooler months may not be adequate in the summer. Increasing water consumption is a major way animals cool themselves.

As feed intake goes down, energy use goes up as the cows expend energy in panting to stay cool. Summer panting has much the same effect on increasing energy use as shivering does in the winter. In fact, the respiration rate of an animal can give you a good clue as to the heat adaptation of the animal. Within breeds of cattle and sheep there are wide differences in heat adaptation.

If you live in a hot climate avoid seedstock animals with an obviously high respiration rate on a hot day. That energy being expended panting could be making milk or gain.

Generally, an Angus born and raised in Mississippi will be more heat-adapted than one raised in Vermont. However, a Vermont Angus after just 100 days in Mississippi will become almost as heat-adapted as the Mississippi-born Angus.

Research presented at the symposium showed that most animals can adapt to a new environment in about 100 days. What they cannot adapt to are sudden changes in climate.

The shipping of animals from a cold temperature to a hot temperature (or vice-versa) results in a severe depression in animal performance for at least 40 days. However, research at the University of Missouri indicated that just a few short exposures to heat prior to being shipped virtually eliminated this severe depression in performance.

The benefits of providing shade for beef cattle were not conclusive. The provision of shade provided no benefit to beef cattle performance in any of the Southeastern research presented at the symposium. In arid climates shade appeared to have some benefit to performance but the results varied greatly from year to year.

A major problem with shedding cattle in the winter or summer was the increase in humidity from the animal's respiration that actually worsened the effects of high or low temperatures on the animals. For example, the continual misting of cattle actually lowered performance by increasing the humidity. In very arid climates, periodically wetting cattle and allowing them to dry increased feedlot gains, but had no effect in humid climates.

Zebu dairy breeds showed a decrease in milk production and average daily gain as the temperature rose, so genetics alone cannot erase the summer slump and even environmentally adapted animals get lazy in the heat. All unnecessary movement is eliminated to keep heat generation down. Bulls and billy goats that fight their peers all winter long suddenly declare peace during the summer.

Graziers needing high production in the hot months should concentrate on high TDN plants such as white and red clover, cowpeas, hay-type soybeans, kudzu, forage rape, chicory and/or the warm-season annuals such as dwarf millet, sudangrass, crabgrass, etc.

Alfalfa is a high-protein, but low-carbohydrate (energy) plant so animal production does not stay as high on grazed alfalfa in the hot months as with the higher-energy forages such as rape.

Another high TDN feedstuff is grain. Given their choice, ruminants will substitute grain for pasture in hot weather, whereas they will usually ignore it in cooler weather if pasture quantity and quality is adequate.

This is why supplementing cattle with grain on pasture in the hot months does not dramatically increase animal performance, but dramatically increases costs. Instead of the grain being an energy supplement to the pasture as intended, the animals substitute the high-cost grain for low-cost pasture.

Dairy cows and European beef cattle in Fiji given unlimited free choice grain refused to eat even the most palatable of forages in hot weather.

Feedlot operators have long noticed that "hot" rations (high grain/low roughage) feed cool. Recent research at the University of Missouri on feedlots using primarily whole-shelled corn rations showed that feed conversions were actually better in the middle of summer than in the cooler months. However, the only way to

maintain spring-like ruminant animal production in the summer would be to provide refrigeration.

The symposium concluded the lowest cost way to beat the heat (or the cold) was to use adapted animals and to gear your peak breeding and production to what your climate naturally provided. This was good advice in 1965 and is still valid today.

Planned Shade Paddocks

There is abundant research showing there is an inverse relationship between high air temperatures and animal production in European breed beef and dairy cattle. The magic threshold appears to be around 86 F/27 C. Add humidity in excess of 45 percent and it is thought to double the heat stress on the animal. Research at the University of Florida found that season-long beef steer gains were lowered by one pound for each day in which the temperature was both above 86 F and 45 percent humidity. (See section on the summer slump.)

While there is widespread agreement that heat and humidity lower animal performance, there is little to no agreement on what to do about it. While the common answer is to provide shade for the animals, there has been no research showing any statistically significant increase in the production of grazing animals provided with shade. In fact, there is no measurable difference in air temperature under a tree as opposed to being in the sun. While it does indeed feel cooler due to the lack of radiation absorption; however, in actuality, it is not cooler in the shade.

With no economic justification for providing shade, it must be seen primarily as a tool to assuage the anthropomorphic feelings of the grazier. We like to go to shade when we rest on a hot day and transfer these feelings to our animals. Seeing animals with no access to shade on a hot day can therefore be a major stressor on many graziers. Stress on graziers is bad and should be relieved whenever possible. The key phrase when thinking about our feelings and our desire for shade is "when we rest."

For example, we do not feel sorry for baseball players playing in the sun on a hot day. We know they are actively involved in what they are doing and probably don't even feel the heat. However, we would feel sorry for them if after the game was over they had to sit in the broiling sun to relax.

In hot weather, the majority of the grazing occurs between the first grey streaks of dawn and 10 AM. The second major grazing period is from sunset until dark. Very little grazing occurs after true dark unless it is a moonlit night. Therefore, allowing your animals access to shade between 11 AM and the late afternoon is unlikely to hurt production. Going to a one-time milking after dark during extremely hot weather can help your animals make the most of their limited grazing time and lower the stress of milking in the hot part of the day on you and your animals.

Multiple Small Breaks Make Cows Forget Heat

Many graziers have noted that the best way to stop animals from milling on a hot day is to give them a fresh break of grass. This gets them mentally involved in something they enjoy and they ignore the heat. Multiple small breaks are a good hot weather stress reliever for your animals and can actually increase production. Shade should be reserved for the very hottest part of the day after the animals have ceased to graze. To maximize productive grazing time, special shade paddocks are preferred over providing shade in each paddock.

Planning For Healthy Shade

Researchers have noted that cows given the choice will always seek out the shade of trees in preference to that of a barn. The vaporization of moisture from the leaves of the tree provides a natural dehumidification that makes tree shade feel cooler. Remember heat stress is more a function of humidity than temperature. Therefore, providing shade with trees rather than putting your cows in hot, high-humidity barns makes them "feel" cooler. And as tight-fisted grazier Gordon Hazard would note, growing trees appreciate while barns depreciate.

However, poorly planned "shading-up" areas can be major infection points for parasitism and disease. Trees used for shade should be numerous, wide spread and should have their lower limbs removed to at least 20 feet in height. The goal here is to have the animals widely dispersed and to frequently have to move to stay in the shade as the sun moves across the sky. A tree with its limbs pruned high will form a moving shade pattern. This prevents an over concentration of manure in any one place and allows the sun to sanitize the area around the tree daily. It is in dark, constantly deep shade areas that disease and parasites lie in wait for your animals.

Research in Florida, Louisiana and New Zealand with pine trees planted in pasture found there was little detrimental effect to grass growth as long as there are no more that 40 to 50 stems per acre. In fact, pine trees in a widely dispersed grazing situation have actually been found to grow faster due to the lack of brush competition, however, they must be hand pruned of their lower limbs several times when widely planted.

The two predominant species used to provide both shade and saw timber are pines and black poplar. In the United States, the primary pine species used with grazing are longleaf, shortleaf and slash yellow pine. In New Zealand, the faster growing radiata pine is preferred. However, it is the black poplar that may have the most to offer graziers.

Poplars are very happy growing in isolation from one another. They can produce a very fine veneer log, they can help dry out a wet spot in the pasture, the grass grows right up to their trunks, they give summer shade, color well in the fall, drop their leaves in the winter to allow maximum sunlight to the pasture and their prunings provide edible forage for the livestock.

In New Zealand, dry beef cows have been wintered for up to two months on nothing but poplar leaves, twigs and branches, and prunings. Poplar trees can also provide a valuable forage reserve during severe droughts.

In rangeland situations, allowing and denying access to fenced shade areas has proved to be as effective a tool as opening and closing water points for creating cattle movement and avoiding overgrazing.

This mixing of animal agriculture and trees is called agroforestry and caused quite a bit of excitement in the Deep South and New Zealand a few years ago. Unfortunately, it did not fit the rigid, single-use mentality of corporate forestry and was poorly thought out from the grazier's more short-term, animal-dominant production viewpoint. No doubt, some foresters will see a great deal of resemblance between a "planned shade paddock" and the agroforestry concepts of the late 1970s.

Needless to say, the growing of a high value sawlog while providing summer shade for your animals is yet another one of those serendipitous events that occur when your grazing management is in sync with nature's overall plan.

Shade's Effect On Pasture Fertility

Manure is one of the most under-appreciated resources on a beef farm. As a walking fertilizer factory, a cow makes an average of a dozen deposits a day, each deposit averaging 5-6 pounds. When converted to fertilizer value that adds up to big bucks.

A cow can make $50 to $100 worth of manure a year. On a 100-cow beef herd that's $5000 to $10,000.

As part of his research at the University of Missouri Forage Systems Research Center (FSRC), Paul Peterson studied factors that affect manure distribution in grazing paddocks. "Some 70 to 90 percent of the fertility taken in with forage eaten by a cow goes out the back end," said Peterson. To be of most value, the cow pies should be evenly distributed over the pasture to return the fertility where it's needed. Without good grazing management, cows will tend to deposit the fertility in a few sites.

When a cow gets up from resting, it will make a deposit. They do the same near spots where they wait for water or mineral or salt. At the watering spots, the beef herd tends to urinate more.

By separating watering and mineral feeding sites, the cows walk back and forth more, increasing the chances of spreading their cow pie deposits.

A shade tree in a grazing paddock can be the site of high fertility deposits. This is why a few shade trees in a paddock will tend to drain the fertility of much of the paddock.

Because cattle tend to pick out favorite "camping areas," cows will tend to lounge under shade trees even in cool weather.

A Few Shade Trees Can Stress Cattle

If shade is provided for your cattle, it should be enough for all animals to have access to it at one time. Having a shade area for only a few animals will create a milling, restless herd and produce stepped on teats and stressed manure-covered cows.

Shade should be plentiful, widely spaced, move with the sun or it should not exist at all.

Action Advice

♣ Run an electric fence around the dense shade areas and keep the cows out.

♣ Graze paddocks with only a few trees only at night.

♣ Create a rolling shade-mobile as grazier Joel Salatin has done so that you place the shade-mobile where you need fertility most.

Florida Dairy Uses Cooling Ponds Instead Of Shade

Put a Holstein cow in the sub-tropics and you've got a pretty miserable beast for about seven months of the year. Florida dairyman, Norm Nickerson of Wauchula, has completely replaced shade with purpose-built cooling ponds on his three pasture-based dairies. These ponds are four feet deep with a slope to an eight-foot-deep manure-collection center. The ponds have to be pumped out and cleaned approximately every 15 years. Each pond is approximately a half acre. Norm provides two of these ponds for every 150 cows in paddocks near the milking parlor. After some experimentation with various pond depths, Norm concluded the cows obviously preferred the four foot depth and didn't like a pond that was deeper. "The cow does not want her body to be totally submerged," he said.

Norm milks his cows before sunrise to allow them to maximize their grazing during the coolest part of the day without interruption. This early morning graze produces the majority of the day's entire grazing during hot weather. Once the temperature starts to soar in the early afternoon the cows are allowed access to the cooling ponds for the hottest part of the afternoon. Clean, piped stockwater is provided in the cooling pond paddocks and the cows prefer to drink from this rather than from the pond.

The cows stand for approximately 20 minutes of each hour in the water and then lay around the edge of the pond for the remainder of the hour and allow evaporation to cool them. Little to no grazing occurs while the cows are in the pond paddocks. The cooling ponds are used from May until early November. The ponds have white sand bottoms and there is no mud.

Norm found a dramatic drop in mastitis since he stopped providing stationary shade and started using the cooling ponds. "The cows were constantly getting dirty from the manure buildup under the shades. Since we switched to cooling ponds the cows come in for the evening milking absolutely clean. In fact, we have taken the cow washer out of the milking parlor," he said.

(Cow cooling ponds may not be legal under some states' Clean Water Act regulations.)

Dairying In A Hot Climate

One thing you can bet on in the South and Southwest is that summer will always be hot. Holstein cows are not genetically adapted to heat and require some thought and management to work successfully in hot weather pasture systems. Here are some hot weather recommendations I have gathered from grazing dairymen in Texas, Alabama, Louisiana and Florida.

Subtropical grasses include the bermudas, bahia, dallis, kikuyu, and pangola, but most of these recommendations are from dairymen grazing Coastal bermuda/winter annuals. Subtropical grasses are usually not thought of as being dairy-quality but can be with the proper grazing management and fertilization. The primary problem with all subtropical grasses is their extremely fast growth and maturity cycle. Subtropical grasses must be kept young and growing rapidly to be of dairy quality.

Times are expressed in the 24 hour military system to minimize confusion.

Breed To Avoid The Heat. Time your breeding season so that all cows are dry or near the end of their lactation during July and August. Subtropical grasses will start to lignify and become less digestible after the fourth of July. Trying to maintain high milk production in July and August is very expensive. Most Southern dairymen find it far more cost-effective to just go with the flow and accept lower summer milk production per cow during hot weather.

A favorite breeding plan with non-seasonal dairymen on subtropical perennial/winter annual pasture is to have one-third of your cows calve in late September and October and two-thirds calve in January and February. The early fall calving herd is used as a follower herd in the spring and dried off in June. The winter calving herd can either be dried off in July and August or milked once a day during the hot weather months. If a milking is dropped it should be the late afternoon one as this one is the most stressful to the cows during hot weather. Milk prior to dawn in the summer.

This one-third/two-third breeding season maximizes the use of spring pasture, allows cows to be bred in cooler weather, and those that don't catch in one breeding season can slide around to another. Do not try to breed Holstein cows in the hot months of the year.

BST Has Southern Cows Sweating. Carl Coppock, a dairy consultant from Laredo, Texas, warned dairy producers that heat was the primary limiting factor in summer milk yield in the South and that using BST increased cow heat stress. BST produces more milk, which causes the cows to eat more, which produces more body heat, which causes the cows to eat less, which causes cows to produce less milk. Cows on BST also drink up to 50 percent more water than non BST cows in an effort to cool themselves, and water must be kept close and plentiful.

Because there is a lag in the time between when the cow increases her milk production and her feed intake, many dairymen are fooled about the true profitability of BST use.

Keep Water Close. Allow constant access to water. Do not make the cows walk more than 500 feet to drink. Have a lot of tank and water pressure redundancy to insure adequate water during hot weather.

Milking Over Before Sunrise. Gradually shift your milking time earlier and earlier as the spring progresses. Do not worry about trying to maintain a 12 hour interval between milking. Try to time your morning milking to be over before sunrise. During the hot months the early morning graze is the most important and makes up nearly 80 percent of the day's total grazing in hot weather. This grazing period starts at first light.

Frequent Paddock Shifts. Give the cows a fresh paddock at 1100 and a small fresh break after the evening milking. Night grazing makes up only a very small portion of the day's graze so this break can be much smaller than the morning break.

If the cows bunch up in a corner and start to mill during the day, give them a small fresh break of grass. Nothing makes cows forget the heat as fast as a fresh break of grass.

Afternoon Access To Shade. Shade is not necessary, nor desirable in the early part of the day. After 1500 allow the cows access to shade until the evening milking at 1800. On some Florida and Louisiana dairies, cows are allowed access to cooling ponds during this extremely hot late afternoon period. Cooling ponds may not be legal in Texas where the State heavily regulates all surface water, so take care.

Avoid Long Walks In Afternoon Heat. Avoid walking cows long distances to milking in the late afternoon heat. Keep salt available and plentiful.

Supplement With Potassium. When temperatures exceed 85 F/27 C, cows get rid of about 75 percent of their body heat load by way of their lungs and skin through evaporative cooling. While sodium is the primary mineral excreted by horses and humans during heat stress, potassium is the dominant mineral excreted by heat-stressed cattle.

Potassium is not stored to any great extent within the animal's body and a lactating cow can rather quickly develop a potassium shortage and increased heat stress. Potassium supplementation is one way to off-set high potassium loss during heat stress and help keep milk production from falling.

Frequent Nitrogen. Apply nitrogen every 20 to 23 days. Subtropical grasses must be kept young and growing fast to maintain dairy cow quality. It will probably be necessary to drop up to one-third of your paddocks out for haying in July to keep your stocking rate high enough (three to four cows per acre in July on Coastal) to keep up with the grass. Use a very fast 10- to 14-day rotation. Use the late lactation cows as a follower herd.

Annual Legume Overseeding. With heavily fertilized subtropical grasses it is very difficult to keep reseeding annual legumes like Crimson and Arrowleaf present without some annual overseeding. Subtropical white clovers will require babying through their first summer with very light grazing pressure to survive but are quite hardy in subsequent years.

Rye Better Than Ryegrass For Overseeding. Annual ryegrass produces a chemical growth inhibitor that can retard the spring growth of subtropical perennial grasses. Cereal rye or one of the new short-season ryegrasses are best for overseeding subtropical grasses. Legumes will help keep quality and dry matter production high during this transition period. Use the full-season, late maturing ryegrasses in conjunction with summer crabgrass and fall oats.

Do not feed subtropical grass hay to cows on subtropical grass as it will lower milk production. Grazed pasture is higher in quality than the best subtropical hay. If you must feed hay on subtropical pasture, feed leguminous hay. Use your subtropical hay for dry cows and as a free-choice dry matter supplement to cows on lush winter annuals.

Stand Loss Precautions. Taking subtropical grasses to a very short residual just prior to a killing frost can result in a stand loss, particularly at the northern end of the subtropical grass zone. A system whereby one-third to one-half of the farm is managed as a crabgrass/oats/ryegrass annual pasture will give a better year-round forage flow than one that is all subtropical perennial/winter annual. This will allow the subtropical grass to go safely dormant before grazing off the residue prior to overseeding or drilling.

Fall Flatspot The Worst. The fall transition from subtropical perennials to winter annuals is the most difficult management period. The subtropical grasses are slowing in growth due to the shorter days but it is still too hot for most winter annuals to grow. The one exception to this is oats. Oats are both drought and heat resistant and make the best early fall pasture.

Also, seriously consider making high quality ryegrass silage from your excess spring pasture for feeding at this time. As this is the driest period of the year, self-feeding silage clamps work well with few, if any, mud problems. Subtropical grasses increase in quality in the fall of the year as their growth slows and temperatures moderate.

Buy Heat-Adapted Replacements. Try to buy your replacements in the South. Replacements that grow up in the South seem to handle the heat better than the imports. Fat, Midwestern replacements can suffer a high death loss if brought South during the hot weather months. Smaller body phenotype Holsteins tend to be more heat tolerant than large body phenotypes and predominantly white Holsteins. Try a few crossbreds and Jerseys in with your herd and just watch. You may find it easier to switch than fight.

Sunlight Purifies Dairy Effluent. New Zealand research has found that using a spray irrigation system is the best way to recycle dairy shed effluent. Dairy effluent is the pipeline water, wash water and manure from a milking parlor. It is not the much-more-concentrated manure produced in a total confinement system. The wash water should be sprayed on a paddock shortly after the cows leave it. This allows time for sunlight to kill any disease pathogens before the cows return to graze. The New Zealand research also found that dairy shed effluent grew from one third to one half more dry matter per hectare than pure irrigation water due to its rich nutrient content.

Drought Management

A rule of thumb is that in the second year of having started a MIG program, the very time period when your enthusiasm is at its highest, one can expect a drought. I guess this is Nature's way of keeping us humble. I often say that it requires three years and a drought to learn MIG and while none of us likes to think about having a drought it is absolutely necessary to think through a drought plan **before** the drought arrives.

In the semi-arid parts of the country, severe droughts can extend for one to several years. Such environments lend themselves better to sheep, goats and seasonal beef production than to brood cows. In the humid parts of the country there are no such extended periods of absolutely no rain and droughts are of two general kinds. One is a significantly lower than normal rainfall year whereby periods and intensities of rain are diminished and less frequent but they still exist, and two, is an extended period of absolutely no rainfall. Such periods of absolutely no rainfall seldom extend beyond six to seven weeks in the eastern half of the country. Often, these two types of drought will exist in the same year or two year sequence.

Warning! You curse winter's rain and mud at your own peril. Winter droughts are much more serious than summer droughts, because they prevent groundwater recharge, reservoir filling and can cause a severe shortfall of spring pasture growth. Most MIG programs are based upon the expectation of a spring pasture surplus. When it doesn't appear, it can ruin a whole year's plans.

The final severe second stage drought usually signals the end of the below normal rainfall pattern and is frequently followed by a period of above normal rainfall. The saying "droughts end in floods" is often true. However, droughts do not just suddenly happen. For the aware grazier, their approach is signaled far in advance by the slowing regrowth of your grass. This is one major value of frequent pasture walking and measuring your pasture's regrowth -there are no surprises.

Here are some considerations for your drought plan:

• **Grazing Management**. Keep in mind droughty pastures are higher in dry matter than normal pastures, so less grass goes further. In many cases, weight gains and milk production actually go up during moderate droughts. This is particularly true in the Southeastern states where the subtropical grasses used there are traditionally grazed when they are too mature.

Pastures that are continuously grazed and not limed and phosphated on an annual basis tend to be very short-rooted and their soils low in water-holding organic matter. Such pastures are extremely susceptible to even mild drought. As your pasture's root systems deepen and organic matter increases with summer and fall rotational grazing, your pastures will become more and more drought resistant and dependable. Fall stockpiling programs will promote the growth of deeper roots to grow on cool season grasses.

Grazing the majority of your pastures to a one inch residual in the winter dormant season will help make them more drought resistant in the growing season. Dead leaves slow pasture growth and water utilization. Young, rapidly growing plants make the best use of the soil's water reserves.

In your first three years of MIG, plan to take off the surplus that will appear as hay and/or silage for a drought reserve. Once this reserve has been built, you should thereafter always try to stock as closely to the maximum of your pasture's carrying capacity as possible to keep overhead costs at their minimum.

Many graziers will go to great extremes to avoid feeding hay during the growing season. This is foolish. Stored feeds are for shortages whenever they occur. You will always wind up feeding less hay in the long run by starting to feed it early than when pasture reserves are totally exhausted. By keeping a leaf area on the plant, regrowth will be rapid when rain does come. Care must be taken so that the surface of the soil is not bared during droughts as this causes the formation of a microbial film on the soil's surface that will prevent any subsequent small rainfall amounts from being effective. If your hay supplies run short, consider buying in grain rather than hay as this is usually more cost-effective. 7 to 10 lbs. of grain per cow per day will double your pasture's effective carrying capacity.

South facing slopes and sandy soils are naturally predisposed toward drought. Using only short-rooting grasses and legumes also increases the pasture's tendency toward drought. Deep rooted species such as Puna chicory, alfalfa and Coastal bermuda are very drought resistant. Woody plants are much less susceptible to drought than grasses and legumes. Allowing cows to browse the woods during droughts can greatly stretch your pasture. (In hardwood forests, cows should be routinely kept out of the woods during the growing season. This will keep your woods thick with young and leafy, quality browse for emergency use.)

At the end of the drought, quickly overseed cool season pastures with more grass and legume seed to thicken the drought-weakened sod and quickly raise stocking rates back to normal. Both of these practices will prevent weed and brush encroachment. Due to the buildup of available soil nitrogen during droughts, grass growth rates at the end of a drought can be explosive and will require spring-like grazing management responses.

• **Flexible stock policy**. Having only dairy and brood stock is less flexible than several classes of livestock as destocking is a good, cost-effective response to drought. Buying in forage to continue to run at maximum output during a drought is very expensive. Much more cost effective is a planned lowering of the animals' forage needs by weaning early and dropping dairy cows to once a day milking. If drought persists, dry the milk cows off and drop to maintenance. To paraphrase Joel Salatin, "It is better to do nothing for nothing, than to do something (such as make milk) for nothing (no profit)."

Because sheep and goats can make up a higher percentage of their diet from browse than cows, they are much less susceptible to droughts. In many cases their weight gains and wool production will increase during droughts. Sheep and goats will also help prevent the weed and brush encroachment that often occurs at the end of a drought due to the weakening of the pasture sod.

• **Stock Water Reserves.** Many graziers will start increasing stock numbers under MIG and forget to increase the amount of stock water they have in reserve. During a drought, graziers will frequently run out of stock water long before they run out of grass. This is particularly true when summer droughts are preceded by exceptionally dry winters. Water reservoirs and ground water reserves are almost completely dependent upon winter rains as there is much less effective run-off once the trees leaf in the spring. Also at the end of a drought the pasture response is almost explosive but stock water reservoirs are very slow to refill after a drought due to the dry soil and low runoff. A planned program of increasing stock water reservoir capacity should accompany all MIG programs.

Drought Review

♣ Winter drought is the most serious drought.

♣ Lack of stock water is usually a more serious problem than lack of forage.

♣ Feeding hay early cuts overall hay feeding.

♣ Plan to reduce your forage needs by short-weaning, once-a-day milking and destocking.

Think About It...

♣ Wind more than the cold makes us and our animals feel cold. What can you do to provide a wind shelter to winter your animals outdoors?

♣ How heat sensitive or cold tolerant is the breed of your animals?

♣ Increasing water consumption is a major way animals cool themselves.

♣ Most animals can adapt to a new environment in about 100 days. What they cannot adapt to are sudden changes in climate. If you must ship animals between two different climates, ship North in the summer and South in the winter.

♣ Genetics alone cannot erase the summer slump. Even environmentally adapted animals get lazy in the heat. Graziers needing high production in the hot months should concentrate on high TDN plants. Have you included white or red clover, cowpeas, hay-type soybeans, kudzu, forage rape, chicory and or warm-season annuals in your pasture mix?

♣ Supplementing cattle with high-TDN grain on pasture in the hot months doesn't dramatically increase animal performance, but it does dramatically increase costs because the animals substitute the high-cost grain for the low-cost pasture.

♣ The lowest cost way to beat the heat (or the cold) is to use adapted animals and to gear your peak breeding and production to what your climate naturally provides. Are you taking the lowest cost route?

♣ There is no measurable difference in air temperature under a tree as opposed to being in the sun. Do you feel guilty about baseball players playing in the sun on a hot day?

♣ The best way to stop animals from milling on a hot day is to give them a fresh break of grass.

♣ Multiple small breaks are a good hot weather stress reliever for your animals and can actually increase production.

♣ Heat stress is more a function of humidity than temperature. Therefore, providing shade with trees rather than putting your cows in hot, high-humidity barns makes them "feel" cooler.

♣ Trees used for shade should be numerous, wide spaced and should have their lower limbs removed to at least 20 feet in height. The goal is to have the animals widely dispersed and to frequently have to move to stay in the shade as the sun moves across the sky.

♣ Do poplars grow in your area?

♣ In rangeland situations, allowing and denying access to fenced shade areas has proven to be as effective a tool as opening and closing water points for cattle movement and avoiding overgrazing.

♣ When a cow gets up from resting, it will make a manure deposit. They do the same near spots where they wait for water or mineral or salt. At the watering spots, the beef herd tends to urinate more. By separating the watering and mineral feeding sites the cows walk back and forth more, increasing the chances of spreading their cow pie deposits. Have you moved your feeding and mineral sites to areas where you need manure most?

♣ If shade is provided for your cattle, it should be enough for all animals to have access to it at one time. Having a shade for only a few animals will create a milling, restless herd. Shade should be plentiful, widely spaced, move with the sun or it should not exist at all.

♣ A favorite breeding plan with non-seasonal dairymen on subtropical perennial/winter annual pasture is to have one-third of the cows calve in late September and October and two-thirds calve in January and February. This one-third/two-third breeding season maximizes the use of spring pasture, allows cows to be bred in cooler weather, and those that don't catch in one season can slide around to another.

Chapter 9: Stored Forages

While every effort should be made to graze as long as possible each year, stored forages are still a big part of grass farming for most parts of North America. Today, graziers have several stored forage options to consider. These are as follows:

Hay

Hay is a good option in arid climates but often a poor choice in humid, rainy climates. The quicker the hay dries the higher its quality. Slow drying hay will respire away much of its nutrient content. Rain on cut hay causes leaching and soluble nutrients are lost. It has been estimated that a producer has only one chance in four of making dairy-quality hay in the eastern half of the United States. For best quality, hay must include a percentage of legumes, although a pure legume hay is not necessarily better than a mixed grass/legume hay. In humid climates, mixed grass/legume swards dry faster and therefore are frequently higher quality than pure legume swards.

Storage: Hay nutrient level declines over time. It is best that hay be consumed within two years of having been made. In humid climates fungi will eventually start to grow in long-stored hay.

Cost: Hay is expensive to make compared to pasture silage but is relatively easy to store and to feed out. Roundbale unrollers that put the hay out in a windrow in the paddock are the best way to feed hay on a paddock.

Because of its weather sensitivity, hay does not lend itself well to contract harvesting in the Eastern half of the United States.

Pasture Silage

Average Silage Requirements Per Animal

Type of Animal	Requirement per month (tons)	5 Month Winter (tons)	6 Month Winter (tons)
Cow	1.5	7.5	9.0
In-calf heifer/Dry suckler cow	1.2	6.0	7.2
Finishing Cattle	1.2	6.0	7.2
Weanling (200 kg)	.7	3.5	4.2
Ewe	.25	1.25	1.5

Source: ACOT Council for Development in Agriculture

Pasture silage if made when the grass is immature and sealed quickly--same day is best--can have a very high feed quality. Animal performance can be almost as high as on pasture itself. Pasture silage should be cut after noon in bright weather to insure a high sugar content in the grass for fast ensilage.

While per acre tonnage yields are lower than corn silage, agronomic costs are much lower and the land, after being chopped for pasture silage, can then be used for fall grazing, or stockpiled for wintergrazing. Also, pasture silage does not have to be supplemented with expensive protein as corn silage does.

Pasture silage is the best way to save and utilize the normal spring pasture surplus for use at other times of the year. It has a lower machinery cost (flail-chopper and wagon) than hay production and is much more weather proof than hay. It is easily self-fed and therefore can reduce winter machinery and fuel use.

Pasture silage offers the opportunity to dramatically reduce grain inputs in growing and finishing cattle, thereby giving the on-farm producer, and high-grain-cost-areas a production advantage over commercial feedyards. Grass silage is a cheaper, more dependable method of capturing pasture surpluses than hay.

Pasture silage offers considerable advantages in the production of leaner beef, particularly from heifers and earn-maturing British breed steers, compared to conventional high-grain rations.

Storage: Silage can be stored for years with no deterioration as long as it remains air tight. If air gets into the silage clamp, it rots and turns to compost.

A drawback to silage is that when a clamp is opened it cannot be resealed and so does not lend itself to short-term feeding such as during a drought, etc. Many producers find multiple small stacks not only add flexibility, but cut the hauling cost of the chopped material and increase quality by allowing sealing the day they are made.

As with all stored forages, care must be taken to prevent severe nutrient transfer either by taking the manure to the pasture or feeding the silage on the pasture.

Cost: Pasture silage is the cheapest stored forage to make with a cost approximately two-thirds that of hay. Machinery cost for the flail chopper and multiple-use silage wagon are the lowest of all stored forages.

Because of the reduced harvest window of good weather needed for pasture silage (an afternoon for direct cut), pasture silage lends itself well to contract harvesting, however, a feed-out wagon and a silage grab will be necessary in climates where the ground does not freeze. In cold winter areas, self-feeding at the silage face is a good low-cost option if the silage is consumed before mud season. Many graziers find self-feeding at the silage face in the fall when conditions are normally dry and allowing pastures to stockpile growth for subsequent wintergrazing is the best use of self-feeding in warm winter areas.

Baleage

This is a good compromise for producers who want the higher feed quality of silage but have already invested in roundbale hay machinery--cutter, swather etc. Not all roundbalers can handle the heavier weight of baleage. Ask your manufacturer. Also, the heavy nature of the high moisture bales may require a larger tractor than you currently own, so take care and consider all the costs of baleage before you leap. Like hay, baleage is best fed on the pasture unrolled in a windrow rather than in a stationary feeder that promotes pugging and parasitism.

Because the grass is first cut and wilted before being baled, it is susceptible to nutrient leaching from rain during the wilting period. Animal performance from baleage is similar to that of pasture silage. Baleage, because of its relatively high plastic cost per pound of feed compared to pasture silage or hay, is most cost-effective when used in high-value dairy situations.

Storage: Use baleage within a year. It is very difficult to keep baleage wraps secure for long periods of time.

Cost: The cost of baleage is very variable depending upon the type of wrap process used. Other than the wrap cost, baleage has the same cost of hay. Baleage can be sealed in individual bags, wrapped individually, packed in long tubes or covered in small groups similar to a pasture silage clamp. These different wrapping methods have widely differing costs and all result in about the same quality of baleage.

One of the lower cost baleage wrap systems is the Hay Wrap system. The wrapping consists of a tractor and three-point hitch fitted with a heavy spear that goes through the bale. The bale is turned hydraulically and wrapped tightly with three layers of 100 gauge plastic. Both ends are wrapped with approximately 10 to 15 inches of overlap to seal out ground water. The bales are then jammed together with the tractor to form an airtight seal. Only the first and the last bales are completely wrapped. This minimalist approach saves considerably in plastic costs.

Baleage lends itself well to contract harvesting. Contractors can harvest hay during dry periods or baleage during humid periods to maximize the use of their machinery. It is this dual purpose use of machinery that makes at least having a baleage option so attractive to machinery owning producers.

Plastic Disposal

All baleage and silage programs entail the use of plastic wrap or sheeting. This plastic is not bio-degradable and can only be disposed of by burning in a very hot, outdoor fire. Take extreme care when doing this as the fumes produced by the burning plastic are poisonous. Do not put it in a landfill as it will not decompose. Researchers are currently trying to find an edible silage wrap that would end this major environmental drawback to baled silage.

French Mini-Clamps

Graziers in the west of France have discovered a low-cost way to make baleage. Six roundbales are placed end to end and covered with two sheets of plastic, one over the other, for greater security against air leaks. The plastic is pressed firmly to the sides of the bales and sealed firmly at the bottom with a thick layer of white sand or agricultural lime. The clamp should be placed directly on the earth and not on concrete or a sheet of plastic, the French insist. The French also advise that no more than six bales be put in any one clamp to prevent secondary deterioration once the clamp is opened. All six bales in the clamp must be consumed within a month once the clamp has been opened.

How To Make Quality Hay

Hay can be of exactly the same feeding quality as silage if properly cured and stored. However, the field curing of hay to a 15 to 20 percent moisture level is very difficult in humid climates where the air moisture percentage seldom falls below 60 to 80%. This is particularly a problem in the cool cloudy months of spring when forage quality is at its peak. Probably at least 75 to 90 percent of the time, hay will be baled at higher than the recommended moisture level in the East. Moist hay should be anticipated and will cause no great problems as long as precautions are taken and the correct bale package is used.

If hay is to be baled at higher than the optimum moisture, it must be loose enough to respire away the moisture through subsequent evaporation. For example, very high quality loose hay can be made even in the drippy climates of Ireland and the U.K. The uncompacted form and the running of the relatively long cut grass and stems in all directions allows air to enter and exit a loose hay stack relatively easily.

The small square bale is a more compact package than a hay stack but is still rather air permeable. Hay storage barns and sheds should be built with air intakes in their floors and roof vents or fans that pull the air from inside the barn to the outside. This will pull outside air through the baled hay and the moisture out to help cure it in place. A thin layer of salt on each bale will both help cure the hay and will make it more palatable to livestock. There is a good example of a hay curing barn at Malabar Farm in Ohio.

They were once widely used all over the Eastern dairy belt.

On the other hand, quality round bale hay in the East is so rare that it is almost an oxymoron. In an attempt to make a waterproof package for outdoor storage, the hay is packed so tight that it can't breathe and shed internal moisture. Even worse, all the stems are faced one way and are locked in the bale's center rather than protruding to the outside as done with square bale hay. If there ever was a package designed to produce moldy hay, this is it. My advice is if you want to use a round baler and need quality, stop making round bale hay and start making round bale silage.

A good rule of thumb to use when evaluating hay balers in humid climates is, "If it is advertised as tight enough to shed water, it is too tight to use for quality hay." Hay in the East must be able to breathe after baling to avoid becoming moldy.

How To Make Grass Silage

It is more profitable to turn your grass into milk, and buy-in your hay needs than to restrict grazing. In a seasonal grazing operation forage conservation programs are primarily used to:

1. **maintain pasture quality** by keeping the grass young and vegetative through the removal of overly mature or surplus material and

2. **to balance out the yearly forage growth** fluctuations and provide insurance against drought and other unexpected weather events.

Low-cost grass silage is an excellent way to accomplish both of these goals. Grass silage has the benefit of needing minimal machinery and labor input compared to hay (still best to hire it done). It also lends itself well to self-feeding. The primary drawback to grass silage is that it is not economically portable over long distances, and therefore not salable as a cash crop.

Hay is a better rumen developer and feed in very light calves (less than 350 lbs.) than silage, but the quality of the hay needed for these light calves is such that it should probably be purchased from Western quality hay sources rather than made from Eastern pasture surpluses. Usually high in selenium, Western hay can be a good source of trace mineral supplementation.

How Ensiling Works. Ensilage first requires the elimination of oxygen. All processes that require oxygen cease fairly rapidly, then bacteria ferments sugars and converts them into acids, which lowers the pH. If desirable bacteria (such as lactic acid) dominates the fermentation, a final pH of 3.9 will result and the silage will be well preserved. An excellently preserved silage will have a feed value approaching that of the grass from which it was made.

The trick then is to fill and seal the silo (one of the least-cost, self-made silos is a silage clamp) as quickly as possible. If the silo is filled fast, well preserved, sealed and the seal is maintained, there shouldn't be any waste or rotted silage on the surface of the silo. The presence of any mold on the silage surface when the silo is opened indicates oxygen has been getting past the polyethylene silo seal.

Once harvesting has commenced it should be done as quickly as possible. The decline in quality from the age of the grass is usually more than the decline from harvesting in less than ideal weather. Take care about waiting too long for ideal weather. Cutting silage in a falling rain will increase effluent (weepage) from the silage. Wait until the rain shower has passed.

Wilting the cut grass prior to ensiling theoretically should increase dry matter intake and animal performance. However, under actual field conditions this has seldom occurred. In fact in most cases wilting produced worse silage because of increased exposure to rain. Therefore, the direct cut method is actually preferred due to its lower machinery and harvest cost.

A major myth is that ensiling a forage crop improves its digestibility and quality. The truth is that no stored forage is any better than the day you cut it, and always loses part of its quality in the translation. The primary decider of your silage quality will be the stage of maturity at which it is cut. Length of chop, silage additives and weather, all pale to insignificance compared to cutting the grass before it makes a seedhead. Too mature silage can actually consume more energy than it produces, and actually cause your cattle to lose weight.

Take Care With Silage Effluent. Direct cut silage produces a lot of silage effluent, and care must be taken that this fluid does not get in water courses. Silage effluent is 200 times stronger than raw domestic sewage and can cause fish kills. This effluent is not poisonous, and is in fact good cattle feed, but promotes micronutrient blooms which kill fish by depleting the water's oxygen supply.

Machinery For Silage Making. Grass silage is an easily consolidated crop. The precision chopping required for corn and drier forages is not needed with grass silage as long as clamps or bunker silos are used. In fact, if the grass is chopped too short the animal cannot regurgitate it and chew its cud, and therefore not get the full benefit of the feed. With grass silage, it is now recommended that the cut be as long as possible to increase cud chewing and have the grass remain in the rumen as long as possible.

Low-cost, durable, direct-cut flail harvesters are used all over New Zealand for the making of grass silage. Research at New Zealand's Ruakura Research Center has shown that flail direct cut silage can actually give better weight gains than chopped, prewilted silage, as long as the grass was relatively mature and chopped after 11 a.m. Economic research in the United Kingdom found that these low-cost flail harvesters were the only cost-effective method of forage preservation for small livestock producers and allowed a one-man, one-tractor operation. These flail choppers can be used to cut pasture for hay as well as silage.

Two major drawbacks to a flail harvester are a tendency to suck up dirt and manure along with the chopped grass and accidentally chop into the soil surface on uneven ground. Getting soil mixed in with your silage will cause poor fermentation and should be avoided if possible. To avoid this problem many graziers prefer a chopper that uses a pickup reel to feed the grass into the chopper rather than the vacuum suck system the flail chopper uses. Graziers using the flail chopper should roll the land they plan to cut for silage during the winter to make a flat smooth surface that will help prevent scalping.

With wet, sappy high legume spring pasture, a higher quality silage can be made by first cutting, swathing, and field drying the grass, to the point where moisture no longer runs out when the grass is squeezed in your hand, before chopping and packing. This pre-wilting cuts hauling costs by reducing the weight of the grass, reduces effluent losses and potential water pollution, and results in a higher dry matter silage that in some studies has produced a slightly higher average daily gain. However, wilting exposes the cut grass to weathering from unexpected rain.

Time Of Day Of Cutting Is Important. Grass that is to be direct-cut (chopped) for silage or hay should be done so after 11

A.M. This is to allow time for the grass to increase its carbohydrate (sugar) level. Pastures chopped in the early morning or on extremely cloudy days often do not ensile well due to low carbohydrate level. Care must be taken to prevent the cut grass from becoming too dry, otherwise it will become difficult to consolidate and result in moldy silage, which can be toxic to the cattle.

In Holland and Germany, self-loading forage wagons that combine the chopper unit with the wagon are used quite successfully, and reduce the capital investment needed to make small amounts of silage. While touted as one-man silage making units, most grass farmers have found having an extra tractor and man to help with the spreading and consolidating of the grass at the clamp greatly speeds up silage making.

Dutch graziers have also found that silage making is easier and quality is higher if several smaller silage clamps that can be filled and consumed rapidly are made rather than one big one as is common in Britain and North America. Hauling chopped forage over one-half mile to a silo greatly reduces the efficiency of a low-capital, one-forage-wagon operation. By keeping hauling distances to only 1500 feet, the Dutch figure 10 to 18 tons of silage can be put up an hour with a single self-loading forage wagon. Most Dutch silage clamps are no more than 50 tons in size or approximately one day's work.

In fact, if hauling distances are kept super-short, the forage wagon can be done away with, and all the hauling done with tractor-mounted buck rates, a method well illustrated in Newman Turner's book **Fertility Pastures**. The tractor-mounted buckrake is probably the ultimate in low-capital forage preservation.

Dr. Raymond Steen of the Hillsborough Research Station in Northern Ireland said Irish farmers were suffering a near-terminal case of "heavy metal disease" due to overly expensive machinery purchases. Irish farmers have moved away from the inexpensive, small, flail choppers to the much more expensive precision and double-chop harvesters. He said this made sense for contractors as the larger silage harvesters allowed them to cover a greater acreage in a day, but made no sense for a small sized dairyman or beef producer. "We have found no significant increases in silage quality between the use of a $5000 flail chopper and a $250,000 contractor-sized chopper."

Chopping finer and wilting the silage before chopping did increase intake but frequently actually reduced animal performance due to the loss of quality during the wilting phase due to unexpected rain. "We have seen animal performance drop by as much as 10 to 12 percent due to trying to wilt cut grass in broken (intermittent rain) weather," he said. The method that produced the greatest amount of beef production per acre at the lowest cost was a direct cut with a low cost flail chopper.

In summary, no difference in silage quality has been found due to the type of harvester used when fed to cattle. Flail, double-chop and precision chop all produced quality feed. However, care should be taken in the machine system of harvest used. There can be a 100 percent difference in cost between a low-cost flail chopper and the most expensive system (big bale silage). In general the more complex and sophisticated the machine system the higher the annual repair and maintenance costs. All machine systems produce feed of similar quality. Simpler and cheaper is always your best economic choice.

Consider Using A Contractor. Care should be taken to determine if the hiring of a contractor might be better than equipment ownership. For equipment to be cost-effective, large acreages are required. Nine times out of ten, using a silage contrac tor is your best choice. If there are no silage contractors in your area, perhaps you should consider becoming one. Silage contractors in Ireland can gross up to $250,000 during a six week silaging season.

The one area where there is little way to reduce cost is in the quality of the polyethylene used to seal the silo. Polyethylene quality or quantity must never be compromised to reduce costs. A silage stack or bunker should always be covered with two sheets of plastic.

When Are Additives Needed?

The decision whether or not to use a silage additive confronts the farmer each time grass is to be ensiled. In trials in Northern Ireland several factors have been found to affect the outcome of this decision:

- **Dry Matter Of The Grass**. It is always advisable when

weather is cloudy to use an effective silage additive particularly on low dry matter, direct-cut grass.

• **Filling Over Long Period**. It is not always possible to fill the clamp in 2-3 days. An effective additive will help if long filling periods occur.

• **Grass Species/Age/Growth Stage**. High carbohydrate grasses such as annual and perennial ryegrass naturally ensile better than lower carbohydrate grasses such as orchardgrass and bermuda. Low carbohydrate grasses are more likely to benefit from an additive as are overly mature grasses. Grass cut in May usually has lower sugar levels than when cut in June and is more likely to need an additive.

• **Nitrogen Use**. Generally the more nitrogen and manure slurry used, the more difficult the grass is to ensile. Grasses with high levels of nitrogen applied are usually difficult to ensile and should receive an effective additive.

• **Late Grazing**. Grazing before closing up for first cut silage is often a problem if the grass is left contaminated and has not had enough time to recover before it is ensiled.

• **Type Of Harvester**. Grass harvested by single chop flail harvester and forage wagons is more likely to need an additive than that produced by precision or double chop equipment.

The most common type of silage additives used are:

Formic Acid. No benefit has been found in animal performance when compared to good silage of natural fermentation. Where silage was poorly preserved, silage intake and animal performance have increased as much as 9 per cent in British trials.

Sulphric Acid. While silage intake and fermentation has been increased with the use of sulphuric acid, animal performance has usually fallen in comparison to untreated silage.

Molasses. A good additive. However, if not applied evenly, silage of variable quality can result. Very difficult to apply.

Enzymes. Responses in animal performances have been relatively small.

Inoculants. Results from various commercial inoculants have been highly variable. Evidence so far indicates that inoculants are less reliable than acids at producing well fermented silage under difficult conditions such as low-sugar grass ensiled in wet weather. However, animal performance has been similar to acid treated silage.

WARNING: Before purchasing any silage inoculant additive, make sure there is independent research that shows it has produced cost-effective improvements in animal performance. Increases in fermentation and animal intake have not translated into increased animal performance in a great many trials. Be aware.

Building A Silage Clamp Stack

The ultimate low-cost silo is the silage clamp. All it requires is a space of flat ground with a slight slope to prevent water-logging. Concrete pads allow mud-free, self-feeding, and prevent soil contamination from possibly muddy tires of the spreading and consolidating tractor.

The clamp is initially built into a tepee shape with a slope of no more than 20 degrees on all sides. Some graziers leave the sides of the wedge steep. It's not necessary to consolidate these sides to prevent deterioration as long as the clamp is covered with plastic, but steep sides are dangerous due to the possibility of tractor turn-over while spreading and consolidating. For safety's sake, it is recommended that the sides be sloped at no more than 20 degrees. The cut material is dumped at the base of the clamp and the tractor picks up a front-end loader full of grass and carries it to the top of the clamp before dropping it. This adds the weight of the new material to the tractor and helps consolidate the stack. Water should be added to the tractor's wheels to increase its weight. In one-man operations, the tractor and silage collection cage wagon are driven over the stack and the silage dumped out at the top. One-man clamps are usually not over three or four feet tall and are necessarily small if they are to be finished in one day.

Grass silage is naturally heavy and needs relatively little tractor consolidation to make it air tight. In fact, too much consolidating activity can create a "bellows" effect, which actually pumps air into the clamp. Let the weight of the grass do most of the consolidating and save yourself tractor time and fuel.

A finished silage clamp will look sort of like a squashed haystack. If the clamp is to be self-fed it should not be over five feet in height. The Dutch seal this one-day clamp with plastic held tight with a layer of dirt or barnyard manure and build a new clamp from scratch the next day. The British and New Zealanders frequently add the next day's cutting to the same clamp, although the British admit the Dutch method produces a superior silage.

Large Clamp Or Bunker Silo Technique

Vaughan Jones recommends that a multiple-day large clamp or bunker silo be covered with plastic and close-spaced tires each night. He said the rising warm air caused by the ensiling process causes cold air to be drawn in and can cause deterioration and mold. The next day the tires are removed, the plastic is rolled back, and that day's cut is then piled and packed against one side with a minimum added depth per day of three feet. The 20 degree slope is again replicated. Each day that day's cut is packed against the filling side.

The real secret to successful grass silage is quickly sheeting and weighting of the cover to prevent wastage. If this is not done quickly or well enough, your whole exercise will have been a waste of time. Remember that cut grass continues to deteriorate as long as it is allowed to breathe. The clamp must be air tight to stop deterioration. Research in New Zealand found the silage from a well-made and sheeted clamp to be statistically equal to that from an American upright, air-sealed metal silo.

The covering plastic can be weighed down with closely-spaced tires or even better six inches of dirt or barnyard manure. These clamps are still covered with car tires. The dirt will prevent the silage from freezing in very cold climates. If the plastic is held tightly against the silage wall, there should be no deterioration or wastage. Seeding the covering soil and/or manure to a quick growing grass prevents erosion. Some Canadian graziers cover the surface of their silage clamp with molasses prior to sheeting. This helps make a glue seal and provides extra carbohydrates for the ensiling process. The clamp should be fenced off with electric fence to prevent cattle and deer from climbing on it, and a shallow trench should be plowed around the site to prevent waterlogging.

Feeding Out And Supplementing Grass Silage

Once a silo or stack has been opened it should be consumed as fast as possible. This is particularly true during warm weather (in excess of 80 F/25 C). This is another good reason for multiple, small stacks.

If the silage is being mechanically brought to the cattle, never give them more than they can eat in a day. Care must also be taken not to unduly disturb the silage face with equipment. Rough treatment leaves a tattered and tossed face into which air can penetrate deeply. Silage shear-grabs, which leave a smooth surface, are far superior to front-end loaders for removing silage from the face.

If the silage is being self-fed (cattle eating directly from the silage face) they must be kept moving forward through the silage at a good pace. Care must be taken to keep the polyethylene on top of the stack fully weighted down, taut and right to the front of the silage face.

The method of feeding does not affect the quality of the silage. As with the harvesting equipment, the method of feeding should be kept simple and cheap. Do not attempt to reseal the silage face between feedings as this will form a greenhouse effect that will speed deterioration rather than slow it. Unfortunately, the better preserved your silage is, the faster it will deteriorate when opened to the air.

Self-Feeding Silage

The next tool you need to buy as a grazier is a pickaxe. That's right, a pickaxe! A pickaxe is used to dress the silage face and drive in the solid-plastic posts that hold the one-wire electric fence that both rations the feed and keeps the cattle from climbing onto the stack.

To prevent waste and allow feed rationing, push solid fiberglass posts with an electric wire attached horizontally into the silage face three feet above the ground. This electric-wire feed bunk will allow the cattle to eat forward through the silage stack until they touch the wire. To feed the cattle, all one has to do is push the posts deeper into the silage. A minimum of eight inches of silage face per animal is necessary to insure a full daily feed. There is some silage waste using this method of feeding but the waste and manure mix makes good bedding for the cattle and will produce heat as it surface-composts--both important factors in areas with cold winters.

The electrified wire is erected in a similar manner to an ordinary electrified fence, but in this case the suspending rods are pushed into the silage face or a special bracket is made to which the wire may be attached. The wire is strained at the correct height by adjusting its length and attaching weights as shown.

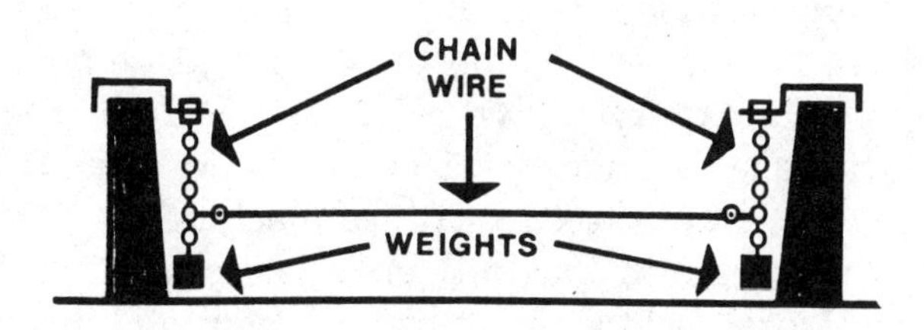

Source: ACOT Council for Development in Agriculture

By adjusting the height of the barrier it is possible to get a clean face with little waste. Don't turn the current on until the animals are accustomed to eating the silage. Electric fence controllers should be **throttled down** to low output for the feeding wire.

Permanent concrete pads can keep the silage face mud-free but require that the manure be captured and respread to prevent severe nutrient transfer from occurring. British dairyman, Newman Turner, moved his self-fed silage stacks across his pastures from year to year using intensive manuring and pugging as a way of improving the tilth and fertility of his soils. Spreading a foot or more of wood chips or sawdust at the silage face helps prevent mud. This mixture of manure, chips and sawdust should only be spread on the pasture's surface and never plowed in to prevent nitrogen tie-up in the soil.

Self-feeding lends itself well to relatively small herds that will be totally off of pasture for an extended period of time. There are no tractors to crank and no need for feed wagons. The primary problem is that your manure and nutrients are concentrated in one very small area and severe soil nutrient transfer can occur.

Such self-fed silage clamps are used in Argentina, Australia and other warm climates in the autumn to allow winter annual pastures time to grow before grazing. Once stacks are broken into in hot weather (above 80 F/25 C) they need to be continuously consumed to prevent secondary fermentation and deterioration. This makes them less flexible than hay for short-term feed deficits.

Working Examples

Mark and Charles Opitz wintered 400 heifers this way their first year using two clamps (stacks) of pasture silage. Paul Bickford wintered 134 heifers on a clamp of pasture silage and a clamp of corn silage. All are dairymen who live near Mineral Point, Wisconsin. "This (pickaxe) is a new grazier's tool," said Mark Opitz. "It cost me $15 and replaced $50,000 worth of machinery."

Both Opitz and Bickford used large round bales to start their silage stacks. Bickford built his on a sloping hill and only put round bales on the downhill side. He then packed silage against these round bales to start the clamp. After running over the silage a few times with a tractor to pack and shape it, the clamp was coverd with a single solid sheet (two are better!) of polyethylene held tightly against the silage with close-fitting tires. Bickford let the size of the sheet of polyethylene determine the dimensions of his clamp. A sheet is 40 feet wide.

Come winter, Bickford simply rolled away the round bales to provide a clear silage face and ran a one-wire electric fence across it approximately two-feet-high. He attached the fence to soild fiberglass posts driven into the silage face. To feed the cattle, he walks across the silage face tapping the posts once a day. Twice a day is even better, since the more frequently the wire is advanced the less wastage there is.

Since the cows cannot reach the silage directly behind the fence, a little dressing of the silage face with the pickaxe is necessary. When the temperature is below zero F, the top of the silage stack will freeze solid and must be broken up with the pickax. The silage face will get crusty at night in very cold weather and make it difficult for the animals to feed unless broken with the pickax. Bickford figures it takes him five minutes to feed 134 heifers when temperatures are above zero and perhaps 15 minutes when temperatuers are below zero.

The Optizs used two rows of large round bales and packed the silage between them. Like Bickford they then rolled away one set of bales to provide a feeding face. After their first winter's experience, both graziers agreed that in the future they would build more, but smaller clamps. This would spread the manure more evenly and allow a higher quality silage to be made.

Both dairies recommend a height of not more than five feet with four feet probably being better for smaller and younger cattle. "The faster the animals can consume a stack the less soil disturbance and manure concentration there will be in one place," Bickford said. This rapid rate of consumption was particularly valuable if the silage was to be consumed in warmer weather and before the ground froze solid. After eating their fill, the animals moved away from the clamp face and their manure was spread more widely than one might think.

By orienting the silage clamps so that the cattle eat from the southeastern side, the clamps can also serve as windbreaks. Both the Optizs and Bickford are convinced windbreaks are all that are needed to winter dry cows and heifers in Wisconsin. Bickford said his outdoor-wintered cattle had much better animal health. Not a single animal had gotten sick. He also found his cattle seldom walk to water if there is snow on the ground.

Spring Thaw Requires Alternatives

"I would recommend that a grazier also have roundbale hay available and possibly the ability to feed on concrete during the spring thaw. I think you need a combination of silage and hay for the best success. I have found any combination of systems is better than just one system," Bickford said.

Highland, Wisconsin, dairy grazier, Dan Patenaude, echoed Bickford's sentiments and said, "Pasture silage alone is not flexible enough." Patenaude went through the winter of 91-92 with only one self-fed silage clamp and no hay. He experienced no problems but considers himself lucky. "If anything had gone wrong, say a long spell of very deep snow, I would have had no backup and no other winter feeding options." He plans to use homemade square bale hay, contractor-made baled silage and purchased hay. "The long wet spring we had this year, sure proved the worth of pasture silage but I think we will still need some hay even if we buy in most, or all of it. Last winter my cows were only in the barn for two nights, but I had small square bale hay to feed them there. I had an option. The more options you have the better."

One option seasonal dairymen have is to buy in the small

amount of hard-to-make, lactating-cow-quality hay they need rather than trying to make it. Patenaude buys in all of his grain and one-quarter of a ton of lactating-cow-quality hay per cow. "All of my haying and silaging is strictly to keep my pastures in control. If it is a little off in quality, so what? My cows are dry in the winter, anyway," he said.

Fenceline Feeding

Permanent feed bunks can cause severe nutrient transfer. Rolling feed bunks prevent pasture pugging and allow the grazier to concentrate manure and hoof action on areas of the paddock that need it. Another alternative is to feed the silage underneath a movable, one-wire electric fence. The fence will prevent the cattle from stepping on and dunging in the feed and wasting it. Unfortunately both of these methods require the daily use of machinery and fuel. New Zealanders use a low-tech wagon that can be used both as a forage cage wagon for the chopped forage and as silage feedout wagon. These are now available in the United States.

Madison, Wisconsin, grazing consultant, Alan Henning, advises placing hay or silage in a paddock before the cows are turned into it. He said the cows would mill around and pug the paddocks if the hay or silage was fed out directly to the cows. Also, always feed supplemental grain or feed on the ground under the electric fence rather than in a feed bunk. "Research at Purdue University has found there is 17 percent more saliva produced when the cow feeds with her head in the grazing position (ground level) than when she feeds with her head up at a feedbunk," he said. "Watch a cow. Where does she graze first? Under the electric fence. That's where she wants to eat. So, feed her there."

There are electrically driven, metered, small feeders designed for the fenceline feeding of grain and protein cubes. These feeders automatically place the grain in small piles of pre-set weights for each cow rather than in one long continuous pile, which tends to allow aggressive cows to eat more than their share.

Spring Mud Season

Self-fed grass silage clamps are wonderful until the spring thaw comes, then the cows sink to their brisket in mud. Roundbale hay is an option as long as it is unrolled and its feeding location varied every day. Paul McCarville, of Mineral Point, WI winters his dry cows outside on roundbale hay. He found the key thing was to keep a rotation going and feed the hay on a different paddock every day or so. This not only spreads the manure and nutrients over the paddocks but helps prevent pasture pugging. He doesn't worry about water as long as there is snow on the ground.

Charles Optiz wants all of his pasture silage clamps consumed before the spring thaw. "What we need to use in the spring is one of those machines that unrolls round bales and leaves the hay in a windrow out in the paddock. We've got to keep these animals moving in the spring to prevent pasture damage."

Bermudagrass Silage

Four years of research at Clemson University have shown that silage made from heavily fertilized Coastal bermuda of less than 30 days of age can produce as much milk as corn silage at a feed cost savings of 25 cents per cwt. of milk.

For good silage quality, bermudagrass should be cut every four weeks, no higher than six inches, and be packed **without wilting**.

Pasture Silage Review

♣ Pasture silage can be a low-cost, high-quality stored forage if it is chopped in an immature stage and sealed quickly.

♣ Quality silage comes from cutting grass when it is at a growing, green, leafy stage. Grass that is too mature will produce low animal performance and may not contain enough carbohydrate to ensile properly.

♣ The first spring cutting of grass for silage will have a quicker decline in quality than later cuts.

♣ Cut grass before it makes a seedhead for optimum silage.

♣ Grass past its prime that has lodged over in wet weather produces a low-quality silage.

♣ Cutting grass for silage in a falling rain increases effluent from the silage stack and lowers quality.

♣ Don't cut too close to the ground. This can lead to soil contamination and poor preservation. Aim for a stubble of 2 inches.

♣ Once harvesting begins, it should be completed as quickly as possible.

♣ Slow filling can lead to variation in the fermentation. Fill and seal as quickly as possible. If filling is temporarily stopped for any reason, cover the clamp with plastic.

♣ A shallow trench around the silage clamp prevents waterlogging.

♣ Most of the disappointments with grass silage as a supplement to pasture have been the result of a too sudden change to silage. This shift must be done gradually over at least a week's time to allow the cows' rumen micro-flora to change. Don't wait until you are completely out of grass before you start supplementing with silage. Keep in mind this gradual transition is also necessary when shifting cattle back to direct grazing after having been on a full silage feed.

♣ Have material of uniform quality and palatability, otherwise stock will pick and choose and cause wastage.

♣ Long chopped material is easier for the cattle to pull from the silage face when self-feeding.

♣ The height of the feeding face must be related to the age of the animals feeding. Younger animals require a lower feeding face.

♣ Cut down silage above animals' reach with a pickaxe.

♣ Clean feeding can be achieved by adjusting height and distance of wire or barrier from the feeding face. The fence should be moved twice a day and be not more than nine inches from the silage face at any time.

♣ Neglecting the feeding barrier (wire) can give rise to wastage and low intake.

♣ Have ground always slope away from feeding face.

♣ Allow six to eight inches of silage face per cow.

♣ Use a low powered energizer or a transformer to lower the voltage on the wire across the silage face if connected to your main fence energizer.

♣ Heifers should be taught to feed at the silage face before they calve.

♣ Multiple, small clamps, rather than a single large one allows the clamp to be built and sealed faster, ensuring higher quality silage. It can also be consumed faster, producing less mud and manure concentration.

♣ If landscape allows, build stacks on rocky outcrops to

lessen pugging.

♣ Use heavy-duty solid fiberglass posts that will not shatter and leave sharp points that could injure the cattle.

♣ Once the clamp is opened feeding should be continuous.

♣ At temperatures below zero F, the silage face may freeze over at night and make it difficult for the animals to feed. In very cold weather make attention to the silage face a regular morning chore.

Think About It...

♣ Here are some grass silage tips from around the world. How many can you adapt for your grass farm?

♣ **Tropical Grass Silage**. Tropical and subtropical grasses such as kikuyu, bermuda, dallis etc. can be used for pasture silage if cut in a very immature stage--4 to 5 inches tall--as the carbohydrate level falls rapidly in the quick maturing tropical grasses. (Burt Smith, University of Hawaii)

♣ **White Sand Can Keep Rats Away**. Lay a ring of white sand or lime around your silage stack (clamp) to seal the edge and help keep rats and other varmints away. (British silage expert Mike Woolford)

♣ **Avoid Windy Ridges**. Avoid building silage stacks on windy ridges. Suction will pull the plastic cover away from the stack, loosen the seal and admit air. Do not put silage stacks or baled silage under trees where falling limbs may poke holes in the plastic. Fence off stacks and bales from livestock with electric fence. (Geoff Greig, Agpac Plastics New Zealand)

♣ **Chop Length Important**. Longer chop length (one inch to two inches) is important in pit and clamp silage stacks as it helps exclude air. Chop length is not so important in round bale silage and the process of making the silage naturally excludes air. (British silage expert Mike Woolford)

♣ **Silage Face Freezing**. To solve problems with the silage face freezing hard during extreme cold (1984's January freeze came with windchill factors of -70 F), take a tractor and break open these faces so the cattle can feed. (Wisconsin grazier, Paul Bickford)

♣ **Fast Harvest Necessary With Lodged Crops**. Harvest crops immediately if they lodge. Grass swards will lose eight to nine percent digestibility units per week in wet weather. (Padraig

O'Keily in **Irish Farmer**)

♣ **Fall Silage Feeding Could Solve Southern Flat Spot**. Argentine graziers primarily use self-feeding, pasture silage clamps in the early fall flat spot when they are stockpiling their perennial pastures and trying to get their winter annuals up for grazing. This normally dry period does not present the pugging and mud problems self-feeding does during the wet mid-winter periods. This is definitely something Southern U.S. graziers should consider.

♣ **Here's Another Argentine Tip**. Thistles make a very high quality feed when chopped and ensiled.

♣ **Averting Silage Spoilage**. Leave the face of the stack (clamp) uncovered when feeding silage. Do not try to resheet it. Trying to recover the face will fuel aerobic deterioration and spoilage. All resheeting does is create high humidity and encourage bugs to spoil the silage stack. Have an overhang of plastic out from the top of the stack to protect the silage face from rain.

Never use a front-end loader on a silage stack face. The tearing action loosens the silage and opens the stack to air and spoilage a yard to two yards in front of the face. Always use a silage shear-grab, which leaves a neatly cut vertical face to the stack.

Silage stacks should be long and narrow so that they do not have a wide face exposed to the air when silage is being fed.

Don't feed out more silage than the animals will consume at that feeding. (British silage expert Mike Woolford)

Chapter 10: Seasonal Grass Dairying

Seasonal grass dairying can produce a very high return per animal and per acre and offers an excellent middle-class living and a superb quality of life from a relatively small acreage farm. Seasonal dairying is particularly suited where the grazier and his family do the milking themselves. Since the cows are not in lactation all year, the grazier and his family can travel and take a vacation like everyone else. With the calving season confined to just a few weeks and the cows harvesting their own feed, the daily work load is light and there is plenty of time for reading, contemplation and quality family time.

Many seasonal dairymen find their highest profit comes from turning all of their grass into milk and buying their replacement heifers. Some have their dry cows wintered by their neighbors on a fee basis and go to Florida or Mexico for the winter.

Seasonal production emphasizes the marginal economics of twice a day milking as the lactation curve declines. Many go to once a day milking or buy calves and graft them on the cows for the last few months of lactation. Seasonal dairymen have quit fighting Mother Nature and soon learn it is more profitable to just relax and go with the flow. The forage flow, that is.

Seasonal dairymen have also found it far more economical to buy in all their grain and quality hay needs than produce it.

Contractors can be used to harvest the spring grass surplus as silage for dry cow feed. This silage can be stored in a pasture clamp or walled silo and the cows can feed directly from the face of the silage. Since the cows are not in lactation during the coldest weather minimal barns and capital structures are needed.

Most seasonal dairymen find one small tractor, a mower-shredder and a manure spreader adequate for their needs. If all other equipment, barns and stored forage structure costs are charged against winter milk production, as they should be since they are not needed for seasonal milk production, green-season milk can be produced for about one-sixth the cost of winter milk.

Answers To Commonly Asked Questions

What are the drawbacks of seasonal dairying?

Seasonal dairymen must manage their money because of its seasonal nature just as all other farmers of other commodities have to do. Seasonal grass dairying is not a low management system but a much higher management system. Less time is spent actually working but a lot more time is spent thinking and walking one's pastures. It is a "thinking person's" form of farming.

Seasonal grass dairying has also been described as a "real time" management system in that it is very dynamic and rapidly changing. Your pastures must be walked frequently and your management adjusted to the growth of the grass. The pasture must be kept young and vegetative with a high legume content for maximum milk production. Pasture surpluses are removed as silage or hay.

What will happen to the price of milk if a lot of dairymen go seasonal?

Realistically, we do not expect all dairies to go seasonal. Large, heavily capitalized dairies will be forced to produce year-round to cover their huge overheads. Seasonal dairying best fits family dairies. Currently, less than one third of the U.S. milk supply is consumed in its fluid form today. Cheese and other manufacturing uses are the other two thirds. In Wisconsin, cheese manufacturing consumes almost 90 percent of total production. Logically seasonal dairies are ideally suited for concentrating on the manufacturing milk market and leaving the fluid market to others.

The mid-winter months represent only eight to ten percent of total fluid milk consumption in the country, which can easily be produced by the large, high capital confinement dairies and by grass dairies in the South whose lowest cost milk production occurs in the winter months. Already, a national milk market is forming with regional surpluses being trucked to areas with seasonal shortfalls. A similar "production sharing" arrangement already exists in South America where summer milk is made in the Andes and winter milk is made in the cool subtropical lowlands.

Many dairymen find that by milking seasonally, using intensive grazing and buying in their feedstuffs, they only need about one half to one fourth of the land their current herd requires. This gives them room for a tremendous expansion in cow numbers if they should so desire.

The shift to seasonal grass dairying will greatly alter the way dairy farms in America look and are designed. For example, the milking parlor will be at the center of the farm to minimize walking distance rather than at one corner as most conventional dairies are currently designed. The parlor will be designed for low-labor, fast-throughput milking.

In the upper Midwest and New England, seasonal dairying offers the only hope for competing against the lower cost dairies in the South and West where costly capital structures such as barns are not required. With separate milking parlors, emphasis on grazing and seasonal milking, barns will be minimal or non-existant. Today's dark, dank barns will be recognized in the future as the pneumonia holes they are and will be discarded.

Inexpensive pole barns with high roofs that allow the sunlight to reach all parts of the woodchip-covered barn floor and equipped with Canadian-style slatted-plank windbreaks on their North and West sides will be used only during the very worst of weather. Otherwise the cows will wintergraze stockpiled pasture or eat directly from silage clamps or roundbales in the paddock they were made.

Many graziers seeking to maximize return-per-acre will winter their dry stock off the farm, buy or farm out their replacement heifers and turn every blade of grass they grow into high value milk.

As management guru Peter Drucker pointed out, normally

90 percent of your income is generated from 10 percent of your effort. Conversely, 90 percent of your costs are generated by 90 percent of your effort. If you are working hard and not making financial progress, you haven't yet identified where you really make your money and where your unnecessary costs are. Productivity increases when all of our effort is concentrated where it gives us the greatest leverage and return. This effort/reward ratio includes efforts in cost cutting.

Drucker said it requires just as much effort to cut 10 percent from a $50 cost as 10 percent from a $50,000 cost. Therefore, you should concentrate your efforts on your biggest costs first because that's where the bill results will be.

Cost Cutters

Here's where the big results in cost cutting for most dairy producers will be found:

Get Your Breeding Season In Sync With The Pasture. This is your number one cost cutter. The market high occurs in a different month every year. Winter occurs at the same time year after year. The cost of milk production on non-seasonal, town milk dairies in New Zealand is not dramatically lower than in the United States. Don't expect pasture to make you financially whole if your cows are not bred to maximize its use.

Stop Grain Farming. Grain farming is a highly specialized, large-acreage enterprise today. A recent financial analysis of less than 100 cow dairies in Wisconsin found that they would net $14,000 more per year buying their grain rather than growing it. Plant all of your land to grass. If you do not have enough capital to immediately fully stock all of your acreage, lease it to your neighbor and let him lose the money trying to grain farm it.

Concentrate On Cutting Feed Costs. Protein is the most expensive part of a dairy ration. Dairy cows need a 12 percent protein feed. Young, green, leguminous pasture is usually around 20 percent plus protein. Why are you feeding very expensive protein on green high protein pasture? Do you really expect your feed salesmen to suggest you cut the most expensive part of the ration out?

Also, I have not been able to find any university research that shows that the increased animal response from grinding, cracking, steaming, and flaking corn will pay for the time, energy and machinery the processing requires. All of these processes were primarily devised to increase the mystique and profitability of feed manufacturing. Steam flaking, for example, allows water to be sold for the cost of grain.

Whole shelled corn works a lot better when fed under a one-wire fence than a finely ground feed. You can buy it direct. You don't need a feed mill or a Ph.D. to feed it. Yes, you will see a little whole corn in the cow's manure. If this really bothers you, get a couple of paddock pigs or a Joel Salatin-style rolling hen house and turn the grain in the manure into a profit center.

Minimize Machinery Costs. You can almost always hire it done for what the interest and depreciation on owning a machine would cost you. If you don't need a machine on almost a daily basis, think hard about buying it. Multiple purpose machinery is much cheaper than single purpose.

Keep in mind the big machinery cost in growing a crop is the harvest cost not the planting cost. Use your animals to direct harvest your crops and you'll be able to dodge the big bullet on machinery costs.

Increase Stocking Rate. Profits are maximized when stocking rates are at their optimal limit because fixed costs are minimized. MIG can provide at least a 30 percent increase in stocking rate in well-managed operations and 100 percent or more in extensive operations. The huge increases in labor productivity from MIG have largely been overlooked because most research operations are so small. On a correctly engineered MIG dairy, one person can easily manage and milk 100 to 160 dairy cows.

Be Realistic About Animal Genetics. Commercial enterprises have to be able to make a profit with the average animal genetics and middle-of-the-road animal performance. If it takes a SuperCow to breakeven, you've got your cost structure too high.

Don't Blame The Animals For Lack Of Profits. Profitability is strictly a human function. Your cows don't care whether you make any money or not. If you'll do all the work for them, they'll sure let you.

Change As Fast As Possible. Costs go up before they go down when you change technological directions because you have to continue to run the old while you are learning the new. The shorter you can make this transition period the faster your profits will recover.

If You Don't Have A Competitive Edge Don't Try To Compete. Peter Drucker said the only two resources any business person has to work with are knowledge and money. If your operation is run at the same knowledge and skill level as your neighbor's you'll never become wealthy. True wealth only comes to the innovator. It is only created at the leading edge of the envelope. As a reader once pointed out, "If it doesn't sound crazy, it won't make any money." Get crazy!

A New Zealand Perspective On Seasonal Dairying

New Zealand's dairy industry is divided into two segments. One is a small segment that supplies the year-round domestic supply dairying requirements and is called "town dairying," and the other is the large, ultra-efficient "export dairying" that is run on a seasonal basis only. The "town dairies" must of necessity use a good bit of stored forages and feeds to lactate year-round, but the huge export dairy industry is built around timing the cow's lactation to the onset of the spring pasture lush so as to minimize all inputs. This allows New Zealand dairymen to sell milk at a profit for less than a third of the U.S. price.

There are currently around 15,000 dairy producers in New Zealand and they milk 2.3 million cows. Milk yield is measured by the acre rather than by the head and dairy quality land sells for US $4500 to $10,000 an acre due to the profitability of all-grass dairying.

A "starter unit" for a young dairyman would be a small (by New Zealand standards) herd of 130 cows. Many dairymen will milk 400 to 500 cows with a husband and wife team alone. To do this, both the milk shed and animals have to be adapted to a minimal labor input per cow system. Cows udders are not washed nor stimulated prior to milking. Mastitis is controlled largely by culling cows that are susceptible to it. Turntable milking parlors in combination with automatic release milkers allow a large number of cows to be milked quickly. Circular holding pens with motorized crowding gates allow one man to handle a large number of cows with a minimum of fuss. No feed is fed during milking nor at any time during the seasonal lactation.

At the heart of the New Zealand "export" dairy is the crucial timing of the onset of lactation to the start of the spring grass lush. The New Zealanders have gotten so good at this that it is estimated that 90% of the cows in the prime dairy district of Waikato begin lactation in a two week period. The average dairy cow in Waikato will only receive 10 to 14 square bales of hay a year. The majority of this hay is fed in the early fall to allow the building of a feedbank of grass. This feedbank is then tightly rationed with strip-grazing to provide a winter rotation of 130 days. This long rotation allows the building of a spring pasture surplus to begin lactating on in the early spring.

Silage and hay are made more to maintain pasture quality than to provide feedstuff. The rule in all of New Zealand grassland agriculture is to never restrict the animal to make hay. Purchasing hay off the farm is far more cost-effective than choking down a production class of animal, they believe.

In the Waikato district around Hamilton on the North Island, the year long stocking rate is 1.6 milking cows per acre. All young replacement stock is grown out off the farm on contract and dry cows are grazed off the farm to save grass. Many of the tails are cut off New Zealand dairy cows as research has shown this results in fewer flies and a lower mastitis rate. The cows are dried off based upon body condition rather than milk production to make winter feeding and breeding management easier.

"In New Zealand, we are grassland farmers, first and foremost, and only very secondarily, dairymen," said John Roadley, a dairyman who grazes some 800 cows on two farms in New Zealand. "Our economics is based on a grass-to-milk to dollar conversion ratio. This gives us a definite bias toward per hectare profitability."

Profitable grass dairying requires a continual compromise between what is good for the grass and what is good for the cow. "When the crunch comes," said Roadley, "we will always do what is best for the grass."

The four main things grass dairymen work with are stocking rate, calving date, calving spread, and cow genetics.

He uses a stocking rate of 2.9 cows per hectare (over a cow per acre), calved six weeks before the onset of the spring lush, has a 45 day calving season with half of those calves born in the first

15 days and uses cows that had been genetically selected and bred to harvest grass.

The only real fudge factor a seasonal grass dairyman in New Zealand has is the length of the lactation. "If we see we are not going to be able to build enough autumn grass cover to take into the winter, we will shorten the lactation."

Roadley stressed that what is most critical is having enough grass in the spring when peak lactation and breeding both occur. In New Zealand, much of this spring grass has to be grown in the autumn and carried through the winter to spring (stockpiling).

Once his cows are dry they are put out on a grazing contract with cropland farmers and wintered off the farm. This allows him to have a higher overall stocking rate and to use his spring grass surplus production strictly as drought insurance.

North American-Style Seasonal Dairying

"Every year since we went seasonal we do less and less and make more and more," explained Bear Creek, Wisconsin, Holstein grazier Carl Pulvermacher. He said his 68 acres of pasture land currently grosses $1430.70 per acre ($1305.20 from milk and $125.50 from meat) compared to only $402 from his corn ground (162 bushels at $2.50 per bushel).

"Looking at my own budget it appears that grazing is at least three times more profitable on a per-acre basis than growing corn. Needless to say we have been cutting crop acres every year," he said.

Two factors are keeping him from completely ending cropping. One, he is an organic dairy and organically grown corn is expensive to buy, and two, a major highway cuts his farm in half and he is reluctant to drive his cows across the road due to liability concerns.

On the controversial subject of shade, Pulvermacher is dead set against it. "We saw we lost milk production for six days after the cows were in a paddock with shade. The reason, of course, was that the cows stayed huddled up in the shade and didn't graze. Now, we only graze shaded paddocks at night."

He starts calving in late April and plans to dry off 30 cows in November and 45 in January. "I originally went seasonal to get more time off. I like international travel and just couldn't do it milking year around," he said. Since going seasonal he has been able to travel to Australia, Mexico and Russia for extended periods.

"By going seasonal you can add 20 percent more cows without adding any more facilities or land," he added. He has also seen his vet bill and culling rate fall by one-half. He is adding a small swing-over 9, New Zealand-style mini-parlor that will allow him to milk 72 cows an hour single-handed.

"A 15,000 lb. herd average is very easy to accomplish with a seasonal dairy without having to push your cows or yourself very hard," Pulvermacher said.

Dairyman Paul Bickford originally planned a five-year conversion to seasonal dairying for his 500-cow total-confinement dairy but accelerated the time table after he saw the huge difference in profitability.

With the shift to pasture, he saw his herd average drop from 21,000 lbs. to 19,000 lbs. on pasture. He feeds 20 lbs. of grain a day and no protein. Stopping the feeding of protein saves him $5000 a month. "Why feed protein on a 22-23 percent protein pasture? I also save $7000 a month on foot trimming since we went to grazing."

When he was a zero-graze confinement dairy he had to have two full lines of harvest equipment just to keep one full line running. Since he has cut back on his cropping both his labor and equipment requirements have dropped dramatically. "I've probably bought the last tractor I'll need in my lifetime," he said.

Such dramatic changes do not come easy nor painlessly. "I want to warn people who are thinking of shifting a traditional crop-based, confinement dairy to a seasonal, grass-based one that you cannot develop a good dairy-quality sod overnight," he said.

He said that while it was frustrating to have to keep running the old high-capital, stored-forage system after one had decided to discontinue it, this was going to be necessary for at least three years while the pasture sods thicken and get up to speed.

Bickford's advice to conventional dairymen is:

1. Don't lay off labor.

2. Have a feed inventory on hand to rescue you from your early grazing mistakes.

3. Don't increase cow numbers until the transition to grass has been completed.

He uses baby calves to graze new seedings as these new pastures are parasite free and the calves are too light to bog and damage the new pastures.

He uses self-feeding pasture silage stacks in the winter. He found these work well as long as they are consumed during the coldest part of the winter when the ground is frozen. "You need a combination effort," he said. "The silage stacks are great but you also need the ability to feed the cows on concrete during the spring thaw period. I have found that any combination of systems is better than any one system." he said.

Bickford is breaking his farm into two seperate mini-farms rather than continue to run it as one large dairy. One reason is because a four-lane highway splits the farm and the cows now have to walk single-file through a long dark tunnel beneath the highway to reach the milking parlor. The other reason is he feels a smaller unit is easier to manage. "250 to 300 cows on 400 acres is a real manageable-size farm. We're building a double-16, New Zealand-style, high through-put parlor for the other farm," he said. "One of the things I have learned, is that if it sounds weird to you as a conventional dairyman, that's what works. For example, we no longer put gates in any of our paddocks. We just drop the wire and let the cows step over. That one thing cuts fence-building time in half." Bickford has also learned to never put sharp corners in the walkback lanes but to use wide sweeping curves. Sharp turns slow the cows down and may cause cow hock damage as she pivots to make the turn. He uses an average stock density of 60,000 lbs. per acre and shifts the cows to fresh pasture every 12 hours.

Charles Opitz said wet springs and summers in the Midwest have proven the value of improved walk-back lanes (race-ways). Opitz uses two inches of sewer rock covered with two inches of finely ground limestone for his lanes. Walkback lanes should never be wider than four steps. Wide lanes encourage the cows to meander rather than get on with getting to the parlor and back to the pasture. "A narrow lanes moves cows faster than a wide lane," Optiz pointed out. Avoid a small stone base in a lane near a concrete surface as these would hurt the cows' feet. Always cover larger base material with finely ground limestone to provide a smooth walking surface. He admits this is expensive ($1.50 per foot of lane) but keeps the cows mud free year around.

Like Bickford, Opitz is also breaking his large farm into smaller, more manageable mini-farms. He built a high through-put New Zealand-style milking parlor for a new 300-cow, seasonal sub-unit of his 1000 cow dairy. The parlor cost $90,000, half of which was for the milking machinery. By being seasonal, the milking parlor can have open sides and ends and be much cheaper to construct.

East Montpelier, Vermont, Jersey-grazier Brian Stone is glad to have made the switch and would never go back to milking 12 months a year. "I am in the second year of seasonal production and have absolutely no regrets," Brian said. "Being seasonal has allowed me to save $8000 to $10,000 a year in grain costs." He has dropped grain feeding to just six pounds of grain a day and has seen production actually increase as his pastures and management got better. "The fastest way to a better bottom line is to concentrate on cutting costs," he said. "My purchased feed cost per cwt. of milk is only a dollar. We're at the point now where we don't really care what the price of milk is." His cows now winter outside on hay stacks with no supplemental feed at all.

Brian recommended that once the decision to go seasonal has been made to change over as fast as possible. "If I had it to do all over again, I would sell everything that didn't fit and replace them." He said that because of the good success of early seasonal converts subsequent dairymen would find their lenders much more cooperative. He starts calving on May 1 and has a goal of having all of his calves born in a 45-day period. He calves on pasture and has been rearing the calves on pasture with a Paul McCarville-style whole-milk-tank. He has found no disappointments with either. He plans to cut his lactation period back to only eight months a year as his cow numbers rise. "Seasonal dairying emphasizes the economic marginality of the late lactation period." Brian's pastures are a mix of white clover, timothy, orchardgrass and Reed canary-grass. All of these were established through overseeding. "The only thing I plow now is the garden."

Lawrence Shearer, a seasonal dairyman from Colrain, Massachusetts, agreed that grain bill savings was a major advantage to going to pasture but having all the cows dry at the same time was also a major advantage to going seasonal. "It is during the dry period where you have the biggest advantage over the conventional dairyman. It is very easy to manage a whole herd of dry cows." Shearer also advised that dairymen should not let cash-flow fears defer them from going seasonal. "We now pay all our bills six months in advance," he said. "Last year my son and I split $100,000 in net income from just 48 cows. Seasonal dairying is the only way to have both a low-labor input and a high income."

Located on the North Pacific coast just south of Eureka, the small town of Ferndale and its associated "bottom," are undoubtedly the center of California grass farming. Here multitudes of small grass-based dairies give lie to the universality of the 1500-cow California drylot dairy. I spoke with Ferndale dairyman Chuck Ozanian and his herdsman, Richard Harpham after they had just completed their first winter of not milking in 1994. They graze 170 Jersey cows on 140 acres of irrigated ryegrass pasture.

A computer cost analysis in 1992 showed winter milk was costing $5.00 cwt. more to make than it was bringing and this spurred their shift to seasonal production. "The winter losses put us behind the eight ball for the whole year. We just never caught up from the winter financially," Ozanian said. The cows were dried off on December 24, and milking started again on February 20. Seasonal production stopped income for two months but dropped costs for 12.

California dairymen are only allowed a 60 day dry period if they want to keep their state fluid-milk quota. However, because California's milk market is 70 percent manufacturing and only 30 percent fluid milk, most dairymen do not use their fluid quota as free-market manufacturing-milk is normally priced over quota, but most feel maintaining the quota adds resale value to the farm. Ozanian said he was selling free-market Jersey manufacturing-milk for $12 to $13 versus the $11 for fluid quota milk.

Several local Jersey-breed dairymen were building a new cheese plant in the area and a new ice cream factory was being built in Ferndale. Such additions augured well for the price of Jersey milk in the future, Ozanian thought. Ozanian is shooting for a 50 day calving season and had no problems with cow breedback so far. He spent only $3000 for breeding including the lease of an Angus bull for cleanup. His cows averaged a 65 day open period. "Jersey's are just the ideal breed for seasonal grass dairying," Ozanian said. The herd average is 12,098 lbs.

His current goal is a stocking rate of 1.5 cows per acre (180), but said if he could find a winter run-off (contract grazier) for the two winter months the cows were dry he could graze 220 cows the remainder of the year. (Contracting out the wintergrazing of dry stock is common in California.) Herdsman, Richard Harpham, said they tried to keep winter feeding down by using fall nitrogen to build a forward stockpile of grass. Their goal is to not have to shut up paddocks for grass silage if they can avoid it. They'd rather use fall nitrogen to build a feed wedge and ration that out rather than use silage.

The previous year late lactating cows received grass silage while the dry cows were wintered on a three-day break of stockpiled grass. On the first day the cows only grazed and on the second and third day they were fed hay. During heavy winter rains, the cows are limit grazed for only a short time each day and then put back in the barn to prevent pasture pugging.

"We use the cows to farm a lot in the winter when they are dry. We'll use an ATV seeder to spin seed out along a break and then let the cows walk the seed in when we let the fence down." Clover seed was also fed to the cows in their ration to help keep pasture clover levels high. During the spring, the cows are put on a 10-day fast rotation but Harpham said a 10-day round still wasn't fast enough. "We start out with a slow first round and pick up the paddock shift rate as the grass growth increases." Harpham said.

All replacement heifers are currently grazed on the farm, but they will use a contract grazier as the herd expands. The heifer calves currently go to pasture at two weeks of age with a Paul McCarville whole-milk-feeder. Male calves are sold.

I asked if there were any drawbacks to seasonal grass dairying. Harpham looked at the ground a moment and then said, "Yeah, one. The work's entirely too much fun."

Grain on Grass--The Problem of Feed Substitution

A common lament of North American farmers is "If we're so productive, why aren't we rich?" The difference, of course, is the economists are measuring the gross while the farmer has to live on the net. What most farmers have failed to realize is that the two are only loosely correlated. In fact, in ruminant agriculture the two can actually be negatively correlated as we will shortly discuss. This is due to the huge cost-differential between grazed pasture and machine-harvested feedstuffs.

In the United Kingdom, grain/soybean meal dairy-concentrate, which costs only slightly more than in the United States, is estimated to cost from seven to ten times more on a dry matter basis than grazed pasture. Pasture silage, the cheapest form of stored forage, costs at least three times as much as grazed pasture and hay four times as much.

British and Irish research has found that young, leafy pasture is worth almost exactly the same as a milk or meat making feedstuff as concentrate-feed and is far superior to any stored forage. Therefore, it seems obvious to everyone in the world but North Americans that the way to maximize profitability is to maximize the use of pasture and minimize the use of grain and stored forages. In fact, the UK goal is that no more than ten percent of a year-long dairy ration should be made up of grain for maximum profitability.

With a pasture-grazing-season of six months, the British want to get 65 percent of the total diet from grazed grass, 25 percent from grass silage and the remainder from grain. In Ireland, a 75-25-5 ratio has made them the lowest-cost milk producers in the Northern Hemisphere. Again, as in Britain, this is with only a six month grazing season.

While gross milk production can usually be increased by feeding more grain concentrate, if this much higher-cost concentrate replaces lower-cost grazed pasture or pasture silage, the result on net profit will be negative. Research at the Hillsborough Research Station in Northern Ireland found that as long as pasture quantity and quality (immaturity) was adequate, each pound of grain concentrate eaten by the cow replaced one pound of pasture on a one-to-one basis. In other words there was no net additive effect whereby the cow ate all she could of the pasture and then somehow managed to eat some more grain concentrate, as many North American dairy nutritionists have assumed would happen. In fact, the cows were observed to decrease total grazing time by 20 to 23 minutes for each kilogram of grain concentrate-dry-matter fed. It was also found that feeding grain concentrates lowered the overall digestibility of the total ration by shifting the rumen to the acid side for several hours.

Relative Costs
(Direct Only)

	$ ton of dry matter
Grazed Grass	$40
Grass Silage	$112
Concentrate	$272

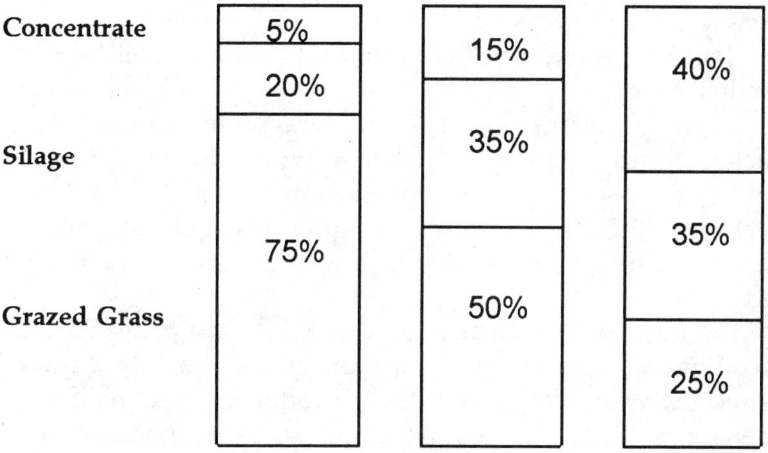

Concentrate	5%	15%	40%
Silage	20%	35%	35%
Grazed Grass	75%	50%	25%
Milk yield lbs/cow	12,320 lbs.	13,420 lbs.	15,420 lbs.
Gross dollars at $11 cwt	$1,355	$1,476	$1,696
Total feed costs	$368	$544	$840
Net return per cow	$987	$932	$856
Difference in net return		- $55	- $131
Feed cost per cwt.	$2.99	$4.05	$5.45

The chart shown is from Con Hurley, Dairy Editor of the **Irish Farmers Journal** and dramatically demonstrates the negative effect of feed substitution on net profit. By increasing the diet from 5 percent concentrate to 40 percent concentrate, milk production per cow went up over 3,000 lbs. but net profit per cow actually went down by $131. The other unstated part of this equation is that the increase in gross production when widely replicated would lower the price of milk thereby worsening the loss. The Irish chart well illustrates the cost-price squeeze North American farmers of all commodities have gotten themselves into by focusing exclusively on high gross production.

Some other North American feeding ideas Hillsborough researched were:

High Producing Cows Need Grain On Pasture: High producing North American Holstein cows were found to have responses to concentrate supplementation similar to lower production British Friesian cows and grain was not cost effective as long as pasture quantity and quality were adequate. Conclusion: Not economic.

Feeding Grain Will Increase Milk Fat On Spring Pasture: The feeding of high starch grains on spring pasture **actually worsened the drop** in spring milk-fat production. The feeding of bicarbonate of soda showed no effect at all. Conclusion: Not economic.

Cows On Pasture Must Be Supplemented With Rumen Bypass Protein: There was **no impact** from the feeding of rumen bypass, high or low levels of protein as long as pasture quantity and quality were adequate. Even though recent studies have shown high losses of dietary nitrogen in the rumen with grass-based diets, there is no evidence to indicate that the supply of amino acids reaching the small intestine may limit milk synthesis. Conclusion: Not economic.

Cows On Pasture Need To Be Supplemented With Pasture Silage And Hay: The feeding of supplemental silage or hay in situations where pasture quantity and quality were adequate **resulted in reduced milk yield and milk protein yield** with variable effects on milk fat yield. Again this was due to the substitution effect. Research at Hillsborough found cows reduced their grazing time by 43 minutes per day for each kilogram of silage DM consumed. Conclusion: Not economic.

Cows On Pasture Need To Be Supplemented With High

Energy Corn Silage: As long as pasture quality and quantity were adequate the feeding of corn silage to cows on pasture **resulted in reductions in milk production**. Conclusion: Not economic.

Cows On Pasture Need To Be Fed A High Concentrate/Stored Forage Diet At Night: As long as pasture quality and quantity were adequate, this method of feeding **resulted in lower milk yields** than pasture alone. Conclusion: Not economic.

So is supplementing dairy cows on pasture with grain or silage ever economic?

Yes, when pasture quantity is short, such as in a drought situation, or when the grazier has let it get too mature due to poor grazing management.

The bottom line on supplemental feeding is that far greater results in net profit will be achieved by focusing on creating dairy-quality pasture and grazing management than upon the myriad of unresearched, uneconomic recommendations on supplemental pasture feeding.

A Most Cost System

State Grassland Specialist for New York, Darrel Emmick said that it was as if we in North America had gone out of our way to create a "most-cost" dairy production system.

Emmick studied the Irish system of producing milk entirely from perennial grass pastures and compared the costs of the Irish system to milk-production from grain and corn silage in New York State. The Irish dairyman gets 65 percent of his cows' diet from pasture, 25 percent from grass silage and 10 percent from grain. This allowed them to produce milk for around $5.00 cwt.

In contrast, in New York a typical dairy ration consists of about 40 to 50 percent corn or other annual crop silage, 40 to 50 percent grain, and less than 10 percent of the diet is derived from pasture. This ration produces milk for around $15 cwt. or three times the Irish cost (and seven times the New Zealand cost). This is hardly world competitive!

We have devised a system where most of the cows' diet is made up of the most expensive rations with the least expensive ration being the one the least used. The way to cut cost is to reverse these ratios," Emmick concluded.

Thank God For Denmark

Cash costs of production per 100 kg. of milk in various countries compared with New Zealand as presented at the 1993 World Grassland Congress by Michael Murphy of Ireland.

Percent of NZ Cost

Denmark	333	Britain	217
United States	300	France	217
Canada	300	Ireland	183
Germany	266	Australia	117
Holland	250	New Zealand	100

The Dairy Breeds As Grazers

Graziers attempting to go seasonal with large body phenotype North American Holsteins have been having great difficulties getting them to reliably calve on a 12 month cycle. Dairy producers who seek to go seasonal should possibly consider the smaller body phenotype breeds.

In the 1939 book **Dairy Science**, W.E. Petersen ranked the major dairy breeds by their grazing ability.

For temperate climates:
1. Ayrshire
2. Jersey
3. Guernsey
4. Brown Swiss
5. Holstein

For hot climates:
1. Jersey
2. Guernsey
3. Brown Swiss
4. Ayrshire
5. Holstein

Peterson noted that the smaller the body phenotype the most grass efficient the cows were. Recent research in New Zealand found the same fact. Smaller Jerseys returned considerably more profit per acre than Holsteins due to their lower body maintenance requirements. This lower feed cost more than offset the Holstein's higher gross milk yield per cow.

Think About It...

♣ Inexpensive pole barns with high roofs that allow the sunlight to reach all parts of the woodchip-covered floor and equipped with Canadian-style slatted-plant windbreaks on their North and West sides need be used only during the very worst weather.

♣ Many graziers seeking to maximize return-per-acre will

winter their dry stock off the farm, buy or farm out their replacement heifers and turn every blade of grass they grow into high value milk.

♣ Productivity increases when all of our effort is concentrated where it gives us the greatest leverage and return. Have you identified where you really make your money?

♣ Is your breeding season in sync with the pasture?

♣ The big machinery cost in growing a crop is the harvest cost, not the planting cost. How can you use your animals to direct-harvest?

♣ Costs go up before they go down when you change technological directions because you have to continue to run the old while you are learning the new. The shorter you can make this transition period the faster your profits will recover and improve.

♣ The four main things a grass dairyman works with are stocking rate, calving date, calving spread, and cow genetics. Have you thought of drying off sooner or going to once-a-day milking?

♣ Eliminating gates cuts fence-building time in half. For paddock changes, just drop the wire and let the cows step over.

♣ In the walkback lanes, never put sharp curves, which slow the cows down and may cause cow hock damage as she pivots to make the turn.

♣ Wide lanes encourage cows to meander rather than get on with getting to the parlor and back to the pasture.

♣ Avoid a small stone base in a lane near a concrete surface as these hurt cows' feet.

♣ Are your cows farming for you? Use an ATV seeder to spin seed out along a break and then let the cows walk the seed in. What other tasks can you turn over to your animals?

♣ What's your non-pasture feed costs?

Chapter 11: Baby Calf Rearing On Pasture

You don't have to milk cows to make a profit in the dairy business. Baby dairy calf rearing, grazing dairy replacement heifers and dairy beef all offer exceptional returns. Take a look at these "dry stock" opportunities and see if dairy cattle don't fit into your pasture's profit picture.

Baby Calf Rearing

The Paul McCarville Whole Milk on Pasture Feeding System has dramatically changed the rearing of baby dairy calves for the good. Graziers using this system report both lower input costs and far healthier calves. Wisconsin dairyman, Paul McCarville, said his feeding system is now used by dairymen in all 50 states, Canada and Mexico. While it is ideal for a seasonal, pasture-based dairy, conventional confinement dairies also use it and some dairy-beef graziers are also using this system with commercial dry-milk-powder milk.

McCarville saw the whole-milk-on pasture-feeding-system described in a New Zealand magazine and wrote and bought some of the nipples used in New Zealand. From the magazine pictures he made his first rolling, pasture "milk bar," as they are called in New Zealand. This consisted of a 35-gallon plastic teat-dip container mounted horizontally on a pair of wheels and with an ATV coupler on one end. The barrel had an opening at the top of the barrel to allow whole milk to be poured in and 19 nipples spaced around all four sides of the barrel. The New Zealand nipples are very durable and have lasted him several years in seasonal service.

These nipples are connected to plastic tubing that leads to the bottom of the barrel. Since a barrel must always be left with a group of calves, two rolling barrels are needed for each group of calves. Paul uses a total of five barrels for the 30-plus calves he raises each spring.

Another 35 gallon barrel with nipples around its mid-section is used for starting calves and is mounted in an upright position with a tire around its bottom to prevent it from being turned over by the calves. A small 5-gallon bucket with several teats attached five inches from the bottom is used to teach newborn calves. Colostrum milk is collected and stored in a freezer for use in growing the calves. Paul collects the first seven days of milk for use with the calves. Antibiotic milk should never be fed to very young baby calves but can be fed to older calves if they are maintained separately from the baby calves.

Calves must receive colostrum within six hours of birth to gain any disease immunity. Paul's calves are calved on pasture to prevent disease. They are removed from their mothers, have their navels disinfected and are fed two to four quarts of colostrum milk with an added probiotic gel for the first seven days. Free choice water and grain-supplementation begins at three days of age. A grain-feeding bottle is used to teach the calves to eat the grain/meal starter ration. Frequent applications of ag lime are used to help keep the calf-barn floor fresh and disease free.

New calves often have to be coaxed up to the barrel by hand with a nipple bottle, but Paul said it is important that you quickly walk away from the upright barrel after filling it with milk so the calves learn the barrel is "mother" and "you're not." It is important that a barrel be left with the calves at all times in case they get the sucking urge. "Leaving the barrel with them keeps them from sucking on each other," he said.

On rainy days when the calves take to shelter, the barrel must be moved under the shelter with them as the calves will not go out in the rain and will start to suckle each other. Calves suckling each other is an excellent way to spread disease from the mud and manure that sticks to their hair.

Paul stands over the fence and watches his calves suck after each feeding. Calves must be constantly sorted by drinking speed. Slow suckers must be sorted off and put in a group of similar drinking speed, or must be fed separately for up to three weeks. He said Holstein/Jersey crosses are particularly aggressive feeders and will knock Holstein and Brown Swiss calves away from the milk bar.

At seven days of age the milk is gradually increased to six to eight quarts of milk per calf per day. The calves are moved to the pasture at two weeks of age if the weather is nice.

Care should be taken to keep birds out of the calves' feed. Birds can land in calf scours and then fly to the trough and create massive scour problems. Birds will be less of a problem if the grain is fed in the afternoon. Also, some graziers use plastic flaps over the face of the grain container that the calf can easily move aside, but that keeps birds away from the grain. These bird-proof "meal bars" are now commercially available in North America.

At one month of age the calves go to once-a-day feeding and the milk portion of the diet is reduced to three to four quarts of milk per day. At six to seven weeks this amount of milk should be again cut in half. If the calves are eating at least two pounds of grain a day at that time, they can be weaned off milk completely.

Paul went two years without cleaning his tanks and nipples and did not lose a single calf. He believes that it is important that the tank retain the colostrum "mother" smell to keep the calves bonded to the tank. However, other graziers have reported fly problems with uncleaned tanks in hot weather and graziers using commercial dry-milk-powder milk have reported the milk feeder lines tend to stop up unless cleaned frequently.

McCarville sells the New Zealand nipples and offers a ready-to-assemble trailer kit. Paul also has an excellent, instructive video available on his whole-milk-on-pasture-feeding-system called "Roll On, Mama." He has an ad in The **Stockman Grass Farmer's** Directory each month.)

New Zealanders, as would be expected, are anxious to get their calves on pasture as quickly as possible and move them to pasture at one week of age. Vaughan Jones offered these tips on calf rearing:

♣ Calves that are raised in hutches are not subjected to competition, stress, immunity against cross infections, and get no grazing or exercise. Vaughan asked, "Would you raise your children like this?" Dairy calves must be raised in groups to be labor efficient and economical.

♣ A hay barn after the hay has been fed is ideal for rearing calves. Calf barns should have a multiple use to keep capital cost down. It should have an open face that faces the sun and should be well ventilated. If you can smell calf or ammonia, you do not have enough ventilation.

♣ Do not use barns with concrete floors as the moisture from the urine cannot get away and makes the bedding a stinking, soggy mess.

♣ For rearing large numbers of calves, multiple small barns scattered over the property are far better than one large barn.

♣ Spraying the calf barn daily with disinfectant can help keep scours away but should not replace daily housekeeping chores of keeping bedding fresh and waterers clean.

♣ Milk is a far better calf feed than milk replacer. Use whole milk whenever possible. Non-dairymen should consider buying late-lactation cows and milking them just for calves. Also, up to four baby calves can be grafted onto one cow for natural suckling.

♣ Bedding can be bark chips, shavings, sawdust, straw, shredded paper, in that order of preference. A thin fresh layer should be added on a daily, or near-daily basis. Do not use old, mouldy hay. The calves will nibble at it and the mouldy air is very bad for them.

♣ Never clean a calf barn when there are calves in it. This is a sure way to make them sick. Wait until the calves are permanently out on pasture to remove accumulated manure and bedding.

♣ In good weather, calves should be allowed on pasture at one week of age. If the weather is poor, provide high quality, legume/grass hay free choice. Overfeeding calves milk and grain will slow rumen development. Make them want to eat hay or graze.

♣ At two weeks of age give them as much warm water as they will drink in the morning and feed them their milk in the afternoon so that they will sleep full and continue growing overnight. Feed grain at night as well to prevent bird contamination.

♣ Calves should be weaned by weight, grazing activity and pasture available, not by age, but this should occur between six and nine weeks of age. Calves should be wormed at weaning, and frequently thereafter, before it is physically apparent that they need it. Paddocks previously cut for silage or hay are preferred for young calves as they will be virtually parasite free.

♣ After weaning, young calves should not be grazed in groups of more than 50 calves. If rotationally grazed, they should be shifted daily.

Action Advice...

♣ For disease immunity, calves must receive colostrum within 6 hours of birth.

♣ Feed 2-4 quarts of colostrum milk with an added probiotic gel for the first seven days.

♣ At seven days of age the milk is gradually increased to 6-8 quarts of milk per calf per day.

♣ Constantly group calves by drinking speed.

♣ At two weeks of age move calves to pasture if weather is nice.

♣ At one month of age put the calves on once-a-day feeding. Reduce the milk portion of the diet to 3-4 quarts of milk per day per calf.

♣ At six to seven weeks of age cut the milk diet in half. If calves are eating at least two pounds of grain a day by this time they can be weaned off milk completely.

♣ Frequent applications of ag lime and phosphate helps keeps the calf-barn floor fresh and disease free.

♣ New calves may need to be coaxed to the barrel by using a nipple bottle. It is important that you quickly walk away from the upright barrel after filling it with milk so that calves learn the barrels is "mother" and you're not.

♣ On rainy days when calves take to shelter, the barrel must go with them.

Dairy Replacements

Tired of selling gain for $25 to $35 cwt. in the beef stocker business? Well, then consider moving up to dairy--dairy replacements that is. Graziers can usually double their income per pound of gain by grazing dairy replacements rather than beef steers. The short production life of most North American dairy cows (less than three lactations) keeps grade, pasture-raised, bred-dairy-replacements in good demand.

Today, the most die-hard confinement dairymen are realizing that pasture-grown replacements tend to have bigger rumens, and therefore greater feed capacity (which makes more milk), than confinement-grown heifers. According to Vaughan Jones, research in Britain has shown that the size of a calf's rumen at three or four months of age remained relative for their lifetime. This is why it is so important that calves get onto pasture very early in their lives.

The value of gain for dairy replacements has traditionally been priced at around one dollar per pound. The reason for this is that it costs approximately a dollar a pound to raise a heifer in a "modern" confinement system. Due to these high costs, more dairymen are seeing the value in contracting out the growing out of their replacement heifers to lower-cost professional graziers. Even pasture-based dairymen have figured out that turning all of their grass into milk is far more profitable than using it to grow their own replacements at home.

In California, some dairymen put their replacements out on grazing contracts for as high as 85 cents per pound and think they are making out like a bandit compared to the cost of raising them at home. Gain payment rates tend to be higher the lighter and younger the animal is due to the higher level of management required. For calves over 400 lbs., cost-of-gain payments in the $45 to $55 cwt. range are typical. This value-of-gain is virtually equal to the average sell-buy from non-leveraged beef-stocker-steer ownership, but of course, gain grazing requires no capital for animal ownership.

Lloyd and Linda Stueve in Oakdale, California, graze over 2500 dairy replacements a year and use a combination of both owned and contracted heifers. The contract heifers are on an approximately 16-month grow-out program. Natural-service

Holstein bulls are used for breeding. The Stueves have access to both winter-annual cool-season range and irrigated summer pasture. Their 800 acres of flood-irrigated pastures are a mixture of annual and perennial ryegrass, Ladino clover, and warm-season dallisgrass. This pasture mix carries a per-acre stocking rate of 2000 to 2300 lbs. of heifers from April 15 to October 15. Summer temperatures in the San Joaquin Valley are often in excess of 100 F/35 C and frequent irrigations are necessary to maintain perennial ryegrass stands.

2500 acres of annual range is leased to lower the stocking rate on the irrigated pastures to one-half of its summer carrying capacity. It takes approximately three acres of winter range to graze a Holstein heifer from November to mid-April with no hay.

Surplus irrigated pasture is cut as pasture silage and short-term contract-grazing animals are brought in to balance feed supply and demand in the spring. The contract heifers are delivered back to their home farms in July, which lowers the summer stocking rate. However, supplemental pasture silage must be fed at times in late summer and early fall. The fast (and multiple) maturity cycle of the warm-season dallisgrass requires the pastures to be kept short during the warm weather growing season. This prevents forward stockpiling for the summer slump as can be done with an all-cool-season-plant pasture. A 100 head beef cow herd is used to scavenge the ranch's ditch banks and roadsides and other areas of excess grass.

"As most graziers can attest, the balancing of animals to pasture growth is an inexact science due to the differences in seasonal growth rates from one year to the next," Lloyd said. "Our primary goal is to keep our pastures short, young and vegetative and then use pasture silage to fill in any gaps that may occur."

He said California graziers were going to have to concentrate on premium-priced niches such as dairy replacements to offset the state's higher-priced land and water costs.

A New Industry In The Making. The contract grazing of dairy replacements is a huge industry in New Zealand with highly formalized grazing contracts, periodic weighups, and guaranteed-minimum gains and target weights. The current U.S. productivity goal is for the heifer to breed at 15 months and calve at 24 months of age. To achieve the target weights this breeding schedule calls for requires a relatively high constant rate of gain year-round with today's large-frame, late-maturing North American Holsteins. Due largely to poor winter-weight gains, a sizable percentage of North American Holsteins do not calve until they are 28 to 29 months old.

Vaughan Jones gives the following **minimum** weights to aim for in a heifer's life:

Mimimum Weights to Aim For
(expressed in pounds)

	Weaning	8 Months	Mating	Before Calving
Holstein-Friesian	165	550	750	990
HF x Jersey	155	420	640	880
Jersey	145	365	525	770

This necessity for keeping animals gaining on schedule earns the contract-replacement-dairy-heifer grazier his premium price-per-pound. No doubt as the contract graziering industry matures over the next few years, periodic every-other-month weighups will become as standard in North America as they are in New Zealand. These weighups will reassure the dairyman customer about the grazier's skill and provide a benchmark for periodic payment to the grazier. (Beef stocker graziers take note!)

In fact, a complete New Zealand-style graziering industry is ripe for development in North America. In this industry, a large master contractor handles the marketing to find dairymen customers, subcontracts out the grazing to smaller graziers, oversees the periodic weighing and reporting of gains, schedules the trucking, and handles the billing and paying of gain money.

(That sound you hear is opportunity trying to kick down your door.)

An Alternative To Contract Grazing. An alternative to contract grazing is buying newborn heifer calves from local dairymen, growing them out and selling them as bred-replacements at 18 to 20 months of age before their second and most expensive winter. Most graziers I talked with report an average value-of-gain from this of around $84 cwt. after figuring marketing costs, price rollback, non-breeders and death loss on the baby calves.

This is far better than the $40 to $50 cwt. value-of-gain

typical with beef stocker steers; however, most of the replacement-heifer graziers I talked with would prefer a grazing contract over owning the heifers themselves to stay away from bankers debt and interest. Very often, they said, they sell the grown heifers back to the same dairy producer from whom they bought them.

A major problem with ownership is the long period a grazier has his money tied up in the animal. Beef-oriented bankers who are used to "touching" their money every six to twelve months (paying off the old loan and then writing a new one) are uncomfortable with the 18- to 20-months their money is tied up in a dairy replacement.

Another risk is that a certain number of heifers will be unable to breed and have to be sold on the beef market for whatever they will bring. Also, unless a replacement-heifer grazier develops a geographically diverse market for the heifers, the traditional market can literally "dry up" in a drought or other feed catastrophy. This can result in a grazier having to winter a lot of very heavy animals, or even worse, a grazier could be forced with having to calve out and milk a bunch of untrained heifers. Most graziers will dump their heifers on the market for whatever they will bring before they will do this.

The increase in seasonal dairying is having an impact upon replacement dairy heifer demand. It is important that the heifers calve slightly later than the older cows so they can become accustomed to the milking routine before they have to do it for real. Northern dairymen increasingly want their replacements bred to calve in April/May while Southerners prefer September/October and/or January/February breeding. Having customers in both the North and the South helps market heifers who fail to breed on schedule.

In the South, many dairy producers traditionally use natural service beef-breed-bulls and buy in all of their replacements. Many contract graziers also use easy-calving beef-breed-bulls to avoid the physical danger of highly temperamental dairy bulls or the hassle of AI. Due to the large supply of these types of calves there is an active market for lightweight, beef/dairy-cross calves in the South and Southwest.

Death losses on calves from first-calf heifers can be extremely high. First-calf heifers frequently do not produce enough colostrum to adequately protect their calves' health and their calves should also receive colostrum milk from older cows.

Three Management Phases. It has been my observation that when any livestock production program extends over six months in length, it results in the animal changing ownership several times as graziers start to specialize in whatever phase best suits their talents and climate. Replacement-heifer rearing lends itself particularly well to North-South partnerships.

The dairy replacement business is broken into three major management phases:

1. Birth to weaning at six to nine weeks of age.
2. Weaning to breeding at 15 months of age.
3. Breeding to calving at 24 months.

The birth-to-weaning period is very management intensive but compensates for this by producing the highest value of gain. Values of gain in excess of a dollar per pound is increasingly attracting small acreage, "specialist" graziers who sell or contract out the weaned calves to others for continued growing. The Paul McCarville whole-milk-on-pasture method of raising baby calves has tremendously increased the profitability of this pre-weaning period by lowering death loss, labor, feed and capital costs.

Vaughan Jones believes that calf rearing is best done by women. "Calves respond to thoughtfulness and tender loving care, and women are usually more gentle and thorough," he said.

If the weather is nice, baby dairy calves should be out on pasture within a week of birth. The overfeeding of milk and meal will result in calves with poorly developed rumens that "crash" after weaning. Calves must be given an incentive to graze, and require very short and tender grass to gain well. To see what a pasture for a week-old dairy calf should look like take a look at your front lawn. Grass in baby calf pastures should never be over four inches in height. To see what a pasture for a baby calf should feel like take your shoes off and walk across it barefoot.

If you use a mower to shorten your pastures, you will find this to be a very unpleasant experience as mowing produces a prickly stubble. The way it feels on the bottom of your tender foot is the way it feels on the calf's tender nose. Baby calf pastures need to be kept in condition with grazing rather than mowing. Keep in mind the microflora, which develop in calves rumens, are passed down to them by adult cattle. This means baby calf pastures have to be periodically grazed by cattle with functioning rumens. If the calves quickly develop a potbelly after weaning, it is usually a sign of a mis-functioning rumen.

Profit potentials for this specialty are probably the highest in California and Florida where large, industrialized dairies traditionally dump their newborn calves for whatever they will bring. As a result, dairy calves of both sexes are often a third or less of the upper Midwest price. Profits in excess of $200 per heifer from a six week ownership are said to be relatively common in these areas of the country.

New Zealand dairy producers typically graze their spring-born replacement calves through their first summer on their own farm and then put them out on contract grazing until breeding at 15 months or until just prior to calving at 24 months. (On many New Zealand dairies all animals are wintered off-farm on grazing contracts. This allows the minimal winter grass growth to accumulate and prevents pasture pugging damage.)

Between Weaning And Breeding. Weaned calves are either set stocked two to three per paddock with the lactating cows rotated through the paddocks or the heifers are grazed as a leader herd in front of the lactating cows. Set stocked young calves are very territorial and do not try to follow the cows out of their home paddock. If rotational grazing is used, mob sizes should not exceed 50 calves.

In Ireland, spring-born weaned calves are used as a follower herd behind the lactating cows. The Irish believe that gains in excess of 1.5 lbs. per day prior to sexual maturity retard the development of the heifer's mammary glands and hurt subsequent milk production. The Irish are careful to control the residual left by the lactating cows in each paddock to prevent extremely high gains on the follower replacements. Higher rates of daily gain are allowed once the heifer reaches sexual maturity at around eight months.

After the heifers are bred at 15 months, they are treated the same as dry cows and used as a paddock clean-up crew. Therefore, a spring calving Irish dairy would have a leader-follower rotation of lactating cows, followed by new crop heifer calves, followed by old crop bred heifers.

No doubt the biggest opportunity for North American contract graziers is the period between weaning and breeding. This is pretty typical of beef stocker grazing with the exception that you are starting out with a less than 200-lb. calf. At this weight, internal parasitism can be a major problem and every effort should be made to keep both the calves and the pastures parasite free.

Newly renovated pastures, or croplands being shifted to pasture, are ideal for new-crop heifers as they are parasite free and the grasses are young and tender. Also, the light body weight of the new-crop calves helps prevent bogging damage on these sodless swards as well, so it is good management for the pastures as well.

Pastures that have been previously grazed with sheep, cut for silage or hayed are also good new-crop calf-pastures. Prepared seedbed pastures of winter annuals such as rye, annual ryegrass, oats and wheat are also parasite free.

Gains per acre with calves less than 400 lbs. can often be quite spectacular (1000 lbs. or more) due to their low body maintenance requirements. As the calves age and gain weight, management intensity drops but so does the per acre profit potential.

Fight The Fat. After the heifers are bred, care should be taken to make sure they are not allowed to get fat on pasture and should be kept in medium flesh. This will help prevent subsequent calving problems. Also, cows that are fat at calving are susceptible to milk fever and are harder to breed back than those in medium flesh.

These bred heifers are excellent to use as follower stock in an Irish-style, leader-follower rotation. Whatever method you use, grazing will have to be restricted in some manner to prevent excessive fattening.

Understanding Value of Gain

The value of gain discussed in this segment represents two things--the value per pound-of-gain after the price-per-pound rollback for the purchased animal is figured or the net payment per pound-of-gain on a grazing contract. Figuring value of gain is very useful because it tends to emphasize the absolute necessity for low cost production methods.

For example, if you buy a 400 lb. calf for 80 cents and sell it as a 700 lb. yearling for 70 cents, the value of the gain you put on is not 70 cents but only 56 cents per pound of gain because you must absorb the decrease in the value of the weight you purchased in the weight you put on.

The math on this is:

400 x .80 = $320
700 x .70 = $490
Difference $170

The difference divided by 3 (you put on three hundred pounds of gain) equals $56 cwt or .56 per pound.

Value of gain tends to be highest when calves are purchased as light as possible and sold as heavy as possible as this allows the price rollback to both be minimized on a per pound basis and amortized over more pounds of gain. (For more on the financial math of graziering read **Pa$ture Profit$ With Stocker Cattle**.)

Dairy Beef Production

Lightweight Calf Grazing. Graziers looking to make dairy returns per acre without having to milk cows should take a look at grazing lightweight male dairy calves, according to Dr. Raymond Steen, dairy beef specialist at the Hillsborough Research Centre near Belfast, Northern Ireland. Because very little of the pasture growth has to go to body maintenance due to the small size of lightweight calves, Steen said gains per acre can be quite spectacular--nearing the 1000 lbs. of gain-per-acre range for a six-month graze with no grain supplementation.

Add to this the fact that the value-of-gain for very light calves is much higher than for older, heavier yearlings and you have a combination that can pay you $1000 an acre dairy wages for beef production. However, to achieve this level of performance and profit you will have to manage your pastures even better than the best dairyman.

Pastures for very young calves (150 to 200 lbs) must be kept short and vegetative, but not too short, according to Dr. Steen. The difference in average daily gain between pastures grazed at 3 1/4" (9 cm) and pastures grazed at 2 1/2 " (6 cm) was over a half pound a day in average daily gain. (1.6 lbs. per day on 2 1/2" and 2.2 lbs per day on 3 1/4".) The above gains are from Holstein bull calves.

In order to keep pastures short and vegetative, a very high stocking rate is necessary during the spring lush. With very young calves continuous grazing is superior to rotational grazing. Understocking early in the grazing season results in a buildup of stemmy grass of low palatability and low feeding value, which reduces the performance of cattle later in the grazing season.

Of course, due to the difference in growth rate between the spring lush and the mid-summer slump, a variable stocking rate must be used. This is accomplished by dropping a large portion of the pasture from grazing and cutting it for pasture silage plus the use of an area of the pasture that can either be grazed or cut for silage depending upon the need for extra grass due to spring weather conditions.

Buffer Grazing Area Needed. This graze or no graze area is called a buffer graze area and a portable electric fence is used to increase and decrease the buffer area according to grass growth to keep the calf pasture at a near constant height of 3 1/4 inches (9 cm.). At 2 1/2 inches (7 cm.) the grass around the dung pats would be grazed. At 3 1/4 inches (9 cm.) the sward is reasonably grazed down between the dung pats but the areas around the dung pats are not grazed. At 4 1/2 inches (11 cm.) large areas of the sward are ungrazed or only partially grazed. An increase of 10 percent (100 lbs. per acre) in the mean, season-long stocking rate is accomplished by keeping the pasture one inch shorter than 4 1/2" with no decrease in calf weight gain.

The first goal of a young calf grazier is to match the requirements of the animals to the rate of the pasture production. Young calves are very fastidious about their grass and must have young, highly vegetative material because their rumens are so small. Pasture blowups that allow the grass to become stemmy or mature are devastating to animal performance with young calves.

Steen estimated that over the course of a six-month grazing season approximately 75 percent of the total pasture area would be harvested as pasture silage at least once to keep it young and vegetative. A good calf-rearing pasture should look like a well-cared for lawn--dense and thick and about 3 and 1/2 inches tall.

The best grasses for use with young calves are those that tiller and produce a thick sward when kept short such as Kentucky bluegrass, annual and perennial ryegrass or bermudagrass. White clover does well under close grazing and should be your legume of choice.

Grain Supplementation. The supplementation of young calves with 3.2 lbs. (1.5 kgs) of 15 % protein grain concentrate produced no significant weight gain in calves with pastures at least three inches in height. It did increase average daily gain by 14 percent (0.25 lb.) at the 2 1/2 inch level.

The very small response to grain on too-short pasture indicates the animals substitute grain for pasture rather than maintaining their former pasture intake. This is very poor economics since the grain costs five to seven times the cost of grazed pasture. However, it does indicate that grain supplementation can help maintain a constant stocking rate when grass is short, such as during a drought.

Steen emphasized that even larger quantities of grain were unlikely to produce the animal performance of an adequate supply of high quality grass.

Grazing Silage Aftermath Areas. To keep the pasture at a constant height of three and half inches requires the use of very high stocking rate per acre during the spring lush (six to seven calves per acre). However, the reduction in the rate of grass growth and the increase in the feed requirements of the cattle necessitates major reductions in stocking rate as the season progresses. This is accomplished by grazing areas of the pasture that have been previously cut for silage.

By September, the stocking rate was down to 1.5 calves per acre. Steen said in most cases the stocking rate used during September and October should be only 25 to 40 percent of that used during May and early June.

Nitrogen Vs. Clover. Nitrogen is the most important input affecting stock carrying capacity of grazing swards. The use of nitrogen rates as high as 300 lbs. per acre have been found to be cost-effective with growing beef cattle. However, the use of white clover plus an additional 100 lbs. of nitrogen applied in split applications has been found to produce the highest profit per acre.

Steen found that the use of a good grass/white clover sward with 100 lbs. of supplemental N carried the same number of stock units as 350 lbs. of N per acre on a pure grass sward.

The Irish program of summer pasture and winter pasture

silage with minimal grain allows long-winter, grain-deficit areas of the world to grow and finish beef year-round, but at a fraction of the cost of the predominately grain-based production systems used in the United States and Continental Europe.

Big Profits From Little Holsteins Down South

Research at the Coastal Plain Branch Experiment Station in Newton, Mississippi, has found grazing baby Holstein steers to be far more profitable than grazing traditional beef breed stocker cattle. Profits for a six month graze have ranged from between $325 and $552 per acre, depending the upon the stocking rate used. In contrast, the ten-year average profit-per-acre for beef-breed ryegrass-stockering in Mississippi has been between $100 to $150 an acre.

"The growth rate of a fall-born baby Holstein steer almost perfectly matches the seasonal growth rate of annual ryegrass pasture," explained station superintendent Bill Brock. "He is extremely small and has minimal feed requirements during the dead of winter when grass growth is low, but as the grass turns it on in the spring, the Holstein does too and consequently very little pasture is wasted."

Due to this excellent mesh of animal and grass growth, gains per acre from heavily nitrated Marshall ryegrass continuously grazed with baby Holstein steers have ranged from 1400 to over 2200 lbs. of gain per acre. The Newton program starts in the early fall with newly born day-old Holstein calves. Due to both market and production advantages, fall calving is recommended for Deep South dairymen.

The baby calves are raised on milk replacer on pasture until they are five weeks old. They are then shifted to small holding traps and fed hay and grain until they are two months old. At two months of age, the calves go on annual ryegrass pastures and are grazed until the following May.

Due to poor heat tolerance, Brock recommends the Holsteins be sold as feeder cattle to midwestern feeders in late May when ryegrass pastures fade. They have had no problem selling the 650 lbs. Holstein feeders through local market channels, but warned that graziers in other areas should make sure they have a market before going into a Holstein grazing program.

Death Loss Must Be Kept Low. A key to dairy-beef profitability, Brock said, is to keep death loss low on newly purchased day-old calves. "For this program to be profitable, you have to keep your baby calf death loss under 10 percent. A death loss of five percent or so is acceptable."

Assistant dairyman, Joey Murphey, said a critical factor in calf death loss is the protein percentage of the milk replacer used. "It absolutely has to have a minimum of 20 percent fat and 20 percent protein. If the replacer is one percent below 20 percent, you'll start losing calves," Murphey said.

Beef breed stocker graziers need to keep in mind that very few dairy calves have had any colostrum and so are very susceptible to disease. "A day-old dairy calf is an entirely different animal than a six or seven month old beef stocker calf. Your management and health practices have to be superb. You definitely need to use the correct milk replacer and work closely with your vet."

To prevent the buildup of disease, new calves are moved to a new starter pasture after each set of calves. The cleansing power of sunlight has proven to be the best pathogen preventer for baby calves. Barns should be avoided.

Calves Start Grazing At 130 Pounds. The Holstein steers at Newton average 130 to 175 lbs. at two months of age when they are ready to go solo on late fall ryegrass pasture. Gains on the calves will be slightly less than 1.5 lbs. per day during the mid-winter period and this is quite acceptable. "Remember, we want to take as little bodyweight through the worst of the winter as possible to minimize body maintenance costs and maximize forage use efficiency and profits," Brock said. If the pasture gets short, he recommends the calves be supplemented with three to four pounds of whole shelled corn a day rather than hay due to their small rumens.

"The real beauty of the Holstein steer calf is the way he turns it on in the spring. Our per-head spring-gains are in excess of three pounds a day. The calves just grow into the spring ryegrass lush and keep up with it. In early May when the ryegrass is at its maximum growth our initial stocking weight per acre has grown from 600 lbs. to 2700 lbs. at our highest stocking rate and little to no grass is wasted or has to be cut for hay. It all gets converted into beef." The station experimented with stocking rates and used an initial November stocking rate of 3.0, 3.6, and 4.5 calves per acre. Calves at the 4.5 stocking rate are supplemented with a 16 percent crude protein corn-soybean meal-grain mix at a daily rate of one percent of live bodyweight. The high stocking rate produced both the highest and lowest profit per acre ($325.13 and $553.33).

High Stocking Rate Is High Market Risk. Due to its variability and the increased market risk from lower per-head-gains, Brock did not recommend the highest stocking rate to commercial graziers. "The 3.6 stocking rate appears to offer the best of both worlds. A high return-per-head and a high return-per-acre," he said. The 3.6 stocking rate has produced a return per acre between $389 and $413 and an average profit per head of around $110.

The pasture used with all stocking rates is a pure stand of Marshall annual ryegrass fertilized with 200 lbs. of actual N. The nitrogen was applied at 70 lbs. at planting, 50 lbs. in mid-December, and 80 lbs. in mid to late February.

"This is not cheap pasture to produce. If you're going to put a lot of weight out there, you've got to put a lot of nitrogen out there," Brock said. He said total agronomic cost per acre is around $160 due to the high nitrogen rate, but that this produced a pasture cost per pound of gain of only eight to nine cents per pound at the 3.6 stocking rate.

Dairy Beef Production In Ireland

I have spent quite a bit of time looking at dairy beef production in Northern Ireland. This small country has the largest proportion of its land area devoted to pastoral pursuits of any in the world and is an exceptionally green and lovely land.

Dr. Raymond Steen of the Hillsboro Research Center pointed out West Virginia-sized Northern Ireland had 1.5 million cattle, 1.5 million sheep, and 1.5 million people. Cattle numbers are almost equally split between beef and dairy breeding and Continental/dairy-cross and Continental breeding are responsible for 90 percent of the country's beef production.

Limousin is the preferred "clean-up" bull by dairymen due to its easy calving and the easy grass finishing of the calves. Charolais crosses are considered the fastest-gaining cattle and

Belgian Blue produce the meatiest carcass. Straight Holstein/Friesians bring almost half the price per pound of the Continental/Friesian crosses and are predominantly killed for veal.

Most calves are born in the early spring, grazed through their first summer with their mother, weaned in the fall and fed grass silage and limited grain for their first winter (1.5 lbs. of gain per day), grazed through their second summer, and finished on grass silage and grain in their second winter. Animals that could "finish" on pasture before their second winter netted from $75 to $100 more per head than those that had to finished in a feedlot during the second winter. Irish grass finished beef has almost uniformly white fat on cattle slaughtered at 24 months or less.

The average male liveweight of the Continental-bred dairy beef is 1500 to 1550 lbs. Cattle of this size require European-style meat cutting, whereby muscle groups are unwound and fileted to keep portion size and cost to the consumer down.

Dairy Beef New Zealand-Style

On a river plain near Palmerston North on the North Island of New Zealand is what is no doubt one of the most intensive grassfed beef production systems in the world. The Burleigh Bull Beef System, devised by local grazier, Harry Wier, produces 1200 to 1500 lbs. of beef per acre per year from intensively subdivided and irrigated pastures of perennial ryegrass and white clover.

The Wiers' 400-acre grass farm is subdivided into four irrigated systems of 60 acres each. The remainder of the farm is too hilly to irrigate and is grazed as a less intensive dryland system. Puna Grassland chicory has been added to increase the mid-summer yield of the dryland acreage. Each of the four irrigated systems runs 120 head of dairy and dairy-cross bulls. These 120-head systems are then further subdivided into six mobs of 20 bulls. This small mob size is due to the use of intact bulls rather than steers.

The New Zealanders have found that mobs of 20 bulls are the most manageable herd size and the group size least likely to fight and ride subdominants in the herd. Dairy bulls are used because of their lower initial purchase price and superior growth characteristics compared to the traditional beef breeds.

Wier has worked hard to make his farm what he calls a

"technosystem." By designing a coherent "whole" production system, easy to understand in both its layout and operation, he hopes to be able to sell a turn-key beef production system that could be replicated elsewhere in New Zealand and the world.

Simon Grigg of Burleigh Beef's hardware division Kiwi-tech International explained that the New Zealand beef market is made up of two sectors. One is the traditional "Prime Grade" (same as USDA Select) produced from 1000 lb. Angus-cross steers, and the other is manufacturing grade beef from the dairy bulls that are primarily exported to the U.S. hamburger market.

Whereas New Zealand lamb and dairy products bring a price far less than their North American equivalent, New Zealand grassfed beef tracks U.S. prices pretty closely with NZ Prime selling at roughly the same price as USDA Select. The manufacturing grade bulls sell for a price equivalent to upper Midwest fed Holstein prices.

In New Zealand the slaughter price is the highest price per pound of any class or weight group, whereas, in the U.S. on the current market it is usually the lowest. This means the New Zealand grazier is actually working with a higher-value per pound-of-gain than the U.S. grazier. Also on the manufacturing grade market there is no quality grade, but premiums are paid for heavier than normal carcasses. This "freedom from finish" and the flexibility it allows have made dairy bull grazing the most profitable pastoral enterprise available to New Zealanders after dairying.

Burleigh aims for a slaughter liveweight on their bulls of 1300 lbs. at 24 months of age. The Friesian (Holstein) bulls are purchased as 600 lb. yearlings from herds of contemporaries. Care is taken to never mix groups bulls at any time during their stay at Burleigh to prevent fighting and riding.

One 60 acre "system" consists of six ten-acre lanes of grass, 55 feet wide by 880 yards long of permanent two-wire (both hot) fence. The grass is then rationed with temporary polywire and portable posts. Two portable polywires, one in front and one in back, stretch across the entire six lanes, and all six mobs of bulls are moved at the same time. Once they reach the end of their lane, they are then driven back over the paddock to start at the other end.

The bulls are shifted every other day as frequent paddock

shifts help keep the bulls from becoming bored and thereby helps stop fighting and riding. The grass rest-period is varied by altering the length of the paddock rather than the number of paddocks.

Permanent wooden fence posts are placed every 22 yards so that each fence post division will equal one-quarter acre. This clearly marked and known minimum paddock size helps make dry matter budgeting easier to figure. The bulls are rotated on a varying paddock size according to so many posts per subdivision. For example, a one-post shift every two days will result in an 80-day rotation. A two-post shift will result in a 40-day rotation, and so forth. This post system of movement also allows the manager to clearly instruct untrained labor as to how far to move the bulls per shift.

Portable plastic water tanks equipped with high-flow valves shoved halfway under the lane wires water two mobs each and are moved with each paddock shift. A unique Wier-designed push-fit "Python" hydrant connector at every second post allows the portable waterers to tap into a black polyethylene mainline water hose laid on top of the ground between every other lane.

A liveweight of around 900 lbs. per acre is over-wintered on the intensive system. Some hay is fed but is used primarily to prevent bloat on low-dry-matter early spring grass. Maximum use is made of compensatory gain and the bulls actually lose weight during the winter due to very tight paddock rationing. However, during the spring lush average daily gains of 4.4 lbs. per day are common and a 365-day average of two pounds a day is achieved despite the winter weight loss.

A high level of pasture management has to be used in the spring to stay on top of pastures and keep them from growing a seedhead and losing quality. During the spring lush the pastures are loaded up with new stock to keep the grazing pressure on the grass high. The number of subdivisions and the rest period are minimized but continuous grazing is never used at Burleigh. Animals nearing slaughter are given more grass per shift than animals in the growing stage. This allows the near-slaughter animals to "pop" any suppressed gain.

If you can imagine looking down on this river plain from the air, it would look like the interior of a piano it is so strung with wire. If traditional gates were used, it would take one all day just to cross a couple of "systems" and tremendously raise the capital cost to build one. Wier solved this problem by inventing a unique flexible fence that allows the interior fences to quickly be driven over by a bottom skid-equipped four-wheeler or truck. The wire is fastened to the permanent posts with question-mark-shaped spring tensioners that allow the wire to give. Flexible round fiberglass posts are used between the permanent wooden posts.

Wier got this idea of a flexible bounceback fence from studying a spider's web and so he named it Spider fence.

This unique fencing feature allows one man to shift the cattle and water of a 60-acre "system" in 20 minutes and the entire farm in less than two hours. Also, a gate can be created anywhere you like by just stepping on the wire and pressing it down. (Insulated boots, of course.)

To cut out a bull from the herd Wier uses a reel of polywire attached to a short fiberglass fishing pole. The polywire has a weight on the end that allows him to cast the wire like a fishing line. Once he has quietly separated the bull from the mob he will cast the polywire line between the one bull and the mob so that it lands over a paddock fence, thereby electrifying the polywire. He then starts to reel in the wire while he walks toward the paddock fence. The bull moves in front of the hot wire to avoid being shocked and is reeled in like a big fish. When the bull reaches the fence, Wier steps on the fence and allows the bull to hop over.

All paddock shifts are performed by the paddock manager stepping on the front polywire and the bulls are trained to the fence-hopping technique. Occasionally, the bulls will make a paddock shift by going through a portable scale so their weights can be recorded.

The paddocks are irrigated by a windup reel/traveling-gun-irrigator using the tractor as a moveable pull post. The irrigator can travel one half of the length of a paddock in 24 hours and irrigates two lanes at a time. The gun-unit hose, of course, has to be laid under the front and rear polywire fences so the entire irrigation unit--tractor, reel wagon, and gun unit are equipped with upside-down U-shaped skids that pick up the polywire and allow them to drive under it, as well as the bottom-mounted skids that allow them to drive over the permanent lane fences.

Grigg said that no bulls had ever escaped while the

irrigator-gun unit had the polywire lifted as they are apparently afraid of the water-squirting gun and stay away from it.

While originally designed to be a turn-key, hardware only "technosystem," Grigg and Wier subsequently learned that intensive grazing hardware doesn't sell well unless accompanied by the "software" or operator knowledge of how to use it.

"A technosystem is a combination of hardware, grass, animals, and the operator. But the skill of the operator is by far the biggest part," Grigg said.

Think About It...

♣ Extremely lean Holstein/Continental cross beef is called "Euro-beef" in the US and sells for a premium price in cities with large populations of recent Eastern European immigrants.

♣ Straight Holstein steers will frequently bring more sold as premium hamburger than as finished beef. Carcass yields on Holsteins are lower than beef breeds due to the large bones and poor muscling. New Zealand Friesians are much more heavily muscled and meaty than North American Holsteins.

♣ How does the grass in your calves' pasture feel to your bare feet?

♣ The grazing of replacement dairy heifers offers a higher profit potential, both from contract grazing and ownership, than beef steers in most years. As with all gain grazing opportunities, it is a reputation business and requires that you start small and build your business a client at a time.

♣ Figuring value of gain is very useful because it tends to emphasize the absolute necessity for low cost production methods.

♣ Graziers looking to make dairy returns per acre without having to milk cows should take a look at grazing lightweight male dairy calves. However, to acheive this level of performance and profit you will have to manage your pastures even better than the best dairyman.

♣ The first goal of a young calf grazier is to match the requirements of the animals to the rate of the pasture production. The reduction in the rate of grass growth and the increase in the feed requirements of the cattle necessitates major reductions in stocking rate as the season progresses.

♣ A key to dairy-beef profitability is to keep death loss low on newly purchased day-old calves. Very few dairy calves have had enough colostrum and so are very susceptible to disease. To prevent the buildup of disease, move the calves to a new starter pasture after each set of calves.

♣ Grazing very light calves offers the highest potential return per acre of any area of beef production. The key management factor is to keep the grass young and vegetative. This requires the use of very high stocking rates in the spring, coupled with a flexible buffer grazing area that can either be grazed or cut for pasture silage depending upon the weather and grass growth.

♣ As more dairy producers calve in sync with the onset of spring pasture, opportunities for light calf grazing will grow as the supply will tend to be more bunched and in tune with your pasture.

♣ The demand for Holstein feeder cattle can be extremely variable. Demand is good as long as feeder cattle of the traditional beef breeds are in short supply but can fall dramatically if beef breed cattle are plentiful.

♣ Frequent paddock shifts help keep the bulls from becoming bored.

♣ Animals nearing slaughter are given more grass per shift than animals in the growing stage.

♣ Flexible fence allows interior fences to quickly be driven over by a bottom skid-equipped four-wheeler or truck.

♣ Occasionally, make a paddock shift by going through a portable scale so weights can be recorded.

♣ Bulls cannot be transported long distances without causing dark-cutting meat. If your packing plant is more than 2 hours away, forget grazing bulls.

Chapter 12:
Beef Production

If a beef cow-calf producer refuses to consider the owning of his calves beyond weaning, there is very little a quality pasture program can do to increase his profitability. If one does decide to pursue a post-weaning grazing strategy, a huge range of options and cost-cutting strategies will appear. However, this decision should be accompanied by a complete rethinking of the traditional cow-calf productivity guidelines.

For example, the emphasis on heavy weaning weights as a primary goal is entirely wrong once a producer decides to own his calves beyond weaning. In fact, actually planning to produce lighter weaned calves by weaning them earlier can be a much more efficient and profitable approach. Here's why.

If we accept that we are really in the business of collecting and harvesting solar energy rather than producing beef, then getting the most gain per unit of plant energy will be seen as the key to making a better than average profit. Energy in forages has traditionally been expressed as TDN, or total digestible nutrients. Auburn University extension beef cattle nutritionist, B.G. Ruffin said that 58 percent of the total TDN consumed in an 1100 lb. slaughter steer is consumed up to weaning at eight months. The intermediate stockering stage consumes only 15 percent and the finishing stage 25 percent. In other words, it takes over two and a half times the TDN to produce a pound of beef before weaning as it does after weaning because of the high body maintenance requirements of a lactating cow.

In other words, we can increase our productivity by getting the calf off the cow quicker. The lighter the calf the less TDN required for body maintenance. This is particularly critical during grass-short times of the year and is why lightweight calves always bring a higher price per pound than heavier calves. They are simply more efficient. A major management goal of a cow-calf producer who plans to over-winter his calves should therefore be to **plan** to produce light calves by weaning them early.

In New Zealand and Argentina, beef calves are traditionally weaned at three to five months of age. Having the calf born at the beginning of the spring lush and weaning it at the end is the most grass-efficient cow-calf production system. In some short growing season environments, this may mean weaning calves as early as 60 days of age. First calf heifers should be weaned when their calves reach 200 lbs to allow them to continue to grow without the calf's nursing dragging them down. Calves can function perfectly well as self-harvesting ruminants from around 150 lbs. onward. Above 350 lbs., the cow's milk of most beef breeds only adds about a quarter of a pound to the calf's average daily gain. Thanks to their very small mouths, calves can select-graze a much higher quality diet than cows or yearlings.

In most environments, a cow that only lactates for three to four months will have time to fatten herself before winter and will be able to more or less winter off the flesh on her back. Once we stop being concerned with brag weaning weights we can start to dramatically cut cow herd costs by only having the cow lactate during seasonally surplus green grass periods.

Calving Season Is Critical

I do not know of any region in the United States where January and February are seasonally surplus in green grass and yet a huge number of our calves are programmed to be born then. Part of this is a holdover from the days of the screwworm, but most of it is due to the misguided emphasis on heavy weaning weights. Calving in such cold, wet weather periods frequently results both in a high calf death loss and a poor subsequent reproductive percentage because the cow is having to lactate on dead grass or limited winter pasture. Most of us do not have a surplus of green grass until May and that's when we should start calving to produce the cheapest healthiest calf and the highest rebreeding percentage in our cows.

With MIG, a great many warm-season pastures and ranges will volunteer enough of a cool-season component that supplementary feeding will be unnecessary with dry cows. Research in the 1950s showed that in most years cows as far north as mid Nebraska could be wintered with no more than 200 lbs. of hay and a fall-grown feed bank of time-limited grazed Abruzzi rye. Even in Canada, hay feeding periods can be cut to 60 days and less if the cow is not lactating.

In most environments, a single calving season timed to mesh with the spring grass lush will be the most profitable method of producing calves. In areas of the country with extremely long growing seasons such as the Gulf Coast states, we have the option of considering a split calving season. Split calving seasons have several benefits. We can run more cows per bull, produce a more even supply of calves, increase our marketing options and have the ability to allow a cow two chances to breed a year.

Care must be taken that all alternative uses for the second cow unit's grass are considered before a second calving season is undertaken. Quite often that grass might be more profitably harvested with a different species of animal, such as sheep, or with a purchased stocker calf than with more brood cows. Investigate all of your options.

Traditionally, split calving seasons have been described as spring and fall calving. However, what most of us were doing would have been more correctly described as a winter calving season and a winter breeding-season with a lot of hay and feed needed for both seasons because of being out of sync with the pasture.

A much more grass-efficient program would be an early spring calving in late March and early April followed by a late summer calving in late July and early August. However, the cows from both seasons should go through the winter dry. This means that the July and August calves would be weaned in October and early November at three to four months of age. The March/April calves could be weaned as early as the end of the bermudagrass lush in late August depending upon the summer grass supply and management's need for it.

This would give you a set of yearlings to sell in late February to early April when prices are at their seasonal high and another set to sell at the end of August, another traditional seasonal high in the South. The grass freed up by the sale of the first set of yearlings would provide the grass for the March/April calving cows. These suggested sale dates are just for illustration purposes. You should always keep your options open and stay flexible in your marketing program.

Here's a brief review:

• All pasture management starts with getting your breeding season in sync with your pasture.

• Quality pasture should be created for weaned calves, not for the cows.

• Weaning should occur at the end of your surplus grass period.

• Lightweight calves have lower body maintenance requirements and so produce more gain per acre of pasture than heavier calves.

• Long growing season pastures can sometimes be best utilized by a split calving season if both are combined with early weaning.

Plan A Forage Sequence For Yearling Cattle

Just as heavy weaning weights may not be a profit-enhancing goal in a retained-ownership marketing system, placing cattle on a grain-based finishing ration at the "traditional" 700 to 750 lbs. may not be the most profitable option either for graziers planning to retain ownership to slaughter.

Research at LSU found the gain between 700 and 900 lbs. is actually more profitable to produce on pasture than the traditional stocker weight gain of 400 to 700 lbs. because there is less price-margin rollback. Much of the weight we have traditionally put on in the feedyard can be put on much cheaper on your own home-grown grass. But, a grazing season this long will require a planned forage sequence.

Yearlings that have grazed range, warm-season tame

pastures, or endophyte-infected fescue will usually have a lot of unexpressed growth in them. This is called compensatory gain or "pop." Yearlings on wheat pasture that are pulled off in early March will also have a lot of pop in them as most graziers graze the wheat too short to maximize animal gains in the winter.

Gains of four to six pounds per day are not uncommon when cattle from the above four forage groups are swapped to a finishing-quality forage. Cattle in southeastern Oklahoma that have been grazed through the winter on infected fescue gained six and a half pounds a day when swapped to ryegrass in May. Research in New Zealand and Louisiana clearly shows that pushing cattle gains on intermediate forages is not cost-effective if you are planning to own them through a subsequent higher-quality forage period. A big part of long-season grass management is planning to maximize compensatory gain to your advantage.

Growing cattle are most profitable when managed so as to grow heavier on a rising plane of forage quality or TDN: for example, warm-season grasses, followed by cool-season grasses, followed by warm-season annuals such as sudan or corn, cowpeas or the brassica types such as rape and turnips.

Allowing cattle to become fleshy on an intermediate forage will greatly hurt the performance in the subsequent stage and indicates that you have probably given up too much gain per acre to produce the exceptional gain per head. We only want to fully express our cattle once and that is in the final forage stage.

Compensatory gain is not a dirty word. It is one of the biggest profit tools we have with cattle and its use should be maximized rather than minimized.

Cull Cow Grazing

Tradition has it that fall open cows should always be culled in the fall to avoid the over-wintering expense on the cow. However, with the advent of low-cost cow wintering methods such as strip-grazed stockpiled fescue and/or time-limited small acreages of cereal rye, wheat or ryegrass, this tradition should probably be reexamined as the cull cow is a major product of cow-calf production. Freshly weaned beef cows will usually be drawn down in body condition and regardless of whether one plans to over-winter them, they should be allowed to reflesh before selling them if the feed is available. This additional flesh is not only relatively cheap to put on but will increase the per pound price by several dollars a cwt.

Over the last ten years, cull cows have brought $5.00 a cwt. more on the first of February and $7.00 a cwt. more in mid-March than in mid-November. That is $50 to $70 more gross dollars per 1000 lb. cow for owning the cow an additional 60 to 90 days. This manufacturing beef market is little influenced by the fed beef trade. In fact, I have seen cull bulls bring within a penny or two of finished steers during fed cattle price declines.

Over-wintering thin bulls and cows that can gain in condition as well as price is a much better economic proposition and in fact can be a very profitable seasonal business. Not only can gain be put on dry cows relatively easily (cheap), but it enhances the marketing margin as well since thin cows sell at a discount to moderately fleshy cows. Consider that a cull cow purchased in mid-November for $42 cwt. and sold in early March for $50 per cwt. produces a value per pound of gain of $82 a cwt. Quite often the value of gain on a fall-purchased spring-sold cow will exceed a dollar a pound! The steer grazier very seldom works on a value of gain much over $55 cwt. and it frequently falls into the mid $30 cwt. range. Bigger cows result in bigger margins and thin culled Holsteins are a favorite of graziers playing this game. Fall-to-spring price spreads are highest during the liquidation phase of the cattle cycle.

Over-wintering thin cows at a low rate of gain on hay as a way to utilize excess hay and excess spring pasture can be economically marginal because cow beef prices start to decline after mid-March. Quite often, dramatically so.

A far better program would be to harvest quality pasture silage in the spring and full-feed it to fatten the cows in the mid-winter period or time limit graze winter annuals. To maximize per-head marketing margin the cows need to be fleshed out between mid-November and mid-February and sold before mid-March.

A good many cows are held over into the New Year each winter for tax purposes and these cows keep the January market depressed. A good market play over the last ten years would have been to buy good fleshed tax-culled cows in early to mid-January and resell them in mid-February. The average forward margin on this play over the last 10 years has been $8.00 cwt. or $80 on a $1000-lb. cow. Having a ready reserve of pasture silage will allow you to take advantage of such short-lived price situations.

Purchasers of extremely thin cows need to have a good receiving program just like a stocker calf operator. These cows are under a lot of nutritional stress and need to be built up in body condition as quickly as possible. They also are probably heavily parasitized and mineral deficient. According to the cow graziers I talked to, a highly profitable by-product of cull cow grazing is that around 50 percent of them will be pregnant. Obviously, the "eye-ball cull" most of us use is not very efficient in judging pregnancy. These pregnant cows should be calved out and the calves short-weaned and the cows sold for slaughter as quickly as possible.

Pasture Silage For Beef Production

Research by Dr. Raymond Steen of the Hillsborough Research Institute in Northern Ireland found that high quality pasture silage is the cheapest source of winter feed for growing beef cattle. High-quality pasture silage can produce relatively high levels of animal performance with a minimum of grain input as long as the grass is cut in an immature stage.

Quality-pasture silage can put 1.5 lbs. of gain per head on over-wintered steers with no supplemental grain and can increase net profit from finishing cattle for slaughter by 60 percent over traditional high-grain finishing programs by allowing grain inputs to be dramatically lowered.

High pasture-silage finishing programs are particularly valuable in lean beef programs where fat deposition is not wanted and in finishing early-maturing breed heifers, which tend to fatten too quickly on conventional high grain rations.

Steen's research showed that beef calves being over-wintered for subsequent spring grazing should not be fed to gain in excess of 1.5 lbs. per day. It is more cost-effective to utilize compensatory gain on spring pasture than to feed for higher performance during the winter. This level of animal performance could be attained on early-cut spring pasture silage with no additional grain input, on medium quality silage with three pounds of grain fed daily, or on poor quality silage with an additional 5.5 pounds of grain per head per day. The grain is fed in one feeding.

Research on using a mixer wagon to mix the silage and grain showed no increase in intake or animal performance over once-a-day feeding of the grain separate from the silage.

Stocker cattle that are allowed to feed to appetite on grass silage will seldom gain over 1.5 lbs. per day and more often gain at half this rate per day. This rate of gain is acceptable as long as the cattle are being wintered for subsequent spring grazing. However, if the cattle will be sold before spring grazing, a higher rate of gain can be produced by supplementing with a small amount of grain and protein.

One British research study found that supplementing stocker cattle on a full feed of grass silage with one kilogram (2.2 lbs.) of barley produced an average daily gain of eight-tenths of a pound of gain per day. This gain was increased to 1.98 per day with a 40% barley/60% soybean mix and increased to 2.09 per day when a 75% barley/25% fish meal mix was used. The latter two mixes were still only a kilogram per day total feed. Such responses to protein are only found in younger cattle. The higher gain from fishmeal was thought to have come because fish meal is only slightly digested in the rumen and becomes a source of bypass protein.

200 to 700 lb. stocker calves fed 3.5 lbs. of an 18 percent crude protein barley/soybean meal gained as well as calves fed 5.5 lbs. of fortified barley. However, adding supplemental protein to concentrates above the 10 percent level will not increase animal performance with older steers or heifers but will significantly increase carcass fatness.

Holstein/Continental cross bulls, on the other hand, show a good response to concentrates containing 15 to 17 percent protein even on very high quality silage. "Bulls have a very high potential for growth and lean meat deposition," Steen said, "and therefore require a high plane of nutrition during the finishing period."

The British have also found that the higher the quality of the silage the less impact grain supplementation had on increasing average daily gain. If your goal is to maximize the use of your home-produced silage and minimize purchased grain, it is seldom wise to feed over two to three pounds of grain/protein mix supplement per day. This level of feeding should be adequate to produce an average daily gain of two pounds a day.

With a spring calving cow herd, a two-cut silage system is normally used. The first cut is made early and of high stocker quality for over-wintering the calves and the second cut is allowed to get relatively mature with very high yield and this is cut for dry cow feed in mid-summer. For graziers with no brood cows, a three-cut system is used to maximize silage quality rather than yield.

Finishing Slaughter Cattle On Quality Pasture

Most of the costs of producing or buying an animal occur early in one's ownership. The longer one can graze an animal and put weight on it the higher the profits per head become. A few graziers are now starting to question if a feedlot finishing period is really necessary at all. In many locations the costs of getting an animal to a feedlot in trucking, shrink and death loss, exceed the profit one can reasonably hope to make there. Is this trip really necessary? Not with quality pasture and the correct cattle genetics.

Grain-on-Grass Cattle Finishing

Grain-on-grass cattle finishing systems were widely researched in the South in the mid-to-late 1970s, and were found to be both cost-effective and capital efficient in the production of quality slaughter beef during the cooler months of the year. This was found **not** to be the case during the hot Southern summers.

Research at Virginia Tech showed that by finishing cattle on bluegrass summer pasture or winter stockpiled fescue and clover, all of the protein needed in the cattle's diet could be furnished by the pasture. Capital outlays for facilities were minimal and the animal's manure was recycled naturally and inexpensively by the pasture. During 154 days of wintergrazing on stockpiled fescue at Virginia Tech 1976-77, yearling steers fed one percent of their bodyweight in grain (i.e. nine pounds of grain in a 900 lbs. steer) gained 2.93 lbs., and when swapped to bluegrass/white clover in the spring gained 2.41 lbs. per day and finished in the high Select range. Another group of yearlings were fed at 0.5 percent of bodyweight until the last 90 days and then fed at the one percent level until slaughter. These steers finished in the medium Select grade. Yearling steers finished solely on grass in this study averaged 1.44 lbs. and finished in the high Standard grade.

When grass amounts were adequate, grain supplementation

was found not to be cost-effective, as bluegrass/white clover pasture could produce average daily gains equivalent to a high grain ration. The one percent level of grain supplementation was found to replace as much as 50 percent of the grass intake of the cattle and allowed more steers to be over-wintered per acre of stockpiled fescue, and thus make better use of the spring pasture surplus. Virginia Tech recommended that grain supplementation not be started on stockpiled fescue until January as the late fall and early winter quality of stockpiled fescue alone was adequate for good animal gains.

Summer Finishing Expensive. Grain fed at the one percent level allowed very heavy summer-finished steers to continue to gain at an acceptable 1.59 lbs. per day although at a far higher grain cost compared to cool-season gains. The grain-to-gain ratio over grass alone increased to nearly 20 to one in the summer over non-supplemented bluegrass/white clover as the animals substituted grain for grass. At a nickel a pound grain cost that would equal one dollar of grain for each pound of additional gain produced! This is hardly economical. Similar high costs were produced on grain-supplemented, warm-season grass, summer pasture in Mississippi and Louisiana as well. **Perhaps, the best advice would be to avoid finishing cattle on pasture during the hot summer months.**

The actual conversion ratio of grain to gain during the cooler months is around 10 to 1 for the pasture system compared to 7 to 1 for the traditional drylot system. This lower feed efficiency was used by many economists to "unsell" this low-input system. On today's grain market with corn at a nickel a pound, the total grain cost would be 45 to 50 cents for a 2.93 lbs. average daily gain or between 15 to 20 cents grain cost per total pound of gain. If you cost in your pasture at 15 to 20 cents per pound of gain, this still looks good compared to commercial feedyard costs in excess of 50 cents for one pound of gain. Attempts to salt-limit grain consumption so that daily feeding would not be necessary produced highly variable average daily gains and were not recommended. Machinery is now available for placing small individual piles of pre-measured grain under a one-wire electric fence and this in-the-paddock feeding method is recommended.

Grain on grass programs should be analyzed "wholistically" and considerations should include their ability to balance pasture seasonality, lack of need for protein input, low capital requirements, natural manure recycling, and the increased marketing and production flexibility. Grain-on-grass is a cost-effective tool when used on a seasonal basis to stretch grass supplies or to push cattle so as to "finish" during premium market price periods.

Genetics And Grass Finished Beef

In the United States, "freedom from finish" has been one of the major benefits of producing and selling commercial grade feeder cattle. One could graze cattle to whatever weight that resulted at the end of the grass season and sell them as feeders without having to be concerned about what their ultimate quality grade or yield was. It was thought that feeding grain for a proscribed minimum amount of time would make all beef of similar tenderness. Alas, this has not been proven to be true. In recent taste tests, no correlation was found between the time on feed and the subsequent tenderness or taste of the product. Beef fed 200 days was just as likely to be tough as that fed 60 days.

This new realization that marbling and tenderness cannot consistently be produced solely through grain feeding has rekindled an interest in achieving these benefits through genetic selection. Dr. Gary Smith of Colorado State said that prior to 1950, almost all beef eaten in the United States was grass finished and from four major genetic groups. These were purebred British breeds, Okies (Jersey x British), purebred dairy (primarily Holstein), and Crossbreds (British x Brahman). Cattle were graded solely by conformation and eye appeal and the British breeds dominated until the early 1960s when the ribbing of carcasses to expose marbling was begun. Marbling made the Okie the preferred choice until 1965, when the present system of Quality and carcass grading was begun and carcass "conformation" was dropped.

The addition of Yield Grade shifted demand away from the heavily marbled Okies toward European crosses with better Yield Grades. The dropping of carcass conformation also benefitted the lighter muscled Crossbreds, Holsteins and American breeds. In the 1970s new American breeds were begun by crossing Brahman with the Continental breeds.

A major problem for all beef producers produced by this genetic goulash was that one steak in four was not tender enough for consumers according to a taste test study. Smith said it was now time to seriously reconsider the direction of cattle breeding. The emphasis must be placed on consistently producing cattle with tender, flavorful, juicy meat.

Too many animal scientists hide behind the old canard, "there is more difference within breeds, than among breeds" but this isn't so. Smith said it is essentially impossible to find Limousin cattle that marble as well as Wagyu, Holstein-Friesians with as high muscle-to-bone ratios as Limousins, or Brahman cattle that produce meat as flavorful and tender as Jersey cattle.

Breeds capable of producing Prime Grade Carcasses were Wagyu, Angus, Jersey, Guernsey, and Red Angus. High Choice could be produced by Angus, Galloway and Red Angus and Low Choice by Hereford, Brangus and Holstein. Select grade can consistently be produced by purebred Charolais, Limousin and Gelbvieh.

Crossing Brahman with the British breeds produces a carcass that will grade Choice about 50% of the time. Brahman and Continental cross carcasses will grade Choice only one third of the time even after long periods of grain feeding. The Brahman breed is most responsible for the Standard Grade, Yield Grade 4 carcass that has fat on the outside but not on the inside.

Intramuscular marbling is thought to be necessary to maintain the "juiciness" Americans desire in steak when it is cooked in the traditional "hot and fast" style of outdoor grilling. Exactly what attributes fat adds to beef flavor are not unanimously agreed upon. However, most meat scientists are now in agreement that marbling has little to do with meat tenderness.

Smith said present thinking is that cattle with relatively high proportions of "red" versus "white" muscle fibers have superior propensities to deposit intramuscular fat that is visualized as marbling after carcass chilling. The Japanese Black Wagyu has the highest ratio of red to white muscling. At the other end of the spectrum are D'Aquitaine, Belgian Blue, and Piedmontese.

For tenderness, Smith ranked the following top ten breeds in descending order from one to ten: Wagyu, Jersey, Guernsey, Angus, Red Angus, Hereford, Galloway, Shorthorn, South Devon, and Piedmontese.

The Piedmontese is an unusual inclusion in that it is very heavily muscled, non-marbling, but very tender. It was this one breed that gave lie to the previously widely held belief that marbling produced meat tenderness. Apparently tenderness is due to the lack of connective tissue (gristle) present in an animal's muscles. Hereford is another breed that does not marble easily but produces very tender meat.

Research by Dr. Larry Cundiff of the U.S. Meat Animal Research Center showed that at the same level of marbling, steaks from Bos Indicus cattle (Brahman) are eight times as likely to deliver a "less than satisfactory in tenderness, eating experience" to the consumer than Bos Taurus cattle.

Breeders of Continental European breeds and Brahman cattle must intensify their efforts to identify and cull out strains with unacceptable levels of palatability and tenderness.

To achieve a U.S. Choice, Yield Grade 1 or 2 carcass, Smith recommended on a one-to-ten descending scale, Charolais x Angus, Simmental x Angus, Limousin x Angus, Red Angus, Hereford x Angus, Brangus, Holstein x Angus, Angus, and Hereford.

Angus was the only breed that has proven consistently to carry the breed crossed with it into the Choice Grade. Needless to say, Smith believes that the color black will be an almost universal trait of American beef cattle in the future.

The importance of this finding of genetics as the key to meat quality rather than grain feeding opens a huge crack in the door against pasture finished beef. In fact, with quality pasture and the correct genetics it is possible to deliver cattle to a slaughter plant that are unrecognizably different from grain finished animals except for the lack of grain in their paunch.

Choice Grade On Grass

USDA Choice Grade beef is possible on quality pasture. The intra-muscular marbling necessary for Choice Grade beef has been widely promoted as only possible through an extended period of grain feeding. However, the New Zealanders have found that this is not the case, and that most other grain-feeding myths concerning fat color, tenderness, and meat texture are also false.

Intramuscular fat tends to be the last fat laid down in an

animal's body and does not occur until the animal has reached its mature body size. Genetics plays a role, but the over-riding factor is the closeness to the mature weight of the animal when slaughtered. The New Zealanders found no relation between grain feeding and marbling in their research. Australian research has also found no difference in marbling between pasture finished and grain-finished beef when killed at the same carcass weight.

A Japanese study of grass-finished steers imported from Victoria, Australia, found that 42 percent of them would have graded at least USDA Low Choice but only 48 percent of them met the fat cover needed to meet minimum Yield Grade requirements (60 percent.) The major problem the Japanese cited with Australian grass finished beef was the wide swing in quality from supplier to supplier and from one shipment to the next. Subsequent research found this variability was primarily due to the age, breeding, and grazing management of the cattle.

Japanese Wagyu, Jersey, Angus, Hereford, Polled Hereford, and Murray Grey were all found to be able to marble relatively easy on pasture with the Wagyu and Murray Grey being the most consistent. A wider genetic range in marbling was found in the Angus, Hereford and Polled Herefords indicating the need to select for this moderately heritable marbling trait in these breeds.

Yellow fat in young animals (less than 30 months) was found not to be caused by grass but by legumes. Animals killed in the summer when pastures were more leguminous produced yellow fat. The fat color of the animals grew whiter as the season progressed until it was snow-white by late fall. The use of "specialist" nitrogen-based "finishing pastures" could solve this summer fat color problem. However, only 11 percent of the Australian animals in the Japanese study had yellow fat.

No correlation was found between nutrition and subsequent meat tenderness. The preferred firmness and texture of grain-fed beef can be produced on pasture by keeping animals gaining steadily throughout their life. (Minimum of 3/4 lb.) Most of the reputation for tough grass-finished beef has come from rangeland steers who lost weight each winter or dry season.

Animals slaughtered at thirty months of age were found not to have coarse muscle fiber. This slaughter age is no great problem with improved, temperate pasture grasses and the winter feeding of high-quality, temperate grass-silage. Most temperate-grass slaughter programs in the world produce animals that die between 18 and 24 months of age.

The reputation for dark cutting meat has also come from rangeland animals who have never been handled by humans. Steers from management-intensive grazing were found to be as gentle as those from feedlot situations. The other cause of dark cutting meat is from the use of non-steered bulls. Bulls must be killed very quickly after leaving their pasture to prevent dark cutting or killed before reaching sexual maturity.

New Zealand research found the bright red meat color preferred by the Japanese occurred within the first six weeks of a grain-fed ration. No benefit in meat color, fat color or any other meat quality attribute was found by grainfeeding cattle longer than 12 weeks. In fact, the only truly profitable benefit found in feedlotting cattle at all was as a marketing platform that could spread slaughter animals more evenly over the year. This market-smoothing function could be realized through the use of pasture silage/low-grain rations such as those used in Ireland at far lower cost than the high-cost, feedlot ration currently used in the United States.

Research at North Carolina State indicates that quality beef could be produced solely from grass. The key to producing quality grassfed beef was a forage quality high enough to produce rapid gains in the cattle. According to the research, grassfed animals have a higher yielding carcass with less untrimmable intramuscular fat. Grain finished cattle show some increase in muscle during the finishing period, however, most of the weight increase is due to fat.

Grass-fattened cattle have slightly yellower fat than grain-finished. Grain-on-grass-finished animals have a fat color almost the same as grain-finished animals.

Tough beef is produced by animals that are kept at a submaintenance level and no fat cover on the body is produced. This results in a phenomenon known as "cold shortening" when chilled in the freezer and results in muscles that are hard to shear through. As long as grass-finished animals have a body fat cover of one quarter to one half inch of fat, there is no difference in tenderness between grass-finished and grain-finished beef.

Trained taste panelists at North Carolina State were unable

to distinguish beef finished on intensively grazed dwarf millet and grain-finished beef. From consumer studies, the typical consumer has shown no preference for steaks and roasts from drylot-finished cattle versus grass-finished cattle based on tenderness, taste and aroma.

Doing It All On Grass

The Kerr Angus Ranch (KAR), near Coyle, Oklahoma, has set itself the ambitious goal of producing high grading 1000 lb. slaughter steers, completely on pasture by 15 months of age.

Midland bermuda with Yuchi arrowleaf clover is used as the base forage. Jose tall wheat grass and time-limit-grazed (four hours every other day) wheat, vetch and annual ryegrass provide the cool season grazing.

A recent carcass evaluation of a Kerr grass-finished steer confirms the New Zealand and Australian observation that grass finished cattle will grade USDA Choice. The evaluation is as follows:

Carcass weight (lb.) -- 620
Fat thickness (in.) -- .35
Ribeye Area (sq. in.) -- 11.9
Kidney, Pelvic and Heart Fat -- 2
Marbling Small -- 20
Yield Grade -- 2.3
Quality Grade -- Choice
Warner Bratzler Shear (lb.) (tenderness) -- 9.46
% Fat (raw) -- 20.84
% Moisture (raw) -- 61.13
% Protein -- 17.77
% Fat (cooked) -- 25.35
% Moisture (cooked) -- 48.79
% Protein (cooked) -- 25.55

Kerr initially planned to sell its beef under the National Organic Certification guidelines but were unable to find a processing plant willing to handle the beef using organic standards. In querying its customers, KAR found they were only concerned about the use of implant steroids and the feeding of sub therapeutic antibiotics and have decided to drop the organic certification. This will allow the use of lower priced non-organic animal husbandry supplies, such as dewormers, insecticides and minerals. Kerr now plans to market its animals as "naturally raised, grass-fed beef."

Grass-Finished Beef--Argentine Style

The **New York Times** food section has named Argentine grass-finished beef as "the best beef in the world." I've been there, tried it and I agree. If you need to be convinced grass-finished beef can be a heavenly eating experience hop a jet to Buenos Aires. I guarantee you'll be sold on grass-finished beef.

The Argentines have long been very conscious of the need for eating quality in their meat. Consequently, there is a lot of long-range planning and mental energy involved in Argentine beef finishing. It is definitely not a "turn-out and gather" system like the Old West.

One of the first things I learned about Argentine grass-finished beef is that it is not extremely lean. Some of it has a rind of fat an inch thick. The average yield is 60 percent.

Their production system for English breed cattle (the Angus/Hereford cross is the predominant breeding) is a late spring calving, a late summer/early fall weaning at four to five months of age with the animal dying as a grass-finished steer before the winter of its second year.

The "finishing zone" is on the western side of Buenos Aires Province with a climate similar to coastal Virginia and Southern New Jersey. Due to the perfectly flat relief of the Pampas, soils tend to be boggy and poorly drained. In the finishing zone are long fingers of wind-blown sandy loam ridges that provide the drier soil needed for the growth of alfalfa, which forms the backbone of their finishing pastures.

According to Argentine rancher and grazing consultant, Pedro Landa, alfalfa is prized primarily for its nitrogen-fixing capability rather than forage quality. He likes a 70 percent grass, 30 percent alfalfa mix for maximum animal performance and minimum bloat problems.

The ranches I visited were all subdivided and use rotational grazing. Permanent pastures are alfalfa mixed with fungus-free fescue, orchardgrass, wheatgrass or brome. The Argentine tradition has been to rotate between permanent grass and annuals on a six-years-in-perennial pasture/three-years-in-annuals basis to utilize the nitrogen buildup in the soil from the alfalfa.

Temporary pastures of cereal rye and triticale (a genetic cross of wheat and rye) are used for supplemental wintergrazing. These temporary winter pastures are then stagger-planted to corn in the spring and are used to graze animals scheduled to "finish" in the summer. That's right, the corn is grazed and provides their primary bridge through their "summer slump" in cool-season grass production. Sudangrass is also occasionally planted for summer grazing in order to shade-out volunteer bermuda grass, which is considered a major plant pest in the finishing zone. Shade has been found to be the most effective herbicide for bermudagrass.

Grazed oats are used to finish animals in the autumn. Hay and silage are made from the spring-pasture surplus and are primarily fed in the late summer and early fall to allow the pastures to stockpile growth for winter grazing. Hay is also fed in the early spring when grass dry-matter is very low.

The rainfall average drops very quickly as one travels west from the coast. The western "dry" Pampas is home to large-acreage-extensive cow-calf and sheep operations. Many ranchers own two ranches, one in the dry zone for the brood cows and one in the wet zone for growing out and finishing the calves.

In the finishing zone itself, most ranchers use brood cows to graze the wet swales between the sandy ridges. Weeping lovegrass is used as a stockpiled winter dry-cow feed-source with a little supplemental alfalfa hay for additional protein.

English Cattle Predominate. The Argentine's ideal slaughter weight for an Angus cross is 900 lbs. (410 kgs.) but they will take them as heavy as 1000 lbs. and will drop down as low as 700 lbs. if the supply of killable cattle is short. The animals are sorted for slaughter based upon the fat cover on their rumps. In order to finish before their second winter, the English cattle are never allowed to gain less than three-quarters of a pound per day and gain between 400 and 450 lbs. in a year. Male animals are steered but not implanted so as to meet European import regulations.

In the subtropical north of Argentina, Brahman (Zebu) cross cattle necessarily predominate. These cattle will not finish before the second winter due to their slow genetic maturity and so are often used as follower cattle to the premium-priced English cattle.

They are roughed through the winter at a very low rate-of-gain and are allowed to make maximum use of compensatory gain the following spring and summer. Argentine packers do not consider the Brahman cross to be "finished" until it reaches at least 1250 lbs.

The third class of "finishing" animal are Holstein steers. These are used as third grazers and are considered a "scavenger" class of animal. They are traditionally killed in the 1400 to 1500 lb. weight range. Most of the Holsteins I saw were not owned by the ranchers but were being contract-grazed for Holstein specialists in the manufactured beef trade.

There is also a small premium market for "pasture veal." These are fleshy weaned calves in the 500 lbs. plus category. Since most Argentine ranchers retain ownership to slaughter, high weaning weights are not prized and calves are traditionally weaned early in life at between 300 and 400 lbs.

Gauchos ride the finishing paddocks daily and sort off animals ready for slaughter. 30 thousand-pound steers are a "load" for the small Argentine trucks. This constant pasture "topping" prevents cattle bunching and helps stabilize the prices. The highest prices for beef are in the winter and early spring and some ranchers will grain-supplement cattle on winter pasture so that they will fatten for this premium-priced market. There are also a few North American-style feedlots (80 percent grass silage/ 20 percent grain) but they have been found to only be economical during the premium-priced winter season.

Cooking Beef Is Great Theater In Argentina. Argentine steak houses are called "Parilladas" and cook their meat with great theater and panache. The cooking of the meat is always done at the front of the restaurant so that it can be seen through the windows as an advertisement to passersby. Near the front door of the restaurant will be the circular "ruedo" with a wood fire in the center. Here beef ribs, lamb halves, whole suckling-pigs and goat kids are slowly cooked on iron crosses placed around the side of the pit. The "asado" (or barbecue) pit is built with two concentric circles of bricks with an open sand-filled space between the two circles to allow the placement of the sharp end of the iron crosses in the sand.

To one side will be one or two "parilladas" or grills for steaks, sausages and chickens. The parillada is divided into the grill portion and a firebox where very dense hardwood is burned in an open fire. Glowing embers are transferred from the firebox to the grill for cooking. The Argentines are very adamant about the absolute necessity of never letting flames touch the meat. They also believe smoke from burning fat juices ruins the taste of the meat and quickly extinguish any open flames with saltwater. The grills are long in dimension and height-adjustible so that heat of varying intensities will be available to the cook.

All of this sizzling action is overseen by an "Asador" wearing a broad leather belt with three or four very wicked looking, 15- to 20-inch knives in attached scabbards. The cooking of meat in Argentina is considered very serious business and is only done by men. (Their attitude, not mine.)

Lean Meats Are A Challenge. Lean meats are considered a true test of an Asador's skill, with goat being the ultimate challenge. Meat cooked on the "asado" iron cross should almost fall off the bones and be easy to cut with a fork. Lamb and goat are cooked around the "asado" for at least three to four hours before serving. Only well-fattened beef is cooked "asado" style as the slow cooking tends to dry the meat. The most popular beef cut for "asado" are the ribs.

The Argentines say the sole purpose of fattening beef is to keep the meat moist while cooking. With thick cut "bife" steaks the less fat there is, the hotter and faster the meat is cooked to prevent drying. The Argentines do not like any kind of meat rare and steaks are traditionally cooked medium to well done. The Argentines also never eat freshly killed meats but also do not believe in aging meat for over 24 hours.

Steaks are only turned once on the grill. They are seared on one side over hot coals to seal the juices, then turned over and moved to less hot coals for the remainder of the cooking. This need to vary the heat of the coals is why their grills are so long.

With lean cuts salt water is periodically applied with the leafy end of a celery or parsley stalk to the seared side of the steak to keep it moist. This brine is ONLY applied to the side of the meat that has been seared. It is never applied to unseared meat.

Lean steaks are frequently marinated for up to 12 hours in a salt and vinegar solution before cooking. Adobos or dry marinades are also used with very lean meats and are rubbed in before cooking. Alinos, uncooked vegetable dressings, are also frequently applied to both grilled and roasted meats. Chimichurri, a finely chopped mixture of garlic, onion, tomato, pepper and paprika is one of the most popular.

Thin beef steaks called Churrascos are working class standard fare and are cooked quickly on a grill or a griddle. These are traditionally beaten with a wooden mallet prior to cooking to ensure their tenderness.

Short ribs can be prepared on the grill as well as on the ruedo and are cooked bone-side down first. Once the bone side has turned brown and crispy the meat side is turned to the grill and the brine solution is frequently sprinkled on the bone side to keep the meat moist.

A favorite beef cut is Asado de lomo, or tenderloin. Because of its innate tenderness and lack of fat it is grilled quickly over hot coals. Tenderloin is never marinated or flavored with condiments due to its superior natural flavor.

All "asado" meals begin with chorizos, or mixed pork and beef sausages. These are similar to North American hot dogs. Usually there will be two of these for each person. A beef-blood black-sausage called morcilla will also be served at this time. Sweetbreads, entrails called achuras, grilled heart, kidney and udder are also served up as appetizers.

The Argentines believe meat must be eaten hot and most restaurants will provide your own ember-filled Brazacero to keep your meats hot. At a full-fledged "asado" the preliminaries will be followed by steaks, ribs, chicken and lamb. Potatoes are served as French fries, mashed or baked. Lettuce and tomato or tomato and onion salads are common. Fresh fruits and custard are the traditional desserts. A full-fledged "asado" meal will take two to three hours to consume and will be worth every minute.

I wish every North American could have one good Argentine steak to break the paradigm that grain feeding is necessary for good eating. After a week of eating grass-finished beef, I found upon returning that American grain-finished beef left an unpleasant greasy taste and feeling in my mouth similar to what most Americans feel after eating fat lamb.

In our quest for marbling and tenderness, I am afraid we have forgotten beef flavor. The Argentine steaks taste like steaks.

Your taste buds go "Wow!"

I think one of the great opportunities left in the United States is to make food fun. Think about serving your own grass-finished beef, lamb, pork and chicken "Argentine Style" with a flaming "asado" pit and grill at your county or state fair.

Carcass Yield And Grass

Several graziers have told me they have been disappointed in the carcass yield percentages they have been getting on their grass-finished cattle. In an ideal grass-finished animal, the ratio of salable meat to liveweight should be around 60 percent. However, many graziers are experiencing yields in the 49 to 50 percent range. Since you are charged on a per head basis for slaughter, a low-yielding animal carries a proportionately higher slaughter cost per pound. Most of this yield disappointment is a result of killing cattle before they are phenotypically mature.

Carcass yield percentage is primarily a function of the ratio of bone to muscle and fat. This ratio of bone to meat is low in growing animals and becomes higher as the animal "finishes" or reaches its mature size and begins to hang meat and fat on the frame it grew in the "stocker" portion of its life. In most beef breeds this finishing phase is reached at around 750 to 850 lbs. However, with very late maturing breeds the "stocker" phase may actually extend beyond 1400 to 1500 lbs.

Continental breed animals are currently killed in the growing stage of life because their final mature weights are too heavy and their portion size too large for the established beef commodity market. This immaturity makes their meat very lean and their heavy muscling helps hold their carcass yield at the 60 percent level. However, if we kill light- to medium-muscled cattle prior to maturity, we will have a lean but low-yielding carcass. To keep the yield high it is important not to mis-match production systems and genetics.

Most graziers like the Argentine system of wintering spring-born animals once and killing them in their second autumn of life at 800 to 1,000 lbs. However, for this system to work, early maturing genetics, such as small phenotype Angus and Red Angus, must be used to achieve a 60 percent yield carcass. In the Deep South where very high-quality winter pastures can be grown, late February-born, early maturing breeds can be "finished" to a high-carcass yield on pasture in May and June at 15 to 16 months of age.

Keep in mind that the above Argentine style beef is not lean. In fact, much of it can grade USDA Choice. As such, it requires no special cooking instructions and could be sold through the same distribution channels as grain-finished beef except that carcass size will frequently be slightly smaller than that required for boxed beef. This small carcass size is an advantage if you are selling on carcass halves or quarters. Yellow fat only appears to be a problem on summer-finished animals grazing legume-dominant pastures.

Angus crosses of one-quarter Brahman, Holstein or Continental breeding will fit the box, but will frequently not finish in the autumn and will have to be finished during the winter on silage/grain, winter annuals or stockpiled pasture/grain. An often overlooked breed cross for this mid-size "American" style beef is the dairy byproduct Jersey/Limousin cross. The Jersey is early maturing while the Limousin adds the muscling for a higher yield. The color of this cross is red.

Straight Brahman, North American Holstein, and Jerseys have a naturally high bone-to-muscle ratio and will have a low yielding carcass regardless of weight. New Zealand Friesians and Brown Swiss have beefier carcasses and are better suited for dairy beef production.

Slow maturing breed crosses such as half-Brahman, Holstein-cross, and Continental-cross cattle must be wintered a second winter and are usually killed in the third summer or autumn of their life to produce the desired high-yielding carcass. These animals are difficult to finish in the Deep South due to the lack of high-quality late summer and fall pastures. Keep in mind these animals are frequently in excess of 1400 lbs. liveweight when slaughtered. This makes them very expensive for your customers if you are selling on a carcass half or quarter system.

Also, this long production cycle also gets most graziers antsy for a faster cash flow and it is hard to fight the desire to turn the inventory over. For example, in Ireland, beef cattle will often change hands five to six times in the 30 to 34 months these slow-maturing animals require to finish. Of course, the more ways you slice the pie the smaller the piece.

The leanness of the carcass will depend upon the beef breed with which they are crossed. Very lean Eurobeef is usually straight Continental breeding or a Holstein/Continental cross. The Holstein/Limousin cross is currently a favorite for this type of beef. Brahman/Angus and Holstein/Angus will be similar to grain-finished beef and can grade Select to Low Choice.

An alternative is to kill the slow-maturing breeds and crosses before the second winter at the Argentine weights. This produces an extremely lean, but low-yielding carcass. Many graziers are finding they can direct-market these extra-lean, small carcasses at enough of a price premium to offset the higher kill costs from the low yield. However, this beef while extremely lean is not Eurobeef. Eurobeef, because it is from fully mature animals, has a higher fat content (USDA Select) and a stronger beef flavor.

Another overlooked alternative is to kill these slow maturing breeds whenever we like, at whatever weight we like, and grind the whole carcass up for lean, premium-priced hamburger as is done with dairy Friesian bulls in New Zealand. More graziers are finding lean, high-quality hamburger to be the easiest and most profitable product to produce and direct market.

A year-round supply of grass-finished beef requires a relatively wide range of body phenotypes and maturities. Attempts to promote a grass-finished product from a single breed group, as has been done in France, results in a highly seasonal product because they will all finish at the same weight and require the same amount of time to reach that weight. It is very doubtful if one ranch, in one location, using one set of genetics will ever be able to produce an economical year-round supply of grass-finished beef. But don't despair!

There is a reason I made you temperate grass graziers sit through chapters on bermudagrass and sub-tropic graziers on fescue and brome. Both regions need to understand the other's opportunities and limitations and work together to realize the potential we have for pasture-finished animals. A year-round supply of grass-finished beef will require production sharing between the temperate grass areas, such as Missouri, and the sub-tropic grass areas, such as Louisiana.

Temperate grass graziers have difficulty in finishing cattle in the spring and early summer. Sub-tropic grass graziers have difficulties in finishing cattle in the late summer and fall. Put the two regions together in a production-sharing arrangement with packing plants located along the Kansas City to Cincinnati axis, and Voilà! A year-round supply of grass-finished beef is not only possible but can be very profitable for all concerned.

The weight an animal will finish (fatten) on grass is determined by its genetics. Argentine grass finishing uses a combination of early maturing Angus cattle and later maturing Braford-Angus cross cattle and a corresponding variable finish weight to provide a year round supply of slaughter cattle. As you can see, an 18 month program requires either a very early maturing animal or exceptional quality pasture to be successful. Late maturing Brahman-cross and continental cattle will require exceptional quality pasture to finish before their third winter.

18 month program (540 days) Dead before the second winter.

Finish weight	ADG required to achieve weight
1000 lbs. ÷ 540 days	= 1.85 lbs. per day
900 lbs.	= 1.66
800 lbs.	= 1.48
700 lbs.	= 1.29

24 month program (720 days) Dead before the third winter

Finish weight	ADG required
1000 lbs. ÷ 720 days	= 1.38 lbs. per day
1100 lbs.	= 1.50
1200 lbs.	= 1.66
1300 lbs.	= 1.80

Think About It...

♣ The quicker we increase total productivity the quicker we can get the calf off the cow. The lighter the calf the less grass required for body maintenance. This is why lightweight calves always bring a higher price per pound than heavier calves. A major management goal of a cow-calf producer who plans to over-winter his calves should therefore be to plan to produce light calves by weaning them early.

♣ Having the calf born at the beginning of the spring lush and weaning it at the end of the lush is the grass-efficient cow-calf production system.

♣ In most environments, a single calving season timed to mesh with the spring grass lush will be the most profitable method of producing calves. In areas of the country with extremely long growing seasons such as the Gulf Coast states, we have the option of considering a split calving season.

♣ Split calving seasons have several benefits--you can run more cows per bull, produce a more even supply of calves, increase your marketing options, and have the ability to allow a cow two chances to breed a year.

♣ Over-wintering thin bulls and cows that can gain in condition as well as price can be a very profitable seasonal business. Not only can gain be put on dry cows relatively easily (cheap), but it enhances the marketing margin as well since thin cows sell at a discount to moderately fleshy cows.

♣ A highly profitable by-product of cull cow grazing is that around 50 percent of them will be pregnant.

♣ Quality-pasture silage can put 1.5 lbs. of gain per head on over-wintered steers with no supplemental grain and can increase net profit from finishing cattle for slaughter by 60 percent over traditional high-grain finishing programs by allowing grain inputs to be dramatically lowered.

♣ Beef calves being over-wintered for subsequent spring grazing should not be fed to gain in excess of 1.5 lbs. per day. It is more cost effective to utilize compensatory gain on spring pasture than to feed for higher performance during the winter.

♣ With a spring calving cow herd, a two-cut silage system is normally used. The first cut is made early and of high-stocker-quality for over-wintering the calves. The second-cut is allowed to get relatively mature with very high yields and this is cut for dry cow feed in mid-summer. For graziers with no brood cows, a three-cut system is used to maximize silage quality rather than yield.

♣ Most of the costs of producing or buying an animal occur early in one's ownership. The longer one can graze an animal and put weight on it the higher the per head profits become.

♣ The Argentine production system for English breed catttle is a late spring calving, a late summer/early fall weaning at four to five months of age with the animal dying as a grass-finished steer before the winter of its second year.

♣ The Argentine tradition has been to rotate between permanent grass and annuals on a six-years-in-perennial pasture/three-years-in-annuals basis to utilize the nitrogen buildup in the soil from the alfalfa.

♣ Temporary pastures of cereal rye and triticale are used for supplemental wintergrazing. These temporary winter pastures are then stagger-planted to corn in the spring and are used to graze animals scheduled to "finish" in the summer. This grazed corn provides their primary bridge through the summer slump in cool-season grass production.

♣ The Argentine flexibility in slaughter weight helps even out their year-round supply.

♣ Grain-on-grass and grass silage feedlotting was profitable only during the grass-short months.

♣ Alfalfa is prized more for it nitrogen fixing ability than for its forage quality.

♣ A forage system of perennials and annuals is necessary to provide a year-round quality pasture.

♣ The major opportunity for graziers is not to produce a commodity product totally undifferentiated from American grain-finished beef, but to sell the "green" benefits of high-quality, "guaranteed tender," grass-finished beef as an ecologically responsible, wholesome, healthy product.

♣ Advertising programs contrasting shiny cattle grazing lush, green pastures to those of cattle standing brisket-deep in mud and manure could go a long way toward making grass-finished beef the premium grade beef in the United States.

Chapter 13: Multiple Species Grazing

Just as the pasture becomes stronger and healthier as we mix plant species together, so do our animals when we mix the species that graze it. Monocultures of animals are no more a part of nature's plan than monocultures of plants. Cattle, sheep and goats are, for the most part, very complementary to each other in their forage selections. A long-term observation in humid climates has been that a grazier could add one ewe for every cow he is currently grazing and never miss the grass.

The two factors preventing most of us from adding species are lack of good perimeter fences and lack of specific production knowledge about the new species. Minimal electric fencing has dramatically lowered the cost of interior fencing and subdivision, but a good, eight-wire, sheep-and-goat-proof perimeter fence can give you a lot of options and a lot of peace of mind. Specific species production knowledge can come from doing it on a small scale first, reading and visiting with other producers.

The best time to add a new species to your operation is when the new species you are adding is at the bottom of its price cycle. Most of us learn by doing it wrong and the best time to make these mistakes is when the experience won't bankrupt us. Since lamb tends to be contra-cyclical to beef, the two price cycles tend to financially compliment each other, and because stocker ewes seldom cost much of a per head total dollar premium over lambs, the return on investment in sheep is much higher than in beef cattle. An analysis in New Zealand showed that on a return on investment profitability basis, sheep are the best investment of all ruminants. Also, because of their lower total body weights and subsequent maintenance requirements, sheep can produce a higher total gain per acre than beef cattle.

Combining sheep with cattle and using intensive grazing greatly reduces predator problems. University of California research found no predator losses in flocks grazed at high stock densities. In New Mexico, female cattle and sheep have successfully bonded emotionally and the cattle have prevented any predator losses. Female donkeys, llamas, and ostriches also make good guardians for sheep. Guard dogs are effective but more difficult and expensive to feed than a grass-eating protector. Cattle and sheep also break each others' parasite cycle. For example, if you gather your animals from pasture, worm them, and turn them back on the very same pasture, you will only relieve them of their worm burden for two or three days. This is not cost effective and it greatly speeds the development of wormer parasite resistance. For the worming of any species to be truly effective, the animals must go on prepared, low-parasite pastures or they are quickly reinfected.

Dr. R.P. Herd of Ohio State University said you should think of pastures as being "safe" or "dangerous." Safe pastures are those that were grazed the previous year by another species of livestock, were cut for hay or silage, or are annuals grown on tilled land. Virtually all parasites are species specific, so grazing a pasture with cattle makes it "safe" for sheep and vice versa. Pastures in the North that have over-wintered without livestock on them are also considered safe. Dr. Herd said "safe" does not mean completely parasite free but only a low level of existing parasitism. Most animal scientists do not want animals to live in an un-natural parasite-free environment as genetic resistance to parasitism is a very important trait to retain in our animals. Gulf Coast Native Sheep, for example, are almost completely naturally parasite resistant because they were never wormed. It appears this resistance can be bred into other breeds of sheep over time.

Studies in Ohio have indicated that there is only one disease-producing generation of sheep nematodes per year. This generation is responsible for dangerous levels of pasture infectivity in the summer and fall. Sheep turned out in the spring were exposed to only light infection from over-wintered pasture but worm burdens escalated to large numbers in July and August. Swapping sheep and cattle pastures on July first helps keep the pastures naturally low in internal parasites for both species. This heavy mid-summer worm burden is often responsible for low gains on growing lambs and calves in the summer more than the heat.

Internal parasites are particularly dangerous for weaned lambs, lactating ewes and young calves of less than six months of age. It is toward these very susceptible classes that your primary efforts should be directed. In many of the major sheep producing countries, ewes are run on extensive upland ranges and the lambs are weaned and finished on specially prepared annual pastures and/or second-cutting alfalfa hay fields in the lowlands. Both of these cultural practices tend to keep parasitism problems low.

In the North where winter cold naturally sanitizes pastures, Ohio research showed all ewes should be treated with Levamisole or Invermectin before turning them out on spring pasture. This kills hyperbiotic worm larvae and prevents contaminating the pasture with worm eggs. Late lambing ewes require a second treatment just before or at lambing if they have already grazed spring pasture contaminated with over-wintered larvae.

Irrespective of the season of lambing, ewes appear to lose their natural resistance to parasitism from between two weeks before lambing until eight weeks after lambing. There is also a tremendous rise in fecal egg counts. This is called the preparturient rise. It is suspected that lactogenic hormones are indirectly involved in bringing about these changes. This, unfortunately, has the effect of infecting winter-cleansed, spring pastures for the highly susceptible new lamb crop. Worms in early lambing ewes were derived mainly from worms that had been hypobiotic during the winter. By contrast, worms in late-lambing ewes were derived mainly from over-wintered pasture larvae. In the Ohio studies a prelambing worm treatment with Levamisole completely eliminated the rise in prepartuient egg counts. In contrast, a worming one month after lambing was too late to be effective.

The advantage of prophylactic treatment in the spring is that it prevents the occurrence of the summer buildup of pasture infectivity and the resulting clinical and subclinical disease. The Ohio studies showed that four treatments at three-week intervals, starting three weeks after spring treatment, were as effective as eight treatments at three-week intervals for the entire grazing season. Ohio research showed that the above method worked equally well with horses and dairy replacement heifers.

For graziers seeking to pasture-finish lambs, a second set of safe pastures is necessary to prevent a high level of fall infectivity. Mid-summer rains appear to stimulate the buildup of pasture worms. This involves two anthelmintic treatments about six to eight weeks apart and the use of two pastures (cells) that were not grazed by sheep that year. It is going to be increasingly difficult for sheep-only operations to continue to exist in humid climates as sheep parasites will invariably become resistant to the current drugs, which probably won't be replaced. Sheep will have to increasingly be integrated with dairy and beef cattle and/or with annual pasture grown on clean-tilled cropland.

Dr. Lowell Wilson of Penn State said there are lots of advantages to co-grazing sheep and beef other than increased parasite control. Co-grazing also lowers market risk, decreases weeds, increases total pasture use and can actually produce an increase in gross production per head. Doesn't this sound like nature's marvelous serendipity at work?

The three main types of co-grazing are cattle ahead of sheep, cattle with sheep and sheep ahead of cattle. A grazier should be flexible enough to use all three depending upon the varying nutritional needs of the two species. Penn State research found that adding beef cows and calves to sheep almost invariably increased sheep performance in both ewe and lamb weight-gain while only marginally decreasing suckling calf weight gain. The most successful pasture species mix Wilson found for beef/sheep grazing in Pennsylvania was a mixture of perennial ryegrass and alfalfa. After ten years of management-intensive grazing they still had an excellent stand of both alfalfa and perennial ryegrass.

New Productivity Standards

A major problem in the Eastern half of the United States is that a commercial sheep industry has never developed. Most sheep in the East today tend to be kept more as pets than commercial production animals. Jim Clay of the Eastern Ohio Research Center in Bellville, Ohio said a commercial sheep industry would require much higher standards of labor productivity than is currently being practiced. He suggested a labor standard of no more than one hour per ewe per year and no more than six hours per beef cow per year.

To achieve this low labor input, disease in the sheep flock must be kept to an absolute minimum. Clay recommended a closed-flock policy where outside purchases are kept to an absolute minimum. The other way to increase productivity and profit is to always build your sheep operation from the grass up. "All successful animal systems are designed to use a resource rather than produce a product," he said.

Since ewes and brood cows are relatively low-value-producing animals, costs have to be kept equally low. The way to maximize profit is to maximize the use of low-cost forages. Clay gave the following examples of ways to lower the cost of forage:

- Extend the grazing period.
- Lower fencing costs.
- Keep reseeding, fertilizer and lime costs to a minimum.
- Lower land costs per animal.

The use of management-intensive grazing and low cost electric fences meets all of these goals. Minimal interior electric fences can be used with sheep if the sheep are first properly trained to respect electricity.

Sheep And Electric Fence

There appears to be a diversity of opinion on the effectiveness of minimal electric fences with sheep. This is largely the result of the way the sheep were first introduced to electric fences. Keep in mind that a minimal electric fence serves solely as a mental barrier. Any animal who is willing to take a short period of pain can easily get through a one-wire temporary electric fence.

Sheep in full fleece are relatively well insulated from electric shock, so the game becomes to build the mental fence before they are introduced to a minimal electric fence. The best way to do this is to make sure the animal is well shocked on a wool-less part of his body. Usually this is his nose.

Sheep should be introduced to an electric fence by baiting

them to sniff or tongue an energized wire. This can be done by placing honey or peanut butter on the wire or by using thin strips of aluminum foil to attract their attention to the wire.

The point of this exercise is to make sure that the sheep's first introduction to an electric fence is a memorable one. Those of you who have accidentally brushed against an electric fence can imagine the lasting impression it would make on you if your first introduction to it was a pop on the tip of your nose.

Sheep graziers should never stint on the size of an energizer. Get the biggest one your favorite supplier makes, even for a small operation. Low power energizers that work fine with dairy cattle and tame beef cattle are worthless with sheep.

A sheep that leaks through an electric fence once will continue to do it and will teach its paddock mates to do it as well. Leakers should immediately be sold or retrained to respect the fence. Some graziers will use a polywire harness that carries the charge to the wool-less area where the forelegs join the body to reinforce the shock and retrain them. Remember, with electric fences it is not the physical fence that needs strengthening but the mental fence in the animal's mind.

Spring Lambing Most Profitable

In studying his and others' research in the Eastern United States, Clay discovered dollar returns were always highest for a spring lambing season even though the lambs might sell on a lower price schedule than winter-born lambs. He said graziers using intensive grazing and stockpiled pastures could also consider fall lambing. Fall pastures in Ohio were of very high quality and much easier to manage than the fast-growing spring pastures.

He found ewes bred to lamb in the spring and fall required fewer ram days to settle than those bred in other seasons. He said to keep in mind older lambs were heavier and of higher quality than younger lambs. Often selling on the higher-priced Easter and Christmas markets does not result in a higher net profit than selling whenever the lambs are most economically pasture finished.

Wool Wethers Ultimate In Low Input Grazing

The most overlooked class of sheep in the Eastern half of the United States is the fine wool wether. Wool wethers are castrated males that are raised strictly for their fleece and were once grazed in the hundreds of thousands in the Midwest.

Wool wethers are very hardy animals since they just coast through life with no production stress. Some wethers have been used for as long as 18 years and most are grazed for at least nine to ten years. Thanks to their low production requirements, they can be used like a rotary mower to keep the farm free of brush and weeds and can be wintered in Ohio with no hay or grain.

"Our Merino wethers didn't get a drop of harvested feed either as hay or grain last winter. As long as you take the wethers into the winter in as good a condition as possible, they can root through the snow and over-winter on frosted grass," Clay said.

Sheep And Dairy Cattle

What's a dairyman to do about those unsightly clumps of grass growing out of the manure clumps? Cows refuse to eat them even at the highest stock densities. But sheep? I visited Louie Lynch's dairy in Northern Ireland to see.

Lynch is a seasonal dairyman who raises his own replacements. His rotation was lactating cows as first grazer, new crop calves as second grazer, and old-crop pregnant heifers co-grazed with sheep as third grazers. The lactating cows and new crop calves are shifted twice a day, but the old crop replacements and sheep are only shifted once a day. Lynch said the bred-heifers, which calve as two-year-olds, are used as cleanup cattle to keep their daily weight gains down and therefore prevent calving problems. "They get the worst care on the place," he said.

As we watched a paddock shift, the ewes and lambs immediately set to eating the grass around the cows' manure pies. I walked over to the paddock the sheep had just come from and it was as smooth and even as if a mechanical pasture topper had been through it.

"Normally sheep and dairy cows are seen as opposition," Lynch said, "but they don't have to be if you've got your ewes' breeding right." Lynch has his ewes bred to lamb at the start of the spring lush and then sells the lambs as feeders when the pasture growth slows down in the early summer. He doesn't have enough extra grass in the summer to try and finish the lambs. "You don't choke back your dairy cows, you choke back the sheep," he said.

Lynch uses the sheep to condition the paddocks for baby calves to graze. Pasture for baby calves should look like a lawn and be no more than four inches high. The sheep remove most of the cattle parasites and graze the pasture tight and short. If a pasture shredder is used it can produce a stubble that pricks the calves' noses and prevents them from grazing aggressively.

Also because the sheep are lighter and don't pug the pastures the way the cows do, they can stay out later in winter and go out earlier in the spring. And because they are not the primary enterprise on a dairy, the sheep can be sold off in a drought or other weather emergency to bring the stocking rate in balance. "I figured it up and for what it would cost me for a pasture topper I could sheep-proof my fences," Lynch said. "Sheep are the only way you are going to be able to sell that grass growing in your cow's manure pat."

Sheep Are Just Little Cows

The reputation of sheep as "an animal looking for a place to die" is largely the result of winter lambing and a seedstock emphasis on non-commercial traits. Sheep should be thought of and managed more like "little cows" than lapdogs. There are now breeds specifically bred to be hardy "easy-keepers" and individual breeders in almost every breed who subscribe to a no nonsense commercial orientation.

In New Zealand, I have stayed with sheep graziers who single-handedly managed flocks in the thousands with less fuss and effort than we put into a 20-ewe farm flock. They did this by lambing (on pasture) in sync with the spring grass season and accepting some lamb death loss as inevitable. Most Americans are shocked to hear New Zealand sheep extension people recommend that a sheep grazier should time his vacation for lambing season and get off the farm, but they have found the increase in lamb survivability from intensive animal management is just not worth the extra effort and expense in a large commercial flock.

In Ohio and Washington, research indicates wool wethers may make a profitable addition to forestry in the humid areas of North America for brush control. Conversely, hair sheep with no wool at all may make more sense in the very hot and humid areas of North America. Genetics, grazing technology and common sense are combining to erase most of the production bugger-bears in sheep production. Today, the big bugger-bear is marketing.

Marketing--Problem Or Opportunity?

It is a real shame that we have allowed our sheep marketing infrastructure to almost completely self-destruct. In many (most?) areas of the United States, sheep production today also entails the responsibility of developing a local market for your lambs. Even the major sheep packers are talking about only killing lambs on a custom basis in the future. While this sounds particularly onerous, almost all those who have bitten the bullet and started direct marketing have told me it was far easier than they would have ever believed and they would never go back to the "commodity" lamb business. This is particularly true if you are producing a quality, lean lamb.

If there was ever an animal that lent itself well to direct marketing, a 90 to 100 lb. grass-finished lamb must be it. Far more people willing to commit for a lamb than a whole or half a beef. Pasture-produced older yearling lamb has a much stronger, beefier flavor than hot-house early lamb and does not put that greasy feel in your mouth that most Americans hate about eating lamb.

Other producers are trying to band together into slaughter and marketing co-ops. However, the real marketing problem is not so much the lamb, but the cull ewe and old wether. Mutton can make a delicious deep fat fried, fajita-like entre, an excellent barbecue (just ask anyone in western Kentucky) or a low-fat, easily digestible hamburger. The traditional low price for cull ewes indicates more market neglect than the quality of the meat. There is a real opportunity here for someone with a little meat marketing and promotional flair.

Pigs In The Pasture

The availability of low cost, effective electric fencing is fueling a revival of interest in pasturing pigs. In the past, a hog-tight fence was extremely expensive to build and seldom completely effective. Luckily, pigs are extremely averse to electricity and quickly learn to respect even minimal electric fences. A low-cost, one-wire fence offers better control today than the hog-wire fence of the past.

Feed costs are 80 to 85% of the total costs of a feeder-pig operation. Grass farmers who are able to grow legume-based, stocker-quality feed can frequently cut these costs in half. Non-legume but high protein and highly digestible brassicas such as turnips, rape, and kale also make excellent pig pasturage.

Pigs can also be used to direct-harvest grain crops as long as legumes or brassicas are interplanted with the grain or provided on adjacent land. Such direct-harvesting can turn a profit from even low-yielding grain crops. Cows can be used as follower-grazers for an even more efficient harvest of the grain crop.

Cow manure provides an excellent vitamin and mineral supplement for pigs and they readily eat it. This helps break the cattle's parasite cycle and provide a more rapid recycling of the pasture nutrients.

Pigs help keep a pasture free of hardwood brushsprouts and provide a harvest mechanism for acorns and other mast crops. Pasture rooting is seldom a problem at low stocking rates and plentiful feed, but can be prevented by "ringing" the pig's nose.

Pigs are useful scavengers in orchards and are used to scavenge sweet potatoes and other horticultural crops following harvest.

Due to their monogastric similarity to man's digestive system, they also make excellent scavengers of table wastes. Red China has the largest pig population in the world and they are all raised exclusively on table wastes.

(It is against the law to buy waste food to feed to pigs without cooking it first, but it is not against the law to feed your own table wastes directly to your own pigs.)

The "hothouse" type of pig production completely ignores the natural scavenging ability of the pig and the high capital costs of confined production ($2500 to $3000 per pig) have taken away the easy-in-and-out response to market prices that was the beauty of pork production in the past.

In the early 1980s the Kerr Foundation in southeastern Oklahoma had a demonstration project of a low investment swine system that would allow producers to get in and out in response to the market by keeping capital costs low. This project soon evolved into a pastured pig project to lower feed costs.

While being mono-species and originally not designed as a pastured pig project (which raised capital costs for housing and fencing unneeded in a pure pasture situation) the research results provide a useful reference for pastured feeder pig production.

Sows require a ration that is 14 to 15% crude protein and quality leguminous pasture can certainly provide that. At the Kerr Foundation, pregnant sows on clover were fed only two or three pounds of feed per day, or half the normal ration when on lush clover pastures.

Sows should not be underfed because a thin sow cannot produce up to her potential, but a fat sow will tend to have smaller litters than sows in proper condition.

Under non-lush pasture conditions, the Kerr Foundation fed dry sows six pounds of feed a day and lactating sows 14 to 15 pounds of feed a day. The eye of the master can adapt these feeding recommendations to both the state of his pasture and the body condition of the sows.

When boars are with the sows they fed the same as the sows, but were fed a little more when separate due to their larger size.

The Kerr Foundation originally used self-feeders for the sows, but the dominant sows tended to get most of the feed. As a result the feeders were replaced with homemade troughs, which proved much more satisfactory on pasture.

The sows were fed twice a day to eliminate the problem of bulk fill in lactating sows.

When pigs are about two weeks old, they should have access to an 18% medicated creep-feed. This will help the pigs know how to eat later when they are weaned as well as improving the rate of growth. Pigs should continue to get this 18% feed up through 50 pounds. From 50 to 125 pounds they should receive a 16% feed. All of these feeds can be purchased at most local feed stores.

Some shopping around may pay because there is quite a lot of variation in feed prices. Pigs should always be fed pellets, but sometimes the mash feeds are cheaper for sow feed.

The Kerr Foundation estimates that a sow will eat 1500 lbs. of grain a year, a feeder pig 50 pounds and a market hog 600 lbs.

A legume-based pasture can support 35 feeder pigs or 12 sows per acre.

The breed of sows to be used in a commercial pastured swine operation is very important. The chosen breed should be fertile, produce a lot of milk, and should also exhibit a strong maternal instinct. At the Kerr Foundation a Yorkshire x Landrace crossbred sow was chosen on the basis of the criteria listed above.

Unfortunately, many of the "hothouse" raised boars do not have enough sex drive necessary for pasture breeding. The Kerr Foundation initially used Hampshire boars in their project but these were found to be unsatisfactory due to low libido and were replaced by Duroc boars which were satisfactory. No doubt, there are some seedstock swine-breeders who are raising their animals on pasture and breeding stock should be purchased from these sources if possible.

The Kerr Foundation also recommends that you only purchase breeding stock from certified specific-pathogen-free (SPF) herds. This classification guarantees that the hogs are free of turbinate atrophy and snout distortion, pneumonic lesions, swine dysentery, lice and mange, transmissible gastroenteritis and parvovirus. These diseases are the major causes of swine health problems in the U.S.

SPF breeding stock will be slightly more expensive, but the Kerr Foundation had a total lack of health problems with their swine as a result of this extra investment. The only vaccination necessary in the herd was leptospirosis. This was needed because this disease can be transmitted by other animals.

The Kerr program was planned around a twice-a-year farrowing program, which was set up to match the farrowing seasons with more favorable weather conditions in southeastern Oklahoma. Sows were bred to farrow during March and April and again in September and October. An attempt was made to breed half of the sows initially and breed the remaining sows four to five weeks later.

All sows were pasture bred, with breeding rates of about five sows per each young boar and up to ten sows per adult boar. This type of breeding program requires a boar with a high level of sex drive in order to have satisfactory reproductive performance. Young boars should be monitored closely as to their breeding soundness.

The Kerr Foundation used a program of close monitoring and movement of pregnant sows to farrowing pens when it was determined they were within a week of farrowing.

However, in a low-input "paddock pig" type of operation, a program of selecting sows that are able to nest and farrow on their own would probably be most economical. Research at Texas A&M indicates that such "range-ability" is a highly inheritable trait in pigs and should be genetically selected for pastured operations.

For example, the Kerr Foundation started with a dismal weaning rate of 4.5 pigs per sow, but through stringent culling raised this to eight. (The national average for hothouse sows is 7.5.) Any sow that failed to wean at least seven pigs was automatically culled as was any sow that produced unthrifty or poor-doing pigs.

The Kerr Foundation recommends a "survival of the fittest" policy with baby pigs. Pigs that had to be helped to nurse were runty and hard to market.

Due to the paucity of pasture-adapted swine-breeding stock, starting a pastured pig program is probably best during the cheap end of the pig cycle. Adaptation will cause a high turnover of breeding stock in the herd. You may find it less painful to chunk a sow or boar when they are cheap than when they are dear.

Feeder pigs from pastured operations are highly desired by finishers due to their superior health and thriftiness. The Kerr Foundation was able to contract all of their production for a premium price to a single finisher.

Finishing Pigs On Pasture. Finishing purchased feeder pigs on pasture and selling them direct to local customers as sausage was one of the most profitable enterprises at Poteau, Oklahoma's Rock Creek Farm. Per-head profits ranged from $51 to $65.

The pigs generally reached 225 pounds in 90 days, but gains were slower in the summer and required 120 days. Besides grazing and rooting in the pasture, they were fed three pounds per-head per-day of 14 percent hog ration and any broken eggs from Rock Creek's rolling pasture henhouse. (See following section on pastured hens.)

Sorghum sudan was planted in the spring and turnips were planted in the fall. The pigs were rotated to a new pasture when they had rooted up the old one. After they were moved, the ground was tilled to eliminate parasites and then reseeded. No chemical dewormers were used.

Paddock Pigs. Buying a few feeder pigs in the spring and letting them run with your cattle all summer and fall is a good way to help keep your pasture's parasite load down and provide you with some late fall sausage. Pigs love to eat the cow manure and are a dead end host to the cattle's parasites. In another example of nature's serendipity, cow manure is considered the ideal vitamin and mineral package for a pig. Some graziers will toss a coffee can of corn to the pigs occasionally to keep them tame, but a few pigs can make a fine living on a pasture with no feed at all if given enough of it.

Pastured Hens

One of the neatest pasture fly controllers and sanitizers I have found is Joel Salatin's rolling henhouse. Designed by the guru of pastured chicken, Joel Salatin of Swoope, Virginia, calls it an "eggmobile." One finds these becoming common on organic beef and dairy farms across the country. Since Joel raises and sells organic grass finished beef he has to be creative in his fly and parasite control measures. He uses no commercial cattle wormers or fly control and relies exclusively on keeping a "clean plate" in front of his cattle.

Joel's eggmobile is a 12 x 20 foot trailer with a mesh floor henhouse built on it. A henhouse this size will house 100 free-range hens. Laying boxes line both sides of the trailer. A trapdoor and gangplank allow the hens to enter the henhouse at night, roost and be protected from night-prowling predators. The open mesh floor allows the hens' manure to drop through onto the pasture. Joel estimates 100 hens will control the flies and bugs on approximately 50 acres of pasture while producing high quality, bright orange yolk eggs for only 20 cents a dozen! Joel uses his eggs primarily as barter money with his neighbors in return for borrowed equipment and tools.

During the day, the hens will range outward from the henhouse for as far as 200 yards and return each night. The henhouse is moved to a fresh paddock when the hens are still penned in by the closed trapdoor. The hens and their rolling house follow the cows through their pasture rotation. Joel likes to leave them in one spot for four days as this matches the hatch cycle of the fly larvae in the cows' manure. He said the hens totally obliterate the cow paddies in their search for fly larvae. Joel has found the non-hybrid Rhode Island Red hen to be the best forager.

He estimates 100 hens eat about seven pounds of fly larvae, grasshoppers and crickets a day. It takes approximately four weeks for a paddock to recover its bug population after the hens have worked over it. Joel matches his rotation to the regrowth of the bug population. It's management-intensive bug grazing!

Whole shelled corn, oyster shell, soybean meal and meat scraps are fed cafeteria style in the eggmobile, but thanks to their highly proteinaceous daily bug feast the birds eat very little until they start to exhaust the bugs in that area. When Joel sees the increase in feed consumption, he knows it is time to move them to another paddock.

Joel is convinced his rolling henhouse would pay for itself in fly control and insect control if it were just stocked with roosters and didn't produce a single egg. In nature birds always follow herbivores and clean up after them. In more of nature's serendipity, the cow's manure contains the exact balance and type of enzymes needed for efficient poultry production.

Think About It...

♣ Do you have predator problems? Combining sheep with cattle and using management-intensive grazing reduced predator problems.

♣ Each animal helps break the other's parasite cycle. Swapping sheep and cattle pastures on the first of July helps keep the pastures naturally low in internal parasites for both species.

♣ In addition to increased parasite control, co-grazing lowers market risk, decreases weeds, increases total pasture use and can actually produce an increase in gross production per head. Have you investigated co-grazing for your operation?

♣ Each ruminant grazes on a slightly different mix of plants. What is a weed to one is ice cream to another.

♣ Cow manure is eaten by and is beneficial to pigs and chickens.

♣ A completely parasite-free environment should not be your goal. This is to prevent the animal from losing its natural resistance to parasitism.

♣ The more plant- and animal-diverse your can make your pastures the more stable and healthier they will become.

♣ Specific species production knowledge can come from doing it on a small scale first, reading, and visiting other producers. With which species can you find the most information support?

♣ The best time to add a new species to your operation is when the new species you are adding is at the bottom of its price cycle.

Chapter 14: The Next Big Thing

If you're ready to follow the quality pasture route to riches, you must understand that, in North America at least, you will be a pioneer. Many people believe pioneering doesn't pay, and there is abundant anecdotal evidence to show that it doesn't. However, there are two very different kinds of pioneers--those pioneering within an accepted paradigm, and those pioneering a new paradigm. A paradigm is a set of rules and regulations (written and unwritten) that tells you how to behave to be successful.

Of course, you know who a non-paradigmatic pioneer is, don't you? He's the guy they send out from the fort to see if there are Indians out there. You know what happens to non-paradigmatic pioneers? They either end up with an arrow through their heart, because there were Indians out there, or they wind up smashed flat by the outpouring of settlers anxious to move West when they yelled back to the fort, "There ain't no Indians out here."

Consider a new chemical or piece of machinery that would increase the yield of a crop by 30 percent! How long would it take for the average farmer to adopt it? How much leverage would it give you? Not much. It is estimated that today an innovation within an accepted paradigm gives the earliest innovator only a six month lead before the settlers (the existing players) rush out of the fort and trample you to death. This minimal lead time is too short to build any real, lasting wealth and is the source of all those naysayers who proclaim, "pioneering doesn't pay."

Quality pasture is a new paradigm. The beauty of being a new paradigm pioneer is that when you discover there are no Indians out there, the settlers still refuse to leave the fort because they don't want to leave the comforts of home and move west. They don't rush after you. They don't try to get ahead of you. They let you have that big, new space all to yourself for years and years until you have become so filthy rich that they can't stand it anymore. Still they don't come. They know they don't know the new rules it takes to live out there in the new paradigm and they hate you for it.

This lack of community support for your obvious success can be quite devastating emotionally. However, your economic progress can not be measured by anything they hold dear as the outward signs of wealth. For example, look at the very different symbols of success between a traditional farmer and a quality pasture grazier on the list on the next page.

The accepted rules for success are 180 degrees in opposition to each other. This is why you won't find any support for what you are doing from people in the old paradigm. Your success is an economic threat to all the rules and roadmaps they learned were supposed to lead to success. A paradigm shift changes to a new game, a new set of rules. When it occurs everyone starts over at zero. People who were way ahead at the old game have no idea of what to do in the new one. Needless to say, people who have become very good at one game and have invested a lot of capital in it do not want to see the rules changed. This is why you should not be disheartened by the refusal of your neighbors to support you. "Negative reinforcement" is a sure sign you are on the best path to real wealth. This is why you will only find support from your fellow pioneers, and it is very important that you do so. At the **Stockman Grass Farmer** we run free listings of grazier support groups and grazier meetings and urge that you participate in these. We all need a pat on the back every now and then.

Indicators For:

Traditional Farm Success	**Quality Pasture Success**
Big tractors	No tractor
Monocultures	Diversity
Heavy weaning calves	Planned early weaning
Bigger cows	Smaller cows
Production per cow	Profit per acre
More milk	Less cost
Bigger barns	No barns at all
Producing beef	Harvesting grass
Soil testing	Forage testing
Blue metal silos	Pasture clamps
Total self reliance	Production sharing
Killing Johnsongrass	Planting Johnsongrass
Hating quackgrass	Loving quackgrass
Keeping cows out of corn	Putting cows in the corn
Corn silage	Grass silage
Killing weeds	Adding sheep
Clearing brush	Adding goats
Spraying flies	Adding hens
Making hay	Stockpiling
Rigidity	Flexibility
TMR	Under-the-fence feeding
Computer feeding	Grazier's eye
West	East
Brag production	Brag profits
Windshield farming	Pasture walking
Buy-sell accounting	Sell-buy accounting
Dairy quality hay	Dairy quality pasture

Are you starting to see why we have such a hard time communicating across the huge gap caused by a paradigm shift?

Learning a new paradigm is said to be a triad of why, how and who. Why is the basic philosophy of the paradigm. For example, one must first make the philosophical shift from seeing your primary role shift from one of producing milk and meat to one of growing and harvesting grass. This shift in thinking is necessary in order for the rest of the rules of the new paradigm to make any sense. The "how" part of the triangle are the proven solutions to problems you will encounter in the paradigm. The "who" are the people who have already done what you are attempting to do and who can lend you emotional and practical support. All three are equally important. Too often, new graziers only want to concentrate on the how-to and skip the rest. This ensures that they will make many mistakes that could have easily been avoided if they had sought out the other two pieces of the triad. People who try to pioneer in isolation of other more-experienced pioneers are guaranteed to make the same dumb mistakes as their predecessors.

New developing paradigms follow the traditional sigmoid flattened "S" curve seen in much of science and nature. Joel Arthur Barker, author of the book **Paradigms** said this "S" curve is divided into three phases, which he labels as A, B, and C. The "S" shape graphs the problem-solving ability of the new paradigm. The faster it solves problems, the steeper the up slope on the "S" curve.

In the A phase, the paradigm is basically writing the rules for success. It defines the boundaries and limits of the problems it can solve and chronicles the most efficient ways to go about solving them. The A phase is basically a time of experimentation and prototype building. The curve is sloping upward but at a relatively flat rate. A few early adopters are starting to get rich, but most are still trying to learn the rules of the game. Management-intensive grazing with quality pasture is nearing the end of the A phase in North America as this book is being written in mid-1995.

In the B phase, enough people have learned the rules the new paradigm requires for success and are able to solve problems at an ever-increasing pace. Prototypes are refined, simplified and a supplier-support industry of products, services and learning is created. The "S" curve steepens dramatically as new wealth is created hand over fist by those who know how to play the new game, and their success becomes visible to even the most uninitiated. This success draws in new players and outside capital, and a new industry working under a new paradigm is born.

In the C phase, the learning curve starts to flatten out as the industry finds problems that are not so easy to solve. Barker said it is human nature to put off to the last the most difficult problems. While I firmly believe the current quality pasture paradigm will give early adopters 10 to 12 years of excellent profits before the competition wakes up, it is not too early to start planning for the flattening out of our learning curve. As the man said, "How much you earn is in direct proportion to how much you learn." We have to keep learning and pushing the edge of the envelope. Success is the train we ride, not a destination.

Everything we have discussed up to now has produced financial progress through innovation. Peter Drucker defines an innovation as something that increases the yield of an existing resource. However, there is a more lasting source of wealth and that is through entrepreneurship. An entrepreneur creates something entirely new--a new customer. Drucker said the surest way to build lasting wealth is to stop selling commodities and start serving people. Between the farmer's gate and the consumer's plate the price of our production doubles! This taking of our production direct to the customer will be the next paradigm shift.

The best example of this new entrepreneurial grass farming paradigm I have found is on the Smith family dairy on Vancouver Island in British Columbia. Edgar Smith and his brothers, Doug and Phillip, own and operate Beaver Meadows Farms dairy operation near Comox about one third of the way up the east side of the island. They have 120 acres of irrigated ryegrass pasture and 150 acres of forested "bush" pasture and currently graze 200 Holstein cows. Unfortunately, Canada does not currently allow seasonal dairying and milk production must be more or less the same each month of the year. This makes a quality-pasture-based dairy very difficult. Edgar has decided to end-run the system by dropping out under the producer-vendor provision of the law and manufacturing his own dairy products. "Vancouver Island is a seasonal tourist-based economy. It is beautifully suited to seasonal dairy production and manufacture," he said. Edgar has a berry-based yogurt in mind as a major product. Toward that end he has recently planted 20 acres in cranberries and blueberries.

The farm already has experience in direct marketing through the sale of "natural" grass-fed beef to island restaurants and logging camps. The Smiths use Limousin bulls for clean up following AI on their Holstein cows and it is these Limousin-cross calves that are grown out and sold locally for beef. They use the beef calves to balance their seasonal spring forage surplus and to take advantage of off-farm grazing opportunities.

For several years, Edgar has been able to get free grazing from vegetable and potato growers who need a pasture rotation to keep their fields disease free. Also, swans do not like to land where there are frequent electric fences, so placing grazing paddocks adjacent to vegetable fields helps keep down crop damage from the protected swans. "There are all kinds of opportunities out there for enterprising graziers. You just have to look for them," Edgar said.

The warm Japanese Current keeps the island temperate year round, and allows a seven month grazing season from March to November. The primary problem in the winter is not snow but an almost-constant rain that keeps the pastures too wet to graze without severe pugging damage. "The first thing you have to do here to graze is to provide drainage. Our drainage ditches also provide summer irrigation for the three to four month mid-summer dry," he said.

Perennial ryegrass makes up the primary forage on the farm. Edgar has found that three things are essential for growing perennial ryegrass on the island. These are in order of importance:

- Pasture drainage.
- Frequent liming.
- Irrigation.

"Perennial ryegrass needs one inch of water every 15 days to be productive," he said. "With irrigation, we can keep a fast 10- to 12-day rotation right through the summer dry. Perennial ryegrass is more difficult to grow than most grasses but we have found it to be superior to both endophyte-free fescue and Matua for making milk."

Edgar has been doing extensive small-plot experimentation with perennial ryegrass varieties from England, Holland and New Zealand. So far the clear winner appears to be the "pasture salad" where they are all mixed together.

One-wire electric fences are used for all interior subdivision. Temporary electric fence is used for both the forward and back fence to allow for a flexible paddock size. Stock water is provided with movable tubs and quick-connect hoses. Pressure is provided by a small hillside reservoir.

The walkback lanes are surfaced with six inches of bark mulch from the island's pole-peeling plants. This provides both a mud- and dust-free surface. Three to four inches of new bark mulch are added every year. The mulch is delivered to the farm free by the forestry companies as getting rid of it is a major problem due to tannic acid leaching when it is kept in large piles.

One half of the irrigated ryegrass pasture is cut for silage in the spring. The farm has also been growing no-til corn silage but have found corn silage's usefulness and quality to be less than ryegrass silage. Edgar likes that by using grass silage there is no problem with twisted stomachs. "By stopping the growing of corn silage, we will be able to stockpile more of our paddocks to extend our grazing season," Edgar said. "Every year we graze a little earlier and a little longer. My brother Doug said he plans to have the young stock out on Matua in February this year."

Young stock are wintered outdoors on grass silage in the woods with a movable electric wire self-feeding system. A trip with the **Stockman Grass Farmer** to New Zealand in 1994 wetted his appetite for integrated livestock-forestry management. 50 acres of forest are now managed for grazing and forestry and 80 acres are pruned frequently as in New Zealand. "We have planted over 8,000 trees since returning from New Zealand for use as windbreaks and cattle shelter," he said. "We now see how we can use planned forests to replace most of our barns."

Along the same dual-purpose approach, the farm's irrigation ditches are also used to grow salmon for release and watercress and Cut-throat trout for sale to island restaurants. The use of the irrigation ditches for salmon culture has turned local fisheries officials from a potential threat to the farm's continued supply of irrigation water due to its need for fishery enhancement to major supporters. Edgar believes that farmers need to look for such win-win compromises to avoid problems with environmentalists and bureaucrats.

Pastured turkeys follow the cows through their summer rotation to provide insect control and another direct sale product. With so many enterprises, Edgar and his brothers have not lost sight of where the big money is. "Pasture-based dairying and beef will probably always provide 80 percent of our income, but we are interested in diversifying through complimentary, less-management-intense enterprises. It may be that when it is time to retire we will drop the dairy altogether, relax and just grow beef and berries."

Think About It...

♣ Did you notice how far along the Smith brothers were in incorporating the ideas outlined in this book?

♣ Quality pasture is for real. It is the next big thing in the farm economy. Go for it.

Glossary:

AI: Artificial insemination.

Aftermath: Forage that is left or grown after a machine harvest such as corn stalks or volunteer wheat or oats. Also called the "Fat of the Land."

Animal unit day: Amount of forage necessary to graze on animal unit (one dry 1100 lbs. beef cow) for one day.

Annual leys: Temporary pastures of annual forage crops such as annual ryegrass, oats or sorghum-sudangrass.

AU Animal unit: One mature, non-lactating cow weighing 500 KGs. (1100 lbs.) or its weight and class equivalent in other species. (Example: 10 dry ewes equal one animal unit.)

AUM Animal unit month: Amount of forage needed to graze one animal unit for a month.

Blaze graze: A very fast rotation used in the spring to prevent the grass from forming a seedhead. Usually used with dairy cattle.

Break grazing: The apportioning of a small piece of a larger paddock with temporary fence for rationing or utilization purposes.

Breaks: An apportionment of a paddock with temporary electric fence. Moving the forward wire creates a "fresh break" of grass for the animals.

BST: A hormone for increased milk production.

Cell: A grouping of paddock subdivisions used with a particular set or class of animals. During droughts, several cells and their animals may be merged and operated as one large cell and herd for rationing purposes.

Clamp: A temporary polyethylene covered silage stack made in the pasture without permanent sides or structures.

Composting: The mixing of animal manure with a carbon source under a damp, aerobic environment so as to stabilize and enhance the nutrients in the manure.

Concentrate: Grain or grain/meal mix.

Continuous grazing or stocking: Allowing the animals access to an entire pasture for a long period without paddock rotation.

Coppice: Young regrowth on a cut tree or bush.

Compensatory gain: The rapid weight gain experienced by animals when allowed access to plentiful high quality forage after a period of rationed feed. Animals that are wintered at low rates of gain and are allowed to compensate in the spring frequently weigh almost the same by mid-summer as those managed through the winter at a high rate of gain. Also known as "pop."

Creep grazing: The allowing of calves to graze ahead of their mothers by keeping the forward paddock wire high enough for the calves to go under but low enough to restrain the cows.

CWT: 100 pounds.

Deferred grazing: The dropping of a paddock from a rotation for use at a later time.

Dirty fescue: Fescue containing an endophyte which lowers the animal's ability to deal with heat. Fescue without this endophyte is called Fungus-free or Endophyte-free.

Dry matter: Forage after the moisture has been removed.

Easy feed silage: The bringing of silage to the animal with machinery. Opposite of self-feeding.

Flogging: Grazing a paddock to a low residual. This is frequently done in the winter to stimulate clover growth the following spring.

Free choice: Non-restricted feeding.

Frontal grazing: An Argentine grazing method whereby the animals grazing speed is determined with the use of a grazing speed governor on a sliding fence.

Grazer: A animal that gathers its food by grazing.

Grazier: A human who manages grazing animals.

Green feeding: Direct grazing of corn.

Heavy metal: Large machinery.

Holistic Resource Management (or HRM): A management discipline and thought model that encourages the seeing of the ranch as a unified "whole." This term is trademarked.

K: Potassium.

Lax grazing: The allowing of the animal to have a high degree of selectivity in their grazing. Lax grazing is used when a very high level of animal performance is desired.

Ley pasture: Temporary pasture. Usually of annuals.

Leader-follower grazing: The use of a high production class of animal followed by a lower production class. For example, lactating dairy cattle followed by replacements. This type of grazing allows both a high level of animal performance and a high level of pasture utilization. Also, called first-last grazing.

Lodged over: Grass that has grown so tall it has fallen over on itself. Most grasses will self-smother when lodged. A major exception is Tall fescue and for this reason it is a prized grass for autumn stockpiling.

Management-intensive grazing or MIG: The thoughtful use of grazing manipulation to produce a desired agronomic and/or animal result. This may include both rotational and continuous stocking depending upon the season.

Mixed grazing: The use of different species grazing either together or in a sequence.

Mob grazing: A mob is a group of animals. This term is used to indicate a high stock density.

N: Nitrogen.

Oklahoma bop: A low stress method of dehorning stocker and feeder cattle whereby a one to two inch stub of horn is allowed to remain. Widely used in the South and Southwest.

P: Phosphorus.

Paddock: A subdivision of a pasture.

Pop: Compensatory Gain.

Popping paddocks: Paddocks of high quality grass and legumes used to maximize compensatory gain in animals before sale or slaughter.

Pugging or bogging: Breaking the sod's surface by the animals hooves in wet weather. Can be used as a tool for planting new seeds.

Put and take: The adding and subtracting of animals to maintain a desired grass residual and quality. For example, the movement of beef cows from rangeland to keep a rapidly growing tame stocker or dairy pasture from making a seedhead in the spring and thereby losing its quality.

Range: A pasture of native grass plants.

Rational grazing: Andre' Voisin's term for management- intensive grazing. Rational meant both a thoughtful approach to grazing and a rationing of forage for the animal.

Residue: Forage that remains on the land after a harvest.

Residual: The desired amount of grass to be left in a paddock after grazing. Generally, the higher the grass residue, the higher the animal's rate of gain and milk production.

Rollback: Light cattle usually sell for a higher price than heavier cattle due to their lower body maintenance. The price spread between light and heavy cattle is called the rollback. See also Value of Gain.

Seasonal grazing: Grazing restricted to one season of the year. For example, the use of high mountain pastures in the summer.

Self feeding: Allowing the animals to eat directly from the silage face by means of a rationing electric wire or sliding headgate.

Set stocking: Small groups of animals are placed in each paddock and not rotated. Frequently used in the spring with beef and sheep to keep rapidly growing pastures under control.

Silage: Pickled forage.

Silage clamp: A wall-less, but covered and consolidated pile of silage.

SPF: Specific-pathogen-free classification for pig breeding stock.

Split-turn: The grazing of two separate groups of animals during one grazing season rather than one. For example, the selling of one set of winter and spring grazed heavy stocker cattle in the early summer and the replacement of them with lighter cattle for the summer and fall.

Spring flush or lush: The period of very rapid growth of cool season grasses in the spring.

Standing hay: The deferment of seasonally excess grass for later use. Standing hay is traditionally dead grass. Living hay is the same technique but with green, growing grass.

Stock density: The number of animals on a given unit of land at any one time. This is traditionally a short-term measurement. This is very different from stocking rate which is a long term measurement of the whole pasture. For example: 200 steers may have a long-term stocking rate of 200 acres, but may for a half a day all be grazed on a single acre. This acre while being grazed would be said to have a stock density of 200 steers to the acre.

Stocker cattle: Animals being grown on pasture between weaning and final finish. Stocker cattle weights are traditionally from 350 to 850 lbs.

Stocking rate: A measurement of the long-term carrying capacity of a pasture. See stock density.

Stockpiling: The deferment of pasture for use at a later time. Traditionally this is in the autumn. Also known as "autumn saved pasture" or "foggage."

Stripgraze: The use of a frequently moved temporary fence to subdivide a paddock into very small breaks. Most often used to ration grass during winter or droughts.

Sward: The grass portion of the pasture.

Swath grazing: The cutting and swathing of a crop such as oats into large double-size windrows. These windrows are then rationed out to animals during the winter with temporary electric fence. This method of winter feeding is most-often used in cold, dry winter climates.

TDN: Total digestible nutrients.

Value of gain: The net value of gain after the price rollback of light to heavy cattle has been deducted. To find the net value of gain, the total price of the purchased animal is subtracted from the total price of the sold animal. This price is then divided by the number of cwts. of gain. Profitability is governed by the value of gain rather than the selling price per pound of the cattle.

Wintergraze: Grazing in the winter season. This can be on autumn saved pasture or on specially planted winter annuals such as cereal rye and annual ryegrass.

Resources

Earthworms:

Two good earthworm books are **The Earthworm Book** by Jerry Minnich. This book is now out of print but can frequently be found in used book stores. A newer book is **The Farmer's Earthworm Handbook** by David Ernst. This book can give you a more in-depth look at earthworm physiology and life but unfortunately is written primarily for arable farmers with only minimal pasture references. It is available from Lessiter Publications, P.O. Box 624, Brookfield, Wisconsin 53008-0624. The June 1993 SGF also had an excellent in-depth article by Vaughan Jones on earthworms.

Pasture Analysis:

For a New Zealand pasture analysis and recommendation, follow the procedures outlined in chapter 3 and mail your samples to R.J. Hill Laboratories, 25 Te Aroha Street, Hamilton, New Zealand c/o Port Ag Officer, Private Bag, Hamiton, New Zealand Permit No. 27522.

Include a check for US$55 made out to R.J. Hill and ask Hill to send the results to Vaughan Jones, 71 Newcastle Road, Hamilton, New Zealand. Send Jones a check for US$40 with your number of acres, type of livestock, annual rainfall figures, soil type (clay, loam, sandy) and pH, fertilizers and limes used over the last three years, pasture species and details (% grass (type) % clover (type)).

Jones will work out a suggested fertilizer mix for you, include the quantity of fertilizer to be applied and/or dollars to be spent.

Additional Sources:

Because the number of seeds, seed companies, grazier products, suppliers, grazing consultants, and grass farmer networks continually changes, we have made no attempt to list these here. For the most up to date information consult the **Stockman Grass Farmer** magazine. For a free sample issue call 1-800-748-9808.

Bibliography

Ball, D.M.; Hoveland, C.S.; Lacefield, G.D. *Southern Forages. Atlanta, GA:* Potash & Phosphate Institute and the Foundation for Agronomic Research, 1991.

Barker, Joel Arthur. *Paradigms, The Business of Discovering the Future.* New York: HarperBusiness, 1993.

Clover, A Guide to Use on the Farm. Belfast: Department of Agriculture for Northern Ireland, 1992.

Drucker, Peter F. *Innovation and Entrepreneurship, Practice and Principles.* New York: Harper & Row, 1985.

Drucker, Peter F. *Managing for Results.* New York: HarperBusiness, 1986.

Ernst, David. *The Farmer's Earthworm Handbook.* Brookfield, WI: Lessiter Publications, 1994.

Forages, The Science of Grassland Agriculture. Under the editorial authorship of Maurice E. Heath, Robert F Barnes, and Darrel S. Metcalfe. Ames, IA: Iowa State University Press, 1985.

Grass and Forage, Fertilizers and Organic Manures for Grass. Belfast: Department of Agriculture for Northern Ireland, 1993.

Grass and Forage, Making Grass Silage. Belfast: Department of Agriculture for Northern Ireland, 1993.

Grass, Yearbook of Agriculture 1948. Washington, D.C.: U.S. Government Printing Office.

Lewin, Roger. *Complexity, Life at the edge of chaos.* London: J M Dent Ltd, 1993.

Minnich, Jerry. *The Earthworm Book.* Emmaus, PA: Rodale Press.

Mortimer, John and Bunny. *Trees for the New Zealand Countryside, A Planter's Guide.* Hamilton, New Zealand: Taitua Books, 1993.

Murphy, Bill. *Greener Pasture On Your Side Of The Fence, Better Farming With Voisin Management Intensive Grazing.* Colchester, VT: Arriba Publishing, 1994.

Salatin, Joel. *Pastured Poultry Profit$, Net $25,000 in 6 months on 20 acres.* Swoope, VA: Polyface, Inc. 1993.

Silage. Prepared by Liam Fitzgerald. ACOT--An Chomhairle Oiliuna Talmhaiochta Council for Development in Agriculture, 1987.

Soils & Men, Yearbook of Agriculture 1938. Washington, D.C.: U.S. Government Printing Office.

Top Milk Yields From Grass. Prepared by J. Sheehy. ACOT--An Chomhairle Oiliuna Talmhaiochta, Council for Development in Agriculture. 1985.

Turner, Newman. *Fertility Pastures and Cover Crops.* Pauma Valley, CA: Bargyla and Gylver Rateaver, 1974.

Voisin, André. *Grass Productivity.* Covelo, CA: Island Press, 1988.

Index

Author's Bio:

Allan Nation has been the editor of the **Stockman Grass Farmer** magazine since 1977. Based in Jackson, Mississippi, the **Stockman Grass Farmer** magazine is the only North American publication specializing in management-intensive grazing and pasture production systems for ruminant livestock.

The son of a commercial cattle rancher, Nation grew up in Greenville, Mississippi. He has traveled the world studying and photographing grassland farming systems and is a frequent speaker in the United States, Canada, Mexico and New Zealand on grassland farming topics.

In 1987 he authored a section in intensive grazing in the **USDA Yearbook of Agriculture** and has served as a consultant and resource for Audubon Society Television Specials, National Geographic, WTBS, PBS and National Public Radio. He received the 1993 Agricultural Conservation Award from the American Farmland Trust for spearheading the drive behind the grass farming revolution in the U.S. He is also the author of **Pa$ture Profit$ with Stocker Cattle** and **Grass Farmers**.

Also From Green Park Press...

GRASS FARMERS by Allan Nation. Tired of reading farm stories of doom and gloom, bankruptcies and despair? **Grass Farmers** will tell you about the many people who are making an excellent living on the land. 37 success stories tell how sheep dairying can produce a quality life from small acreages; how a grazier paid for his farm in six months; how grass farming became a retirement job; how heifer grazing can give a grazier a mid-winter vacation, and more. This book won't tell you how big to make your paddocks or when to move your stock, but it is a quick and inspirational read that has put thousands of graziers on the path to higher profits. Softcover, 192 pages. **$23.50***

PA$TURE PROFIT$ WITH STOCKER CATTLE by Allan Nation. This is the first book on stocker grazing written for those who want to get rich with a minimum of financial risk. In **Pa$ture Profit$ With Stocker Cattle** Allan Nation illustrates his economic theories on stocker cattle by profiling grazier, Gordon Hazard. Hazard has accumulated and stocked a 3000-acre grass farm solely from retained stocker profits and without bank leverage. Nation backs his theories with good, hard dollars and sense budgets, including one showing investors how to double their money in a year by investing in stocker cattle. Softcover, 192 pages. **$24.95***

SHELTER & SHADE, Creating a healthy and profitable environment for your livestock with trees by John & Bunny Mortimer. This is the first book for farmers who want to beautify the landscape, add a healthy, natural environment for their livestock, and at the same time improve their bottom line. **Shelter & Shade**'s guided suggestions show you how to plant shelterbelts to protect livestock from harsh winds, snow, and fierce summer sun, eliminating the need for expensive confinement facilities. Specific tree species can be used to enhance your livestock's diet and cut purchased feed costs. Chapters show how to use trees to add humus to the soil, prevent erosion, and dry out wet spots. Includes planting design guidelines. Softcover, 160 pages. **$20.00***

** Plus shipping and handling.*

To order call 1-800-748-9808.

Request our free catalog for a complete list of Green Park Press titles. See last page for ordering information.

THE STOCKMAN Grass Farmer

Green Park Press books and the **Stockman Grass Farmer** magazine are devoted solely to the art and science of turning pastureland into profits through the use of animals as nature's harvesters. To order a free sample copy of the magazine, or to purchase other Green Park Press titles:

Please make checks payable to:

Stockman Grass Farmer
PO Box 9607
Jackson, MS 39286-9607

1-800-748-9808
or 601-981-4805
FAX 601-981-8558

Shipping:	Amount	Canada	Mexico
Under 2 lbs.	$3.50	$5.50	$7.50
2-3 lbs.	$4.75	$7.50	$12.00
3-4 lbs.	$5.25	$8.50	$15.00
4-5 lbs.	$6.50	$10.00	$16.75
5-6 lbs.	$8.50	$11.75	$21.00
6-8 lbs.	$12.00	$13.50	$24.00
8-10 lbs.	$14.50	$16.75	$30.00

Foreign Postage: Add 35% of order.

- -

Name ______________________________
Address ______________________________
City ______________________________
State/Province______________ **Zip/Postal Code**__________

Quantity	Title	Price Each	Sub Total
_______	Grass Farmers (weight 1 lb.)	$23.50	________
_______	Quality Pasture (weight 1 1/2 lbs.)	$32.50	________
_______	Pa$ture Profit$ With Stocker Cattle (1 lb.)	$24.95	________
_______	Shelter & Shade (weight 1 lb)	$20.00	________
_______	Free sample copy Stockman Grass Farmer magazine		
_______	Free book catalog		

Sub Total ________
Postage & Handling ________
Mississippi Residents Add 7% Sales Tax ________
U.S. Funds Only, Please **TOTAL:** ________

Name ____
Address ____
City ____
State/Province ____________________ Zip/PostalCode _____

Quantity	Title	Price Each	Sub Total
_______	Grass Farmers (weight 1 lb.)	$23.50	_______
_______	Quality Pasture (weight 1 1/2 lbs.)	$32.50	_______
_______	Pa$ture Profit$ With Stocker Cattle (1 lb.)	$24.95	_______
_______	Shelter & Shade (weight 1 lb)	$20.00	_______
_______	Free sample copy Stockman Grass Farmer magazine		
_______	Free book catalog		

Sub Total _______
Postage & Handling _______
Mississippi Residents Add 7% Sales Tax _______

U.S. Funds Only, Please TOTAL: _______

Shipping:	Amount	Canada	Mexico
Under 2 lbs.	$3.50	$5.50	$7.50
2-3 lbs.	$4.75	$7.50	$12.00
3-4 lbs.	$5.25	$8.50	$15.00
4-5 lbs.	$6.50	$10.00	$16.75
5-6 lbs.	$8.50	$11.75	$21.00
6-8 lbs.	$12.00	$13.50	$24.00
8-10 lbs.	$14.50	$16.75	$30.00

Foreign Postage: Add 35% of order.

Please make checks payable to:
Stockman Grass Farmer
PO Box 9607
Jackson, MS 39286-9607

1-800-748-9808
or 601-981-4805
FAX 601-981-8558

Green Park Press books and the **Stockman Grass Farmer** magazine are devoted solely to the art and science of turning pastureland into profits through the use of animals as nature's harvesters.